N J P SMITH
G A KIRBY
T C PHARAOH

CONTRIBUTORS

A G Hulbert
K L Shaw

Structure and evolution of the south-west Pennine Basin and adjacent area

Subsurface memoir

Library Copy

Keyworth, Nottingham: British Geological Survey   2005

Bibliographical reference

SMITH, N J P, KIRBY, G A, and PHARAOH, T C.   2005. Structure and evolution of the south-west Pennine Basin and adjacent area.   *Subsurface memoir of the British Geological Survey.*

Authors

N J P Smith, BSc, MSc, CGeol
G A Kirby, BSc, PhD
T C Pharaoh, BSc, PhD, CGeol
BGS Keyworth

Cover photograph
From the Longmynd looking northwards is Pontesford Hill comprising Uriconian volcanic rocks, and in the background the Cheshire Plain underlain by Carboniferous and Triassic strata. Bordering the hill to the west is the Pontesford–Linley Fault, one of the main long-lived faults that limits the Lower Palaeozoic Welsh Basin and was rejuvenated, with other faults farther north, to control the margin of the Carboniferous Pennine Basin and Permian–Jurassic Cheshire Basin (Photographer J M Pulsford, 1969; A11103).

Other BGS publications dealing with this and adjacent areas
A full list of BGS publications may be found in the current BGS catalogue and on the web site.

BOOKS

Subsurface Memoirs
Structure and evolution of the Northumberland–Solway Basin and adjacent areas
Structure and evolution of the Craven Basin and adjacent areas

British Regional Geology
Pennines and adjacent areas. Fourth edition, 2002
Eastern England from the Tees to The Wash. Second edition. 1980
Northern England. Fourth edition, 1971
Central England. Third edition. 1969

MAPS

1:1 500 000
Colour shaded relief gravity anomaly map of Britain, Ireland and adjacent areas, 1996
Colour shaded relief magnetic anomaly map of Britain, Ireland and adjacent areas, 1996
Tectonic map of Britain, Ireland and adjacent areas, 1996

1:100 000
Pre-Permian geology of the UK (south), 1985
Groundwater vulnerability maps of England and Wales, Sheets 16, 17, 18, 21, 22, 23, 28, 29, 30

1:625 000
Solid geology map UK South sheet. Fourth edition. 2001
Aeromagnetic map of Great Britain (and Northern Ireland), South sheet, 1965
Bouguer anomaly map of the British Isles, Southern sheet, 1986
Hydrogeological map England and Wales, 1977

1:250 000 Solid geology
53N 04W   Liverpool Bay, 1978
53N 02W   Humber Trent, 1983
52n 04W   Mid Wales and Marches, 1990
52N 02W   East Midlands, 1986
52N 00   East Anglia, 1986
51N 04W   Bristol Channel, 1988
51N 02W   Chilterns, 1991
51N 00   Thames Estuary, 1989

ATLAS

Regional geochemistry of Wales and part of west-central England: stream water. 1999

Subsurface structural features of southern Britain — a seismic atlas. 2005

CONTENTS

PREFACE

Traditional methods of geological surveying do not always provide reliable indicators of subsurface structure. Nor is any deep borehole necessarily a good guide to what may be at depth at other nearby localities. To overcome such difficulties, seismic reflection profiling methods have been developed and refined in recent decades. Such exploration methods are of particular importance to the oil industry and the application of these and other basin analysis techniques to the sedimentary basins of the United Kingdom has significantly increased the economic resources of the nation, and greatly enhanced the knowledge of the structure and geological evolution of both the land and of the adjoining continental shelf.

Many recent maps and memoirs of the British Geological Survey have made use of seismic reflection profiles, but generally only in a limited way. This book is based on an exhaustive use of such data, and aims to present a concise review of the tectonic and sedimentary history of the Carboniferous and older rocks of the Cheshire Basin and adjacent areas. It is the third in a series of subsurface memoirs relating to Upper Palaeozoic basins, and forms a sequel to a previously published account of the adjacent Craven Basin.

This account is essentially regional in scope, dealing particularly with the deeper, concealed parts of the Carboniferous and older succession and associated structures not considered in earlier publications on the Permian to recent evolution. The results of the study are largely contained in the accompanying 1:625 000 scale structure contour and preserved thickness maps and associated palaeogeographical maps. The accompanying written account is intended both as a regional review, as an explanation and partial amplification of these maps, and as a summary of basin evolution and tectonic history.

This book provides an up-to-date summary and distillation of information obtained during the search for, and extraction of, mineral and energy resources of the region. It will serve as a basic reference source when economic conditions change or new commodities are required, or when new exploration models are developed which once again result in new interest in the region by the exploration industry.

David A Falvey, PhD
Director

British Geological Survey
Sir Kingsley Dunham
Keyworth
Nottingham
NG12 5GG

ACKNOWLEDGEMENTS

NOTES

The interpretation of the seismic data and the production of the structure contour maps were carried out by Mr N J P Smith, Dr D J Evans and Dr T C Pharaoh, who also prepared the written account in conjunction with Dr G A Kirby. Mr A G Hulbert was responsible for the final computer generation and production of the maps, including the calculation and presentation of the thickness maps. Miss K L Shaw undertook data digitisation and manipulation. Dr G A Kirby compiled the book, which was edited by Drs A A Jackson and D W Holliday; figures were drawn by R J Demaine, and G Tuggey, pagesetting by A Hill.

The word 'region' refers to the area of the map shown in Figure 1.
The United Kingdom Onshore Geophysical Library (UKOGL) is the trustee of the UK onshore exploration seismic database with Lynx Information Systems Ltd managing the archive and release of data on behalf of the Library.

ONE

Introduction

This report presents a review of the tectonic and sedimentary history of the north-western part of the English Midlands and the north-east and eastern Welsh Borderland (hereafter referred to as the region) with an emphasis on the structure and evolution of the Carboniferous basins and their fill. It is the third in the *Subsurface Memoir* series of the British Geological Survey, following the Northumberland–Solway Basin (Chadwick et al., 1995) and the Craven Basin (Kirby et al., 2000) and forms a sequel to a previously published subsurface study of the Mesozoic basins of England and Wales (British Geological Survey, 1985).

The region includes areas of high urban population density contrasting with remote upland and moorland countryside (Figure 1). The Birmingham conurbation forms the main industrial area in the region, other urban areas including southern Merseyside, southern Greater Manchester, Stoke-on-Trent and Sheffield. Elsewhere, much of the lower lying land is put to agricultural use. More remote and bleak landscapes are characteristic of the hill country of the Welsh Borderland in the west of the region and the Peak District in the north-east.

The geology of the region (Figure 2) is both complex and extraordinarily varied, with many classic localities and areas that were of major importance in the development of British geology. Strata ranging in age from Precambrian to Jurassic crop out in, or immediately adjacent to, the region. Deformation of the rocks occurred during a number of tectonic phases, producing a series of important structures that control their nature and distribution. The surface and near-surface geology have been described in the British Geological Survey 1:50 000 Series maps and memoirs (Appendix 1). This account examines the deeper, concealed parts of the Permo-Triassic and, in particular, the Carboniferous successions not considered in earlier publications. Over 800 seismic reflection profiles have been interpreted during the course of this study, and the results are contained largely in the accompanying 1:625 000 scale structure contour and isopach maps (Maps 1 to 9) and associated text figures. This account provides both a regional review and an explanation and amplification of these maps and figures.

The Carboniferous rocks of the region have long been of economic significance. Coal, ore minerals, building stone, aggregate, limestone, ironstone and materials for the ceramic industry have been worked in the past. Prior to the 1980s, only limited investigation of the concealed geology was possible, mainly through base-metal mining, coal exploration and extraction, oil exploration and from scientific drilling and geophysical surveys. More recently, many parts of the region have seen renewed exploration for hydrocarbons, which has involved the drilling of deep boreholes and the acquisition of good quality seismic reflection data. This, in combination with Coal Authority seismic data, has resulted in an extensive network of seismic reflection profiles (Figure 3) except where older 'basement' rocks crop out in the west and south-west, in the central Peak District, and also in the main conurbations. This account relies heavily on these data, which for the first time elucidate the detailed structure of the Carboniferous strata beneath much of central England. Where seismic coverage is sparse, tunnel, adit and other horizontal underground sections in mines locally provide some control on subsurface geology. The seismic reflection data date from the 1960s to late 1980s, and are variable in fold of stack (12 to 60) and data quality (poor to good). Where Carboniferous rocks are exposed at the surface, or lie beneath a thin cover of Quaternary deposits, the entire Upper Palaeozoic basin fill is generally resolved. However, data quality commonly deteriorates in areas of locally thick drift and particularly in areas where there is a thick Permo-Triassic cover, most notably beneath the Cheshire and Needwood basins (Figure 2). The scatter of deep boreholes, together with surface exposures, provides stratigraphical calibration. However, on some seismic profiles there are prominent reflectors below the deepest borehole proving, and geological identification of these is therefore less certain. The very thick, early Carboniferous deposits that form the lower part of the sedimentary fill of the Cheshire Basin are not penetrated by boreholes, and this combined with sometimes poor data quality makes interpretation more difficult and less well-constrained locally.

Depth conversion of interpreted seismic data to produce the structural maps was complicated by a number of factors, including the variable age of the data, quantity and quality of the data and rapid lateral changes in thickness of the Permo-Triassic cover. The chosen method of calculating thickness was one involving conversion of a series of two-way-travel-time (TWTT) intervals from the base Permo-Triassic downwards, using a series of interval velocity grids and the summing of the resulting isopach grids to produce depth maps. Interval velocities were obtained from the borehole sonic logs.

Particular attention was paid to the depth conversion of the Dinantian interval, due to the known variation of Dinantian lithologies (and thus interval velocities) at crop and in boreholes in surrounding basins (i.e. platform carbonates and basinal mudstone facies). A contoured interval velocity map reflecting the postulated distribution of these facies in the subsurface was produced by hand. To achieve this, a Dinantian TWTT isopach map was generated, from which an interpretation of the basinal and platform areas was attempted. Dinantian interval velocities from boreholes across the

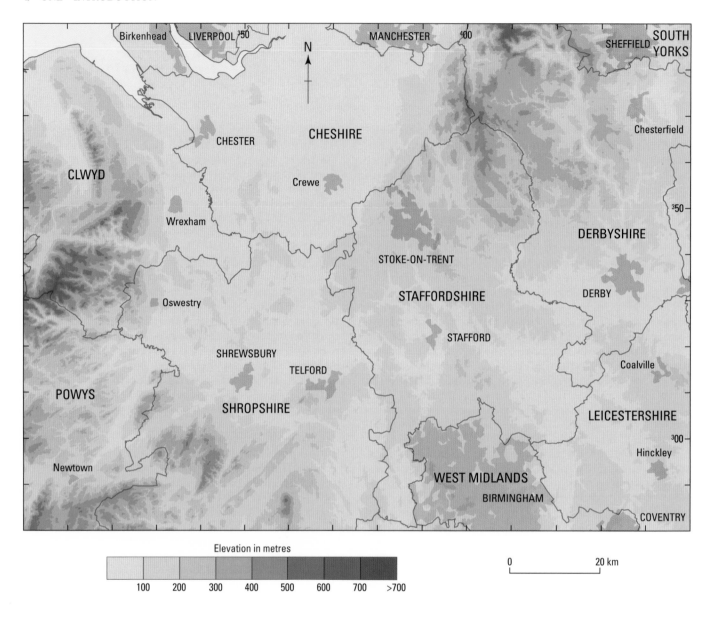

Figure 1 Location map of the region showing generalised topography, urban areas and county boundaries.

area were then plotted on an overlay map and contoured with this 'structural template'. However, deep borehole data in the region are limited and it was necessary to plot the velocity ranges of similar facies just outside the area to assist the interpretation.

SUMMARY OF PREVIOUS RESEARCH

This is a region of complex and economically rich geology, which has attracted such emminent early workers as Murchison (1835, 1839, 1854), Sedgwick (1835) and Lapworth (1879). Perhaps the earliest account of the geology of the region however, appears in the description and correlation of Coal Measures in the 'Natural History of Staffordshire' (Plot, 1686).

The Geological Survey commenced systematic geological mapping across the region in the Welsh Borders, publishing maps on a scale of one inch to one mile (1:63 360) for virtually all of the area, between 1844 and 1880. In Derbyshire, mapping commenced at the southern end of the Pennines in 1850 and extended into the adjacent parts of Nottinghamshire, Cheshire and Lancashire. The memoirs that accompanied the maps were focussed primarily on the economic aspects of the geology, dealing in particular with coalfields such as the South Staffordshire Coalfield (Jukes, 1859), the Warwickshire Coalfield (Howell, 1859) and the Leicestershire Coalfield (Hull, 1860). Between 1886 and 1891, several other volumes appeared dealing with the geology of parts of Northamptonshire, Leicestershire and Warwickshire. Subsequently, various economic memoirs were published

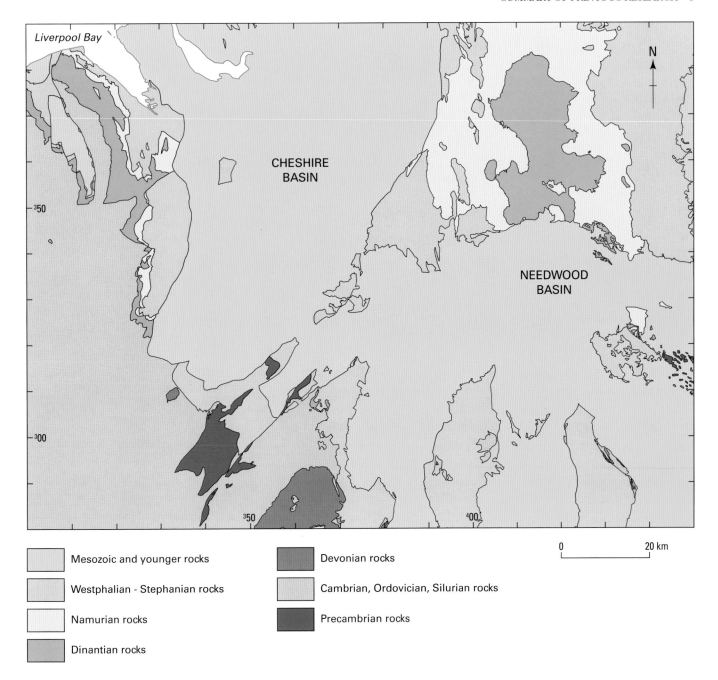

Figure 2 Simplified geological map of the region.

Legend:
- Mesozoic and younger rocks
- Westphalian - Stephanian rocks
- Namurian rocks
- Dinantian rocks
- Devonian rocks
- Cambrian, Ordovician, Silurian rocks
- Precambrian rocks

dealing with gypsum, rock salt, iron ore, coal, refractory minerals and water supply. The first maps to show the distribution of drift were published in 1871. Rapid progress in mining led to an equally rapid increase in knowledge and revision of older maps between 1903 and 1909. Several special memoirs have also been published, including the *Concealed Coalfield of Yorkshire and Nottinghamshire* (first published in 1913, with subsequent editions appearing in 1926 and 1951).

Geological mapping and research, other than that by the Geological Survey, includes a *General View of the Agriculture and Minerals of Derbyshire* (Farey, 1811), and Hall (1832) published a map of the Lancashire Coalfield.

Other workers such as Binney and Sorby were active in the Lancashire and Yorkshire areas at this time. Lapworth (1879) contributed to the early understanding of the Precambrian and Cambrian rocks of Central England. The classic works of Wills (1951, 1956) have greatly improved understanding of, for example, the Triassic system and its palaeogeography in the region.

The region includes two classical areas of Lower Carboniferous (Dinantian) strata in Derbyshire and northeast Wales. In Derbyshire, there has been significant geological research for the greater part of two centuries: summaries of the early research are found in Smith et al., (1967), Morris (1969), Stevenson and Gaunt (1971),

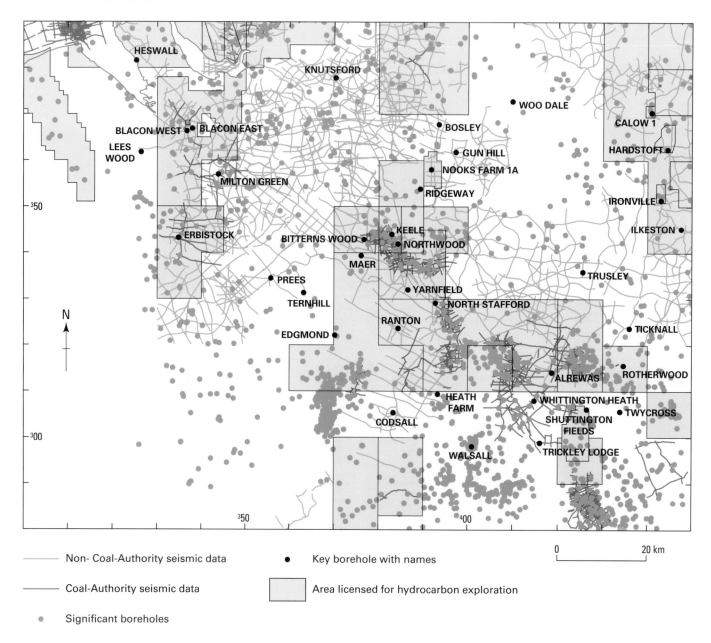

Figure 3 Summary of data location and areas licensed for hydrocarbon exploration.

Ford (1977) and Aitkenhead et al. (1985). The succession of limestone and basaltic lava in the Matlock area was first described by Whitehurst (1778) and the general succession and structure of the Derbyshire Dome later illustrated by Watson (1811). Accounts of the igneous rocks of the area were published by Arnold-Bemrose (1894, 1907). The first stratigraphical work started with Sibley (1908) who applied the coral-brachiopod subdivision of Vaughan (1905), attempting a correlation of the limestones of Derbyshire with those in the Bristol area. The account by Parsons (1922) of the dolomites and dolomitic limestones in the south-eastern part of the Dinantian tract remains the standard work on the subject. Modern stratigraphical work on the limestones started with Cope (1933, 1936, 1937, 1939a, b). Further

important studies of the limestones around the area followed from Parkinson (1950), Prentice (1951, 1952), Morris (1969), Wolfenden (1958), Sadler and Wyatt (1966), Shirley (1959), Butcher and Ford (1973) and Walkden (1977).

The deep boreholes in Derbyshire at Edale, Alport, Eyam and Woo Dale, and around Stoke-on-Trent at Gun Hill (Hudson and Cotton, 1945), Bowsey Wood and Apedale have contributed significantly to understanding the distribution and evolution of 'shelf' and 'off-shelf' areas in Dinantian times, confirming, for example, the presence of a shelf to basin transition from Derbyshire northwards (Gutteridge, 1987, 1991). In the East Midlands, deep boreholes have also demonstrated the presence of the Lower Carboniferous Edale Gulf, Goyt

Trough and Widmerpool Gulf (Strank, 1987). The Gun Hill and Bowsey Wood boreholes provided details on the Market Drayton Horst and the western margin of the North Staffordshire Basin (Corfield et al., 1996; Rees and Wilson, 1998). However, because the borehole provings are well scattered, there are contrasting interpretations of the disposition of the basement beneath the Derbyshire Dome (Miller and Grayson, 1982; Smith et al., 1985; Lee, 1988; Gutteridge, 1987, 1991).

In north and north-east Wales, the first detailed description and subdivision of the Lower Carboniferous rocks were made by Morton (1870, 1878, 1886) and the Geological Survey (Strahan, 1885). A four-fold lithological subdivision of the Dinantian limestone succession was recognised, the basal unit was thought to rest conformably on red siliciclastics, referred to as 'Old Red Sandstone' by Morton and 'Basement Beds' by Strahan. Applying Vaughan's (1905) classic coral/brachiopod zonal classification from the Bristol area, Hind and Stobbs (1906) achieved the first palaeontological zonation of these limestones, concluding that the oldest limestones could not be older than S_2/D zone boundary (Holkerian–Asbian). Jones (1921) and Neaverson (1929–1946) presented petrological and faunal data, the latter upholding the earlier conclusions of Hind and Stobbs (1906). In the middle to latter part of the 20th century, great advances were made in the stratigraphical palaeontology (biostratigraphy) and sedimentology of the Dinantian to Silesian succession. Further works (Lacey, in Sommerville et al., 1989) drew comparisons of the flora with the basal parts of the limestone sequence in Ravenstondale, northern England, although it was concluded that miospore data indicated an Upper Visean (Holkerian to Asbian) age for the Basement Beds. The Geological Survey returned to this area, erecting a new stratigraphy to supersede Morton's lithological divisions, although it was still thought to be Asbian in age (George et al., 1976; Warren et al., 1984). It has subsequently been recognised that strata older than Asbian are present in north Wales (Somerville and Strank, 1984; Somerville et al., 1986, 1989; Davies et al., 1989).

Namurian rocks of the Central Pennine Basin have been the subject of fundamental sedimentological (Sorby, 1859) and biostratigraphical studies, including the pioneering work of Bisat (1924) on the goniatite faunas of marine bands. The first major petrographical studies of the Millstone Grit included that of Gilligan (1920), who concluded that it was derived from sources in Greenland and Scandinavia, with tectonic uplift controlling sediment input into the basin. Subsequent studies have illustrated the stratigraphical and sedimentological detail of particular stratigraphical intervals (e.g. Allen, 1960). Shackleton (1962) studied the palaeocurrents and the sedimentology of the Rough Rock, concluding that it was deposited by a host of small rivers and occasional flash floods. Studies of the large scale controls on sedimentation in the Namurian of northern England and the deposition of these sediments is limited to the pioneering review of Reading (1964) and later work of Jones (1980), in which the progressive fill of the Central Pennines Basin by the various facies of the Millstone Grit is demonstrated.

During Westphalian times, the region lay within an area of continuous sediment accumulation that has been termed the 'Pennine Province' (Trueman, 1947; Wills, 1948, 1951, 1956; Calver, 1968a; Ramsbottom et al., 1978). These authors suggested that the province was bounded by landmasses that formed important palaeogeographical elements throughout the Carboniferous to the north (Southern Uplands Massif) and south (Wales–London–Brabant Massif). Much of the early work on Westphalian successions was concerned with stratigraphy and palaeontology; sedimentological research did not commence until the late 1960s. Indeed, the sedimentology of some coalfields is still poorly known (Guion and Fielding, 1988). Stratigraphical nomenclature of the Westphalian developed in each individual coalfield so that there was a proliferation of local names. Early workers in the Flintshire and Denbighshire coalfields (Strahan, 1890; Wedd and King, 1924; Wedd et al., 1928) attempted to correlate the succession with the well-documented Lancashire and Staffordshire successions. However, a lack of biostratigraphical control led to significant correlation problems, subsequently reviewed by Jones and Lloyd (1942). Since the Second World War, the subdivision and correlation of the British 'Coal Measures' has relied more heavily upon the identification of marine band faunas (e.g. Stubblefield and Trotter, 1957; Ramsbottom et al., 1978). It has been suggested that the bases of the Westphalian A, B and C stages should be defined by stratotypes in the Pennines, two of which lie in or just on the margins of this region: the base Westphalian B at Duckmanton, Derbyshire and base Westphalian C near Bolsover, Derbyshire. The status of these stratotypes has not as yet, been fully resolved. The presence of an unconformity at the base of the Westphalian D in the Midlands (the 'Symon Unconformity'), identified by Wills (1956), means that the original extent of the Westphalian A and B, which are truncated by this unconformity, at the southern margins of the basin may never be known precisely. However, descriptions of alluvial facies from rocks in the south of the region (Besly, 1983), indicates that it lay very close to the basin margin.

The Westphalian of the Flint Coalfield in north Wales was summarised in Calver and Smith (1974) with Ramsbottom et al. (1978) providing a regional correlation of the Westphalian that still forms the basis of many works.

The cause of cyclicity in the Carboniferous rocks of northern England has been the subject of long and varied debate. Bott and Johnson (1967) favoured tectonic control as the main driving force for sea-level changes. Eustatic sea-level oscillations on the other hand have long been held to be an important control on sedimentation (Ramsbottom, 1973, 1974, 1977; Maynard and Leeder, 1992; Holdsworth and Collinson, 1988). The prolonged debate on the relative importance of these effects may be moving towards resolution by the application of the concept of sequence stratigraphy (Fraser and Gawthorpe, 1990; Fraser et al., 1990; Read, 1991; Maynard, 1992; Martinsen, 1993). More recently, the widespread marine transgressions controlling the cyclicity of Silesian strata are increasingly being seen as glacio-eustatic in origin

(Martinsen et al., 1995), a theory supported by evidence of glaciation in Gondwana during the Carboniferous (Heckel, 1986; Veevers and Powell, 1987).

Much of the Permo-Triassic history of the region is now seen as being closely associated with the evolution of other important Permian and Mesozoic basins, both offshore, for example in the East Irish Sea Basin (Jackson et al., 1987; Jackson and Mulholland, 1993), and onshore, for example in the Staffordshire, Needwood and Worcester basins (e.g. Chadwick and Smith, 1988; Chadwick and Evans, 1995).

Aside from the Quaternary deposits, the youngest preserved sedimentary rocks in the region are the Lower to Middle Lias in the Prees area (Walker, 1914; Poole and Whiteman, 1966; Warrington et al., 1980).

Intrusive dykes of olivine-dolerite and related rock types in the Butterton–Swynnerton area, were probably first identified independently in the 1840s by Kirkby and Darwin and were reported by earlier workers (Garner, 1844; GSGB, 1857; Cherry, 1877). Radiometric age determinations of between 52 ± 2 and 52.4 ± 1.4 million years have been obtained (Miller in Cope, 1966a; Fitch et al., 1969; Evans in Rees and Wilson, 1998). However, it is the use of geophysical methods which have led to a greater knowledge of the extent of the intrusions at depth (Sowerbutts, 1987, 1988; Rees and Wilson, 1998), which with their composition and age, led Musset et al. (1988) to suggest that they form the most south-easterly intrusions of the British Tertiary Igneous Province.

The Mesozoic and Cainozoic evolution of northern England is poorly understood and has been the subject of much controversy; in particular with regard to the thickness and nature of any former cover over the Palaeozoic rocks of the Pennines and the present-day landmass. A Lake District–Pennine Island, emergent for much or all of Mesozoic time was popularised by Wills (1951) and supported by Kent (1974), Moseley (1978), Ziegler (1982) and Cope et al. (1992). However, as early as 1929, Trotter calculated that up to 2100 m of Mesozoic rocks, in addition to an unknown amount of Carboniferous strata, had been eroded from blocks in northern England; this was supported by Eastwood (1935), Taylor et al. (1971) and Arthurton et al. (1978). Depth of burial and eroded overburden studies based upon well log data and apatite fission track studies now provide support for the former presence of kilometre-scale cover successions, most of which was subsequently removed by post-Cretaceous uplift and erosion (Green, 1986; Lewis et al., 1992; Evans et al., 1993; Chadwick et al., 1994).

Modern sedimentological research on the Namurian rocks of the region was stimulated by the classic synthesis of Reading (1964). Several authors have published on the sedimentology of particular intervals within the region (Walker, 1966; Trewin and Holdsworth, 1973; Collinson and Banks, 1975; Collinson et al., 1977; McCabe, 1977; Chisholm, 1981; Okolo, 1983; Bristow, 1988; Maynard, 1992). Collinson (1988) provides the most recent review of the stratigraphy and sedimentology of Namurian rocks, with Holdsworth and Collinson (1988) reviewing the concepts and nature of the cyclicity associated with the Millstone Grit and its deposition.

Despite early work on the coalfields of the region, relatively little sedimentological research on the Westphalian rocks was carried out until the pioneering work of Elliot (1968a, b) on the East Midlands Coal Measures. Subsequent work suggested deposition was in an overall delta plain setting that included lakes, lacustrine deltas, fluvial systems, distributaries, overbank and crevasse splay environments (Guion, 1971, 1978, 1982; Fatona, 1980 and Hawkins, 1972 in Guion and Fielding, 1998, Guion 1984, 1987). Since the work of Wills (1956), exploration by British Coal has defined the southern boundary of the Pennine Basin in more detail. Their results have shown that Westphalian A and B deposition took place farther to the south, for example in south Warwickshire, where new coal prospects are proven and Guion and Fielding (1988) stated that further work was required to determine the precise extent of the Wales–London–Brabant Massif. Detailed study of Westphalian A–C sand body orientations and palaeoslope analysis has led to important new understandings of sand body connectivity and the resultant implications to basin-fill (Rippon, 1996). During the 1980s and 1990s, Geological Survey mapping in the coalfields of the region has also led to a greater understanding of the Variscan Orogeny and its timing and effect on sedimentation (e.g. Waters et al., 1994). These authors have demonstrated how early effects of the orogeny were felt in the region from Westphalian C times, and these movements greatly influenced sedimentary facies and distribution.

The advent and application of geophysical techniques provided a key source of information in the understanding of the concealed geology. Drilling in the search for oil beneath the East Pennine Coalfield and in Nottinghamshire also, particularly from 1939 onwards, greatly increased knowledge of the subsurface form and extent of strata. Gravity and magnetic surveys (e.g. Lee, 1988) have outlined the complex distribution of Dinantian basins in the northern parts of the region. Seismic data have been of particular use in this respect and have revealed details of hitherto unknown subsurface features such as faults, folds, structural highs and basins. This new knowledge has convincingly demonstrated that the Palaeozoic and Mesozoic history of the region was often controlled by the reactivation of major lines of basement weakness and some of the overlying syndepositional normal faults. Early Palaeozoic synsedimentary faults were identified by Whittard (1952) and Smith (1987) and inversion of the Welsh Basin along such faults was accomplished by re-activation with thrusting (Smith, 1987) and dextral transpression (Lynas, 1988). It is now widely accepted that in Upper Palaeozoic and Mesozoic times, basement structures controlled the location and movement on important syndepositional normal faults, which in turn had a profound effect on the nature and distribution of sediment during the Carboniferous (e.g. Smith et al., 1985; Gutteridge, 1987, 1991; Fraser et al., 1990; Fraser and Gawthorpe, 1990; Corfield et al., 1996; Rees and Wilson, 1998) and the Permo-Triassic (e.g. Chadwick and Smith, 1988; Evans et al., 1993; Chadwick and Evans, 1995). The behaviour of the Carboniferous syndepositional faults during the Variscan Orogeny and their relationship to the Variscan folds seen around Britain is now well documented (e.g. Fraser et al., 1990; Fraser and Gawthorpe, 1990;

Corfield et al. 1996). Under compression, they are reactivated and pushed back up, deforming the cover sediments, producing what are termed inversion anticlines.

Aspects of the structural evolution of the region have also emerged through the Cheshire Basin Mineralisation Project (Plant et al., 1999) and 1:50 000 mapping around Flint, Stoke-on-Trent, Birmingham, Wolverhampton and Loughborough.

Interpretation of borehole geophysical logs has aided stratigraphical correlation. Dinantian and Namurian sequences have very distinctive log signatures that, as in other areas (Evans and Kirby, 1999; Kirby et al., 2000), may allow correlation within the region. Coal seams and marine bands not only possess characteristic faunas, but also have characteristic gamma-ray and sonic values (Knowles, 1964; Spears, 1964) that aid in correlation (e.g. Whitaker et al., 1985; Bridge et al., 1998; Rees and Wilson, 1998; Powell et al., 2000) and supplement the traditional schemes based on fauna and flora (Calver, 1968a, b). This has permitted classification of Westphalian successions that were previously poorly constrained, and a more detailed correlation both within and between coalfields.

TWO

Precambrian basement

The Pre-Carboniferous basement of the region is thought to comprise complexly structured Precambrian (Neoproterozoic) rocks unconformably overlain by Lower Palaeozoic rocks that were deformed during several Caledonian orogenic cycles. This chapter deals with the Precambrian rocks of this region, which crop out along the Welsh Borderland Fault System (Woodcock and Gibbons, 1988), in Charnwood Forest and near Nuneaton, and are encountered in several deep boreholes (Figure 4). Where demonstrable, the seismic character of much of the Precambrian succession is rather uniform. At outcrop the rocks may show clear bedding planes, but the general lack of compositional contrast suggests that good reflectivity is only likely to be generated by gently dipping intrusive contacts or shear zones.

Various authors have applied plate-tectonic models to the Precambrian of southern Britain (e.g. Dewey, 1969; Baker, 1971; Wood, 1974; Barber and Max, 1979), emphasising such tectonically diagnostic features as blueschists (subduction metamorphism), mélange (trench-fill) and ignimbritic volcanic rocks (arc volcanism). These early models generally infer late Proterozoic subduction of oceanic lithosphere to the south-east beneath Wales, and assume all of the components represent part of one contemporaneous subduction system, paying little or no attention to the possibility of transcurrent displacement. However, U-Pb zircon and Ar-Ar mineral dating techniques have subsequently enabled recognition of a sequence of events in the history of this destructive margin (Tucker and Pharaoh, 1991). Regional analysis of Precambrian rocks of southern Britain at outcrop, and of gravity and magnetic anomalies, has led to the proposal that they define a series of 'terranes' separated by important structural lineaments (Figure 4). The largest outcrops of Precambrian rocks in this region occur along these lineaments. Many of these lineaments and also some of the structures within the terranes have been reactivated during subsequent orogenic and rifting episodes, and have thus played a significant role during the Palaeozoic, Mesozoic and Cainozoic structural evolution of the region. For this reason, a description of these important features is given, together with an account of the rocks encountered at outcrop and in boreholes.

Four of the five proposed terranes, namely the Cymru, Wrekin, Charnwood and Fenland terranes (Pharaoh et al., 1987a, b; Pharaoh and Carney, 2000) are believed to underlie the region. Each terrane comprises volcanic and sedimentary rocks that are distinct from those in the adjacent terranes, but which together are nevertheless broadly similar to the Avalonian successions of the type area in Newfoundland (Pharaoh et al., 1987b; Pharaoh and Carney, 2000). They were accreted to the margin of the ProtoGondwana Supercontinent while it was located at low southerly latitudes in latest Proterozoic time. Together they form the Avalon Superterrane (Gibbons, 1990; Gibbons and Murphy, 1995; Gibbons and Horák, 1996) or Composite Terrane (Keppie, 1985). Lateral movements along terrane boundaries is thought to be of great importance during the terminal phases of Neoproterozoic subduction, c.570 to 540 Ma, when oblique subduction gave way to the development of a sinistral transform system (e.g. Gibbons, 1983, 1987, 1990; Gibbons and Horák, 1996; Nance and Murphy, 1996).

LINEAMENTS

NE–SW trend

The Pontesford–Linley and Church Stretton faults form part of complex belt known as the Welsh Borderland Fault System (Woodcock and Gibbons, 1988), which is imaged on the BGS Longmynd seismic reflection profile (Smith, 1987). The Pontesford–Linley Fault is the inferred boundary between the Neoproterozoic Avalonian, Wrekin and Cymru terranes (Figure 4) and defined the north-west edge of the Midlands Microcraton in early Palaeozoic times. Eastward-directed thrusting occurred on the Church Stretton Fault in post-Silurian times (Smith, 1987).

N–S trend

A series of north–south-trending crustal structures, the most important of which is the Malvern Lineament, separate the Wrekin and Charnwood terranes (Pharaoh et al., 1987b). They are marked by prominent magnetic anomalies in the south, due to the highly magnetic nature of the Malvernian rocks (Barclay et al., 1997). The nature of the northward continuation of the Malvern Lineament beyond the Midlands Microcraton, perhaps along the line of the Pennines, is a matter for speculation. Isotopic and geochemical similarities between the basement of the Cymru and Fenland terranes suggest that correlation of these may be feasible, in which case the Malvern Lineament (in its Proterozoic sense) may not extend beyond the limit of the microcraton. To the south, the Malvern Lineament can be traced to the Variscan Front. However, weak north–south gravity and aeromagnetic anomalies continue farther south suggesting that the Precambrian basement extends south beneath the Variscides (Lee et al., 1990).

NW–SE trend

A system of lineaments here referred to as the Charnwood Boundary Fault System, and which includes the Thringstone Fault, is inferred to delimit the main Charnwood

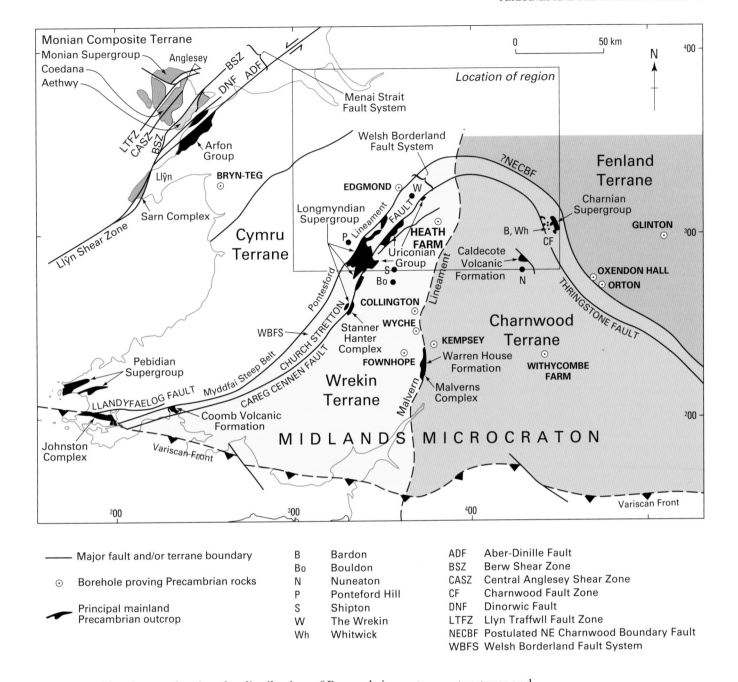

Figure 4 Sketch map showing the distribution of Precambrian outcrop, structures and main terranes across the region and immediate surrounding areas of southern Britain.

outcrop, at the north-east edge of the Midlands Microcraton (Smith, 1987; Pharaoh et al., 1987a); these lineaments represent the boundary between the postulated Charnwood and Fenland Terranes (Figure 4).

TERRANES AND PRECAMBRIAN ROCKS

Wrekin Terrane

This terrane occupies part of the south-west of the region (Pharaoh et al., 1987b) and includes the outcrops along the Welsh Borderland Fault System near Church Stretton

and Telford. These outcrops form four distinctive rock groupings: the Uriconian Group, the Longmyndian Supergroup, the Rushton Schists and Primrose Hill Schists and Gneisses, and the Stanner Hanter Intrusive Complex. Rocks of this terrane were also encountered in boreholes in the Telford area and most significantly, by the Heath Farm Borehole (Pharaoh and Gibbons, 1994). This is the most easterly proving of this terrane and is used to constrain the location of the inferred northward extension of the Malvern Lineament in Figure 4. Using the analogous development of the Worcester and Knowle basins and the pre-Devonian subcrop map (Smith, 1987), the Malvern Lineament is here extended along a north-east trend to the Hopton Fault. Outcrops of the calc-alkaline Malverns Complex, emplaced at about 680 Ma (Thorpe et al., 1984; Tucker and Pharaoh, 1991), lie just to the south of the region and also form part of this terrane.

The oldest dated rocks of the region are the (bimodal) gabbros and granitic rocks of the Stanner–Hanter Intrusive Complex, dated by the Rb-Sr whole-rock isochron method at 702 ± 8 Ma (Patchett et al., 1980). The Rushton Schists, sedimentary rocks metamorphosed in the amphibolite facies at about 670 Ma (Beckinsale et al., 1984), occupy a small outcrop near the Wrekin.

Uriconian bimodal volcanic and commonly ignimbritic volcaniclastic rocks form a discontinuous outcrop east of the Church Stretton Fault, but are interpreted to form the pre-Permian (and pre-Devonian) floor west of Lilleshall (Smith, 1987, fig. 1), extending to the Edgmond Borehole. They were erupted in an ensialic, largely subaerial marginal basin at 566–560 Ma (Tucker and Pharaoh, 1991). The magnetic properties of some of the Uriconian lavas and intrusions make these rocks traceable at depth, along an eastern and western line of anomalies bordering the Longmynd. Anomalies follow the eastern Uriconian outcrop, especially Wart Hill, Ragleth Hill, the Wrekin, Lilleshall and an outlier to the south of the region at Stanner. An anomaly at Shipton was linked to Uriconian rocks (Greig et al. 1968) at a depth of just over 1750 m. This anomaly extends south-west to Bouldon and coincides with a positive Bouguer gravity anomaly (Smith and Rushton, 1993). The western anomaly fails south of Pontesford Hill, where the Pontesford–Linley Fault emplaces Longmyndian rocks, instead of Uriconian, on its footwall. Uriconian rocks unconformably underlie early Cambrian strata at the Heath Farm Borehole.

Approximately 6500 m of strata of the Longmyndian Supergroup were deposited following eruption of the Uriconian rocks. All contacts between Uriconian and Longmyndian rocks are faulted however (Pauley, 1990a) and it is thus not possible to demonstrate the unconformable relationship invoked by Blake (1890), Cobbold (1900, 1925) and James (1956). The Longmyndian Supergroup has been interpreted as a post-orogenic molasse by Greig et al. (1968), and more recently, as a marine, deltaic to fluvial braidplain deposit by Pauley (1990b). Volcanic horizons within the supergroup indicate a continuation of Uriconian volcanism. The structural position of the Longmyndian Supergroup, located between the Church Stretton and Pontesford faults, suggests deposition in a rift (Dewey, 1969; Smith, 1987), perhaps related to latest Proterozoic transtension. Longmyndian strata at crop here were folded into a recumbent syncline and repetition of Longmyndian strata by thrust faulting is suspected but not proved. Stratigraphical evidence for a pre-mid Ordovician age for this folding is provided by unconformably overlying Caradoc and Silurian rocks. Ar-Ar ages of 545 Ma are believed to date the formation of the associated cleavage, which occurred immediately prior to deposition of the basal Cambrian sequence that overstepped on to the

Uriconian near the Wrekin. This latest Proterozoic deformation established the strong north-east-trending structural grain observed in this part of the region, enhanced subsequently by early Palaeozoic reactivation of the individual strands of the Welsh Borderland Fault System, which may have formed the original faulted boundary to the Longmyndian pull-apart basin (Smith, 1987).

Charnwood Terrane

Representatives of this terrane (Pharaoh et al., 1987b) are inferred to underlie the south-east part of the region comprising a large area of outcrop in Charnwood Forest and a smaller outcrop near Nuneaton. The Charnwood Terrane forms the eastern half of the Proterozoic Midlands Microcraton that includes the Charnwood Boundary Fault System along the north-eastern edge. In the Charnwood Forest massif, the Charnian Supergroup is over 3000 m thick, and lies within the Charnwood Boundary Fault System. It consists largely of well-bedded volcaniclastic rocks that were deposited in moderately deep water, and represent the fill of a marine, marginal basin that was located adjacent to a calc-alkaline volcanic arc. Local eruptive and intrusive centres at Bardon and Whitwick are inferred to represent domes of andesite and dacite emplaced into wet volcanic sediment. The magmatic arc itself is not exposed; on sedimentological criteria (Moseley and Ford, 1985) it has been inferred to lie farther to the north-west, but geophysical evidence suggests that it lies farther to the south-west (Pharaoh et al., 1991). Geochemical data suggest that the arc was founded on immature continental crust (Pharaoh et al., 1987b), rather different to that underlying the Fenland Terrane to the north-east. Numerous bodies of diorite that are locally granophyric (North and South Charnwood Diorites and equivalent rocks at Nuneaton) and represent a more evolved, high-K calc-alkaline suite (Pharaoh et al, 1987b) were emplaced at about 603 Ma (Tucker and Pharaoh, 1991). They intrude most of the bedded volcaniclastic strata, which includes strata containing the Ediacaran faunal assemblage. Epiclastic strata of the Brand Group contain the trace fossil *Teichichnus* sp. that is indicative of a Cambrian age (Bland, 1994), and rest unconformably on the volcaniclastic rocks. Both volcaniclastic and epiclastic sequences were folded on west-north-west–east-south-east-trending folds and cleaved during the late Caledonian Acadian deformation phase (Pringle, personal communication). Previously, it was assumed that this 'Charnoid' trend represented a Precambrian deformation, but it now appears that structures showing this trend are entirely 'Caledonian' in origin. Use of the term 'Charnoid' to describe basement structures of presumed Precambrian age and a north-west to west-north-west trend should therefore be avoided. This observed strong Caledonian deformation suggests these rocks form part of the largely concealed Caledonides of eastern England and that they lie on the margins or just outside of the 'Midlands Microcraton'. There is no direct evidence of structural trends in the remainder of the Charnwood Terrane. However, a strong north-west-trending aeromagnetic anomaly extending from South

Staffordshire towards Reading is interpreted as the expression of a concealed magmatic core to the Charnian volcanic arc, suggesting a similar trend to the Caledonian trend observed at outcrop. A local contribution to the anomaly from Carboniferous volcanic rocks and intrusions (Kearey, 1991), however, cannot be ruled out.

Cymru (Wales) Terrane

Representatives of this terrane, defined by Pharaoh and Carney (2000), are not exposed within the region, but are believed to occupy most of that part lying to north-west of the Pontesford–Linley Faults. In north Wales, calc-alkaline plutonic rocks of the Sarn Complex and volcanic rocks of the Arfon Group on the Llŷn were generated by subduction magmatism at about 615 Ma (Tucker and Pharaoh, 1991; Horák, 1993; Horák et al., 1996), and crop out in the vicinity of the Menai Strait Fault System (Gibbons, 1987). Calc-alkaline tuffs, tuffites and lavas proved by Bryn-Teg Borehole in the Harlech Dome (Allen and Jackson, 1978) demonstrate continuity towards the south-east of this late Proterozoic basement beneath the thick fill of the early Palaeozoic Welsh Basin. The Cymru Terrane is in faulted contact with the Monian terranes of Anglesey and Llŷn along the Menai Strait Fault System, which is interpreted as a 'suspect terrane boundary' (Gibbons, 1987;

Gibbons and Horák, 1996). A continuation of the Menai Strait Fault to the north-east would pass just beyond the north-west corner of the region.

Fenland Terrane

This terrane, defined by Pharaoh and Carney (2000) as lying to the north-east of the Charnwood Boundary Fault System, comprises the unexposed Precambrian basement of the concealed Caledonides of eastern England (Pharaoh et al., 1987a). Ignimbritic ash-flow tuffs of felsic composition (Dearnley, 1966), encountered in the Glinton and Orton boreholes outside the region, have yielded precise U-Pb zircon ages in the range 616 to 612 Ma (Noble et al., 1993). Although they are rather similar in age to Charnian magmatic rocks, they are petrographically and geochemically distinct, with ϵNd isotopic ratios indicating the involvement of mature continental crust (Noble et al, 1993). Other boreholes in this region encounter apparently unfossiliferous chloritic phyllites and clastic metasedimentary strata, for which a Precambrian age is possible (Pharaoh and Gibbons, 1994). There are closer petrographical and isotopic similarities to the ignimbritic tuffs of the Arfon Group in north Wales, and indeed the Cymru and Fenland terranes may be correlatives.

THREE

Lower Palaeozoic

Lower Palaeozoic rocks outcrop extensively in the west of the region and occur at depth throughout much of the remainder of the region (Figure 2). They are unconformably overlain by late Devonian and younger rocks. Their distribution is complex as a result of the structures produced by various phases of the Caledonian Orogeny, outlined below.

PLATE TECTONIC SETTING AND STRUCTURAL EVOLUTION

During early Palaeozoic times, the geological evolution of the region was complex and varied, having been influenced by the opening and closing of the Iapetus Ocean, which was formed between Laurentia to the north-west and Baltica and Avalonia to the south-east and east. The closure of this ocean marked the final phase of the - Caledonian Orogeny and consolidation of the Caledonian Orogen, which traditionally includes the early Palaeozoic areas of the British Isles and Scandinavia, together with adjacent areas of Svalbard, Greenland, Ireland and the northern Appalachians. The early concepts of the Caledonian Orogeny as a single event have proved to be simplistic (Harris and Fettes, 1988). Instead, there appear to have been a series of events relating to several small microcontinents that were calved off the northern margin of Gondwana and which drifted northwards to be sequentially accreted to Baltica and Laurentia (Figure 5). Each collision and closure of a small ocean represented collisions between arcs, mobile terranes and adjacent continental margins of Laurentia, Avalonia and Baltica (McKerrow and Soper, 1991, McKerrow et al., 2000; MacNiocall et al., 1997; van Staal et al., 1998).

Therefore, the 'Caledonian Orogeny' has been redefined (McKerrow et al., 2000) and restricted to tectonic events within, and on the borders of the Iapetus Ocean from Cambrian to Late Devonian times. These were often localised and in many instances diachronous, spanning a time interval of some 200 Ma. They include the Taconian and Shelveian (mid and late Ordovician), Scandian (late Silurian), Acadian (early Devonian), Ligerian (mid Devonian) and Bretonian (latest Devonian) phases. Final closure of the Iapetus Ocean completed the Caledonian Orogen (or 'Old Red Sandstone Continent').

Cambrian to early Ordovician rifting

In Cambrian times, the region formed part of the Pannotia or Proto-Gondwana Supercontinent, located at high (>60°S) palaeolatitudes. Rift-induced break-up of the supercontinent locally commenced in earliest Cambrian time (Brasier et al., 1978; Dalziel, 1997). In southern Britain, the initial basal Cambrian succession of coarse-grained clastic rocks was followed by deposition of generally fine-grained strata across a gently subsiding shelf region. Differentiation into fault-controlled basins and highs probably occurred in mid Cambrian times, with accelerating rates of subsidence in late Cambrian times. During early Ordovician (Tremadoc) times, an elongate piece of Gondwanan crust broke away to form the **Avalonia Terrane** (Ziegler, 1990; Smith and Rushton, 1993; Prigmore et al., 1997) of which the region occupied the eastern part (Figure 5a). It drifted rapidly northwards from high southerly latitudes to around 30°S by early Silurian times (Torsvik and Trench, 1991; Trench and Torsvik, 1992; Trench et al., 1992). Together with the onset of subduction of the Iapetus Ocean along the northern margin of Avalonia it marked the beginning of subduction-related calc-alkaline magmatism in north Wales (Kokelaar et al., 1984).

Shelveian (late Ordovician) deformation phase

The first orogenic phase to effect the region is the late Ordovician (Ashgill) **Shelveian** deformation phase (Toghill, 1992) which involved an element of dextral transcurrent shear (Torsvik and Trench, 1991; Trench and Torsvik, 1992). It resulted from the docking of Avalonia with Baltica to produce Balonia (Torsvik, 1998). Late Ordovician calc-alkaline arc magmatism related to these plate movements can be traced from northern England through eastern England to Belgium (Fitton and Hughes, 1970; Pharaoh et al., 1993; Van Grootel et al., 1997). There is however still controversy regarding the polarity of this subduction; most models invoke a south-east-dipping subduction zone to account for the Leinster–Lake District arc. However, evidence from deep seismic profiles could be interpreted as indicating subduction to the north-west.

Shelveian deformation is generally not very intense within the region (Figure 6), and associated strain is rather heterogeneous in aspect, but on the Ringkøbing–Fyn High, some 500 km to north-east, the contemporary metamorphic grade attained amphibolite facies and deformation was far more intense (Frost et al., 1981; Pharaoh et al., 1995). Within and close to the region, it led to the re-activation of the south-west-trending Menai Straits and Welsh Borderland lineaments, in particular uplift along the Tywi Lineament/Anticline (Woodcock, 1984a; Woodcock and Gibbons, 1988; Lynas, 1988; Arthurton et al., 1988; Toghill, 1992). In addition, it is associated with reverse movement and dextral transpression (Lynas, 1988) on the Pontesford–Linley Fault (previously a synsedimentary

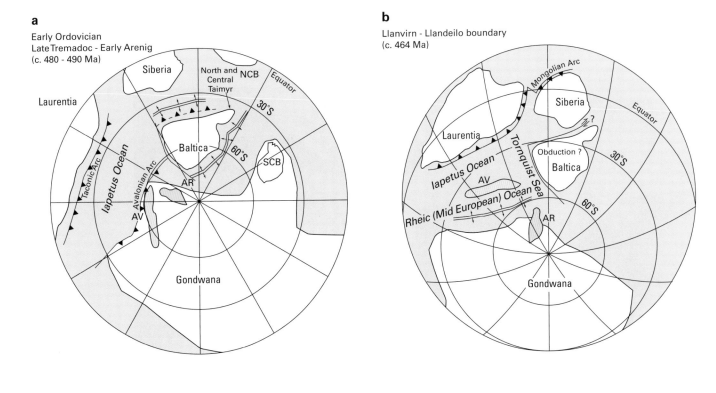

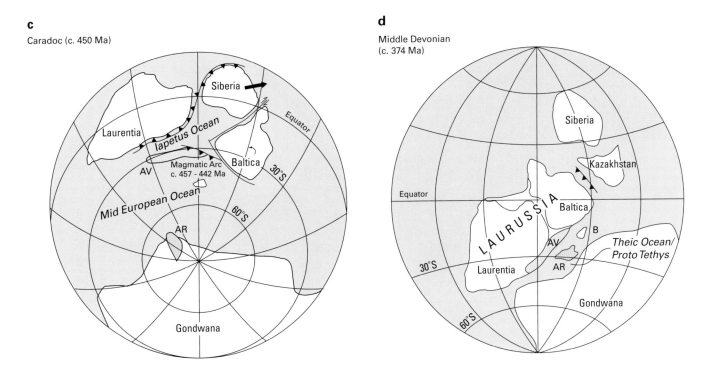

Figure 5   Palaeogeographic reconstructions to illustrate the accretion of key terranes during Palaeozoic times (after Torsvik, 1998; Pharaoh, 1999).

AR European massifs, including Armorica, Iberia and Bohemia;   AV Avalonia Terrane;
B Bohemia Terrane;   NCB North China Block;   SCB South China Block.

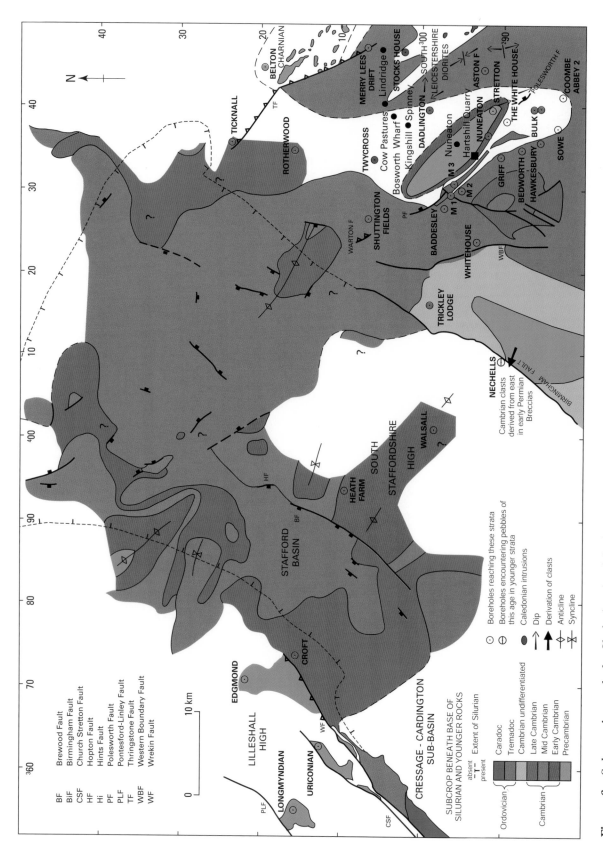

Figure 6 Subcrop beneath the Shelveian (end-Ordovician, Ashgill) unconformity over part of the region, interpreted from borehole and seismic reflection data. The extent of Silurian rocks is indicated. Beyond the limit of the Silurian rocks, the subcrop is at the Caledonian unconformity (reworked Shelveian unconformity).

growth fault) relative to the Longmynd Block that led to the formation of the Shelve Anticline (Smith 1987). Localised folding and faulting of Cambrian–Tremadoc strata (the 'Hartshill Event') associated with dextral transpression of probable late Ordovician age is also recognised near Nuneaton (Carney et al., 1992; Bridge et al., 1998). The intimate relationship of deformation and intrusion at this time is illustrated in Hartshill Quarry where a chevron-fold deforming Cambrian strata is intruded by a dyke of the Midlands Minor Intrusive Suite along its axial plane (Bridge et al., 1998). The Midlands Microcraton was uplifted during this phase, with associated thrust faulting along the north-west and north-east margins (Smith, 1987). The Thringstone Fault, encountered in the subsurface in the Merry Lees mines, dips north-eastwards, emplacing Tremadoc rocks over Westphalian to the south-west (Butterley and Mitchell 1946). Farther south-east, Charnian rocks are probably emplaced over Carboniferous strata along this fault. This is considered to be the probable deformation boundary of the East Anglian Caledonides.

South of Church Stretton the BGS Longmynd seismic profile is interpreted as showing that late Precambrian Longmyndian with unconformably overlying Caradoc strata have been thrust south-eastwards over the less deformed, but more complete, early Palaeozoic succession of the Welsh Borderland (Smith, 1987).

The Midlands Microcraton occupied the buoyant back-arc region during Ordovician arc magmatism as indicated by: the near absence (due to nondeposition, or erosion) of post-Tremadoc Ordovician strata, emplacement of numerous minor intrusions of generally lamprophyric affinity (Thorpe et al., 1993), and a strong thermal overprint on sedimentary fabrics in Cambro-Tremadocian strata (Merriman et al., 1993). The emplacement of one of the intrusions has been precisely dated by U-Pb method at 442 Ma (Noble et al., 1993). The distribution of rocks below the Shelveian unconformity of part of the region is presented in Figure 6.

Silurian basin and shelf formation

The north-westward subduction of Iapetus beneath Laurentia continued throughout Llandovery and Wenlock times (Leggett et al., 1979). During this time, two deepwater basins became established, the Welsh Basin in the west and the Anglian Basin in the east (Figure 5c), respectively overlying the Precambrian Cymru and Fenland terranes. The merged Wrekin and Charnwood Precambrian terranes formed a buoyant block; the wedge-shaped Midlands Microcraton. On this block, there was episodic development of carbonates, contrasting strongly with flysch deposited in the rapidly subsiding deep water basins of Wales, northern England and East Anglia (Woodcock and Pharaoh, 1993). There are also substantial differences in deformational history between the Midlands Microcraton and surrounding basinal areas relating to the ensuing Acadian orogenic phase. The Midlands Microcraton has undeformed Silurian shelf facies, familiar from outcrop in the Welsh Borders and West Midlands (e.g. Dudley) and various boreholes in the region (Walsall, Codsall, Heath Farm) that contrasts strongly with the intensely deformed strata deposited in the deep water basins (Turner, 1949; Pharaoh et al., 1987a; Woodcock, 1991; Woodcock and Pharaoh, 1993).

Acadian deformation phase (Lower to Middle Devonian)

The final phase of Caledonian orogenic activity, referred to as the Acadian deformation phase (McKerrow, 1988; McKerrow et al., 2000) began at the close of Silurian times and led to the inversion of the deepwater Silurian turbidite basins. Strata were deposited first under shallowing marine, then brackish and eventually estuarine to braid plain conditions (Downtonian–Dittonian succession of the Welsh Borderland). This deformation arose due to impingement, then collision of yet another Gondwana-derived terrane, Armorica, with the southern edge of Avalonia following closure of the Rheic Ocean (Ziegler, 1982; 1990). During this process, the triangular-shaped Midlands Microcraton, the 'rigid indentor' of Soper et al. (1987), was driven northwards into the still slightly pliant, loose accretionary mosaic resulting from the soft collision/accretion of Laurussia some 20 to 30 Ma previously (Figure 5d). The north-east-trending Precambrian crustal lineaments lying to the north-west of the Midlands Microcraton, the Menai Strait and Welsh Borderland Fault Zones, were reactivated in a sinistral sense, whereas those with a north-west-trend, the inferred Charnwood Boundary Fault Zone, and the Dowsing–South Hewett Fault Zone of the southern North Sea (Pharaoh et al. 1995), are inferred to have experienced dextral transpression.

Acadian deformation was most intense in the thick sedimentary successions that lay on either side of the Midlands Microcraton, as basinal sediments that had accumulated in the deep basins of Wales and northern and eastern England marginal to the microcraton suffered strong folding, cleavage formation and metamorphic recrystallisation. It produced the 'paratectonic Caledonides' or 'slate belts' that wrap around the northern limit of the Midlands Microcraton (Soper et al., 1987) and also the cleavage affecting the Charnian Supergroup at outcrop. Representatives of these slate belts have been proved in the subsurface of the region. In the north-west, Milton Green and Prees boreholes sampled undated slaty rocks representative of the Silurian Welsh Basin, and the Ironville 5 Borehole penetrated cleaved Tremadoc strata to east of the apex of the microcraton (Figure 7). By contrast, the Silurian and older strata of the microcraton itself appear to have been little affected by Acadian deformation. The metamorphic grade of these rocks is diagenetic, and only locally, low anchizone (Merriman et al., 1993). In the Welsh Borderland, deformation was restricted to the open folding and tilting evident in the Ludlow Anticline just to the south of the region, and comparable structures. Folding of comparable style is believed to affect Silurian strata on the eastern flank of the microcraton under the Permo-Triassic Needwood Basin. Acadian thermal effects were sufficient however to reset Ar isotopic systems, as demonstrated by the K-Ar ages of about 405 Ma from the igneous amphiboles from the layered sills of the Nuneaton area (Bridge et al., 1998).

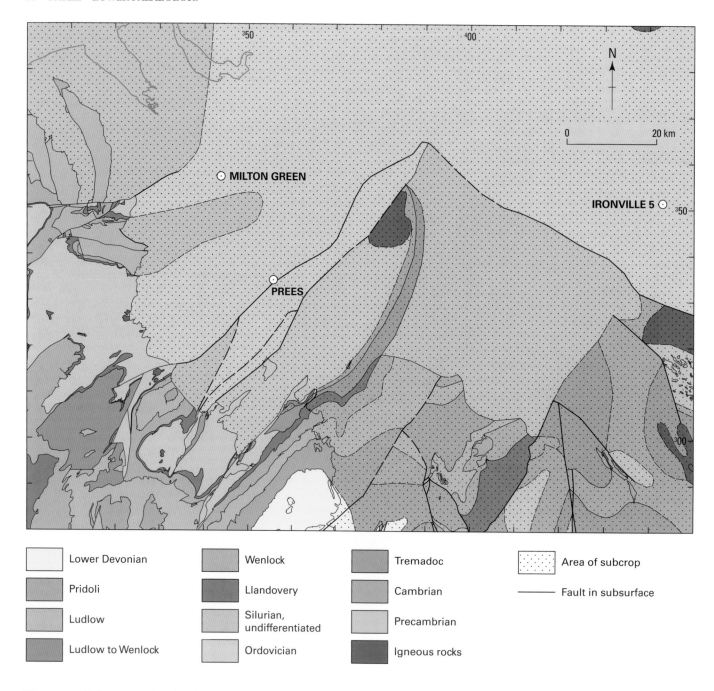

Figure 7 Subcrop to the Acadian (end-Middle Devonian) unconformity.

Lower Old Red Sandstone strata in Anglesey and possibly in East Anglia (Pharaoh et al., 1993) are cleaved, and Rb-Sr and K-Ar isotopic data suggest that the Acadian deformation lasted until Emsian time. The Rb-Sr whole rock isochron age of 399 ± 9 Ma obtained from the volcanic rocks in the Woo Dale Borehole of the Peak District is believed to reflect Acadian resetting of this system. Deposition of Upper Old Red strata in the region, in Frasnian time, followed a significant period of uplift and erosion. The distribution of rocks below the Acadian unconformity is presented in Figure 7.

LOWER PALAEOZOIC ROCKS OF THE REGION

Lower Palaeozoic rocks outcrop extensively in the west of the region, where there are few seismic profiles. In the east of the region this relationship is generally reversed, with several small inliers and more seismic profiles. Some of these inliers however, have no seismic profiles nearby, for example that at Dudley. Mapping the subsurface distribution of these rocks therefore relies on extrapolation from outcrop and borehole provings to provide control on the seismic interpretation. Because of the fragmentary nature of these data, it should be noted that there are

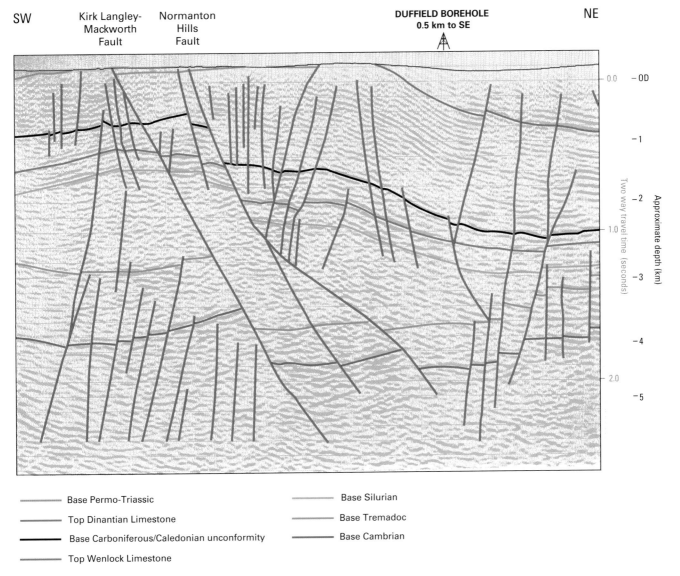

SW   Kirk Langley-   Normanton   **DUFFIELD BOREHOLE**   NE
        Mackworth   Hills   **0.5 km to SE**
        Fault   Fault

— Base Permo-Triassic

— Top Dinantian Limestone

— Base Carboniferous/Caledonian unconformity

— Top Wenlock Limestone

— Base Silurian

— Base Tremadoc

— Base Cambrian

Figure 8   BGS Duffield seismic reflection profile, southern part only. Seismic line illustrates the structure of the Pre-Carboniferous rocks and the structure of the southern margin of the Carboniferous Widmerpool Gulf to the north-east of the Normanton Hills Fault.

inevitably some gaps in knowledge about these strata in the region. For example, although successions of Lower Palaeozoic age in some boreholes (e.g. Heath Farm and Codsall; Figure 11) can be matched to well-developed reflections, these reflections cannot be identified on all seismic lines. In some cases a package of reflections may be defined that can be assigned to a particular age-range by correlation of reflection packages above and below but not of the unit itself. The geological identification of the reflections within these intervals may then rely on a qualitative correlation of seismic character with known stratigraphy, or with reflection packages on other seismic lines where the stratigraphy can be proved. An example

of this is the BGS Duffield seismic line (Figure 8) where a package of reflections is assigned to the Cambrian, by the correlation of lower reflections via adjoining seismic lines to Uriconian strata at the Heath Farm Borehole. The Tremadoc age of basement rocks at Ironville 5 to the north of the profile, and of higher reflections attributable to Carboniferous strata at crop are the other constraints. Elsewhere a borehole may prove rocks of a particular age at its terminal depth, but this may still leave room for uncertainty as to the geological identity of reflections below or laterally away from this point, for example on seismic profiles in the Sheffield–Chapel en le Frith districts, the nearby Eyam Borehole (Figure 9b) encountered rocks of early Arenig age (information from S Molyneux, 2001) beneath the Carboniferous unconformity. A seismically 'transparent' unit along the section that is stratigraphically higher is interpreted to arise from strata of Silurian age, but these could also contain Lower Devonian strata, whereas a strong deeper reflection, defining an unconformable relationship with still deeper reflections, is interpreted to represent the basal Cambrian succession, although there is no direct proof of this. However, in other areas, for example beneath the Cheshire Basin, there may be reflections that cannot be assigned unequivocally to any particular stratigraphical unit because there are no borehole provings or ties to other seismic lines where those reflectors or younger and older units have been identified.

Cambrian

Outcropping Cambrian rocks are restricted to the eastern margin of the Welsh Basin, where there are small and discontinuous outcrops along the Church Stretton Fault system, the eastern margin of the Midlands Microcraton at Charnwood (Carney et al., 2001) and the Nuneaton inliers within the Midland Microcraton (Figure 9a). Cambrian rocks are also proved in several boreholes (Walsall, Heath Farm, Rotherwood, Ticknall, Trickley Lodge) and the Sandwell Park Shaft. Reflectors assigned to Cambrian rocks, particularly the base Cambrian unconformity, have been identified on some seismic profiles, and extend to below 6000 m below the Permo-Triassic Needwood Basin. No rocks of Cambrian age are exposed or have been proved by drilling in the region within the Anglian basin to the north and north-east of the Midlands Microcraton.

Cambrian rocks at outcrop and in boreholes comprise basal quartzite and sandstone with overlying shale containing thin limestones. Stratigraphical nomenclature of the succession near Comley is outlined in Table 1. It should be noted that the Lickey Quartzite that crops out just to the south of the region in the Redditch district, and which was formerly correlated with the other basal Cambrian quartzites, is now considered to be no older than Ordovician (Molyneux, 1987a, b).

Cambrian syndepositional movement, controlling in particular the distribution of middle Cambrian rocks, has been postulated for the Leinthall Earls Fault, which is thought to have subsequently controlled the formation of the Ludlow Anticline just to the south of the region (Smith and Rushton, 1993). Seismic evidence suggests that the Brewood Fault to the east may also have undergone a similar movement history, with middle Cambrian rocks only preserved in the east, near to the fault (Figure 10). Middle Cambrian to Tremadoc strata may also be present beneath the Permo-Triassic Needwood and Knowle basins. Seismic profiles indicate an eastwards thickening of this succession towards the Western Boundary Fault at the eastern margin of the Knowle Basin, suggesting that this fault may have also been active during this time. Middle Cambrian strata are also present locally along the Church Stretton Fault zone where there is some evidence of synsedimentary fault

Table 1   Cambrian strata in the Comley area.

Age	Names	Lithology	Thickness (m)
Late	Black Shales and Grey Shales	mudstone	25
Mid	Billingsella Beds	sandstone	2
	P. rugulosus Sandstone and Grits	sandstone	6
	Shales	mudstone	90
	Comley Breccia Bed	blocks of Lower Cambrian	11
	Sandy flags	sandstone	2
	Shales	mudstone	90
	Paradoxides groomi Grits	sandstone	9
Early	Lapworthella Limestone	sandy limestone	0.1
	Protolenus Limestone	limestone	0.15
	Strenuella Limestone	limestone	0.23
	Lower Comley Sandstone Formation	glauconitic sandstone	150
	Wrekin Quartzite Formation	containing Uriconian clasts	46

movement; Middle Cambrian strata thicken towards the Wrekin Fault on the west of the fault, but are likely to be thin on the eastern side.

The distribution of clasts derived from Cambrian rocks has helped to locate basement uplifts and these clasts have been identified from Permian breccias in the Nechells Borehole and from 'espleys' within the Etruria Formation either side of the Knowle Basin.

The inferred distribution of both Cambrian and Ordovician rocks in the region has been strongly affected by the Shelveian deformational phase and the associated unconformity. The Lilleshall and South Staffordshire Highs are defined, underlying the Permo-Triassic Stafford Basin (Figure 6). These are separated by a basinal succession and bounded by north-east-trending faults. Anticlines and synclines within these structures trend north-westwards. On the central part of the South Staffordshire High, Upper Cambrian and Ordovician rocks are locally eroded and lower Cambrian strata (probably quartzite) subcrop beneath the Shelveian unconformity, as proved in the Heath Farm Borehole and the Walsall and Sandwell Park shafts. Similarly, there is evidence of erosion in the vicinity of Nuneaton in the south-east of the region, and on the north-east extension of the Lilleshall High, where Precambrian rocks subcrop in the core of anticlines.

Ordovician

Ordovician rocks crop out to the west of the Pontesford–Linley Fault in large tracts or in inliers surrounded by Llandovery strata (Figure 9b). At Shelve and the Breidden Hills, they form part of the Welsh Basin succession and contain volcanic rocks and intrusions. The Welsh Basin succession is much thicker and more complete than that on

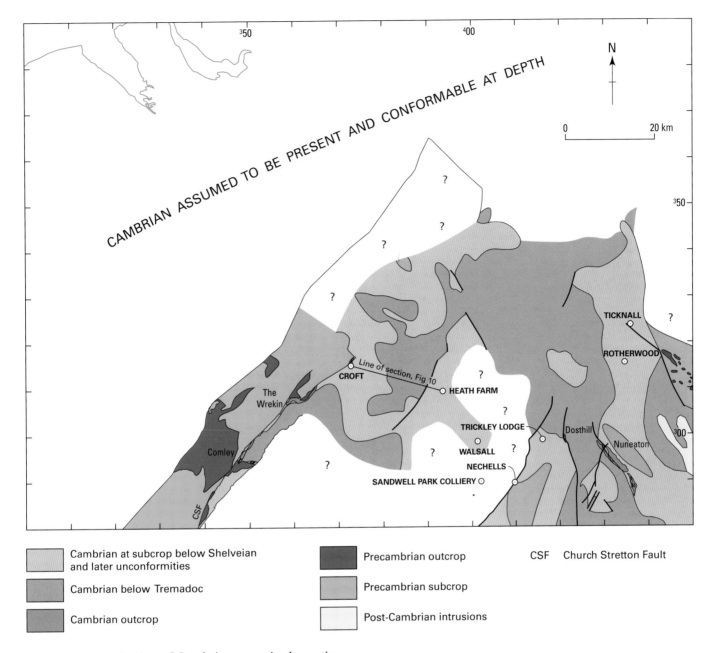

Figure 9a   Distribution of Cambrian strata in the region.

the Midlands Microcraton (Smith 1987) and strata range in age from Tremadoc to Ashgill (Williams et al., 1976). It is thought that the Pontesford–Linley Fault, with downthrow to the west, marked the edge of the Welsh Basin during Ordovician times.

On the Midlands Microcraton, Ordovician rocks were proved in a number of boreholes allowing their distribution to be partially mapped (Figure 6). As with Cambrian rocks, their distribution is much affected by the Shelveian and subsequent deformation. Most Ordovician strata on the Midlands Microcraton are of Tremadoc age, although the latest Tremadoc is generally absent. This succession is thought to have ranged up to 2000 m thick prior to erosion associated with the Shelveian deformation. Arenig and later strata are not present here (Smith,

1987) except at Lickey, just to the south of the region (Molyneux, 1987) where Arenig strata are encountered. This outcrop includes possible Tremadoc volcaniclastic beds of unproved thickness overlain by quartzites (Old et al., 1991). At Caradoc in Shropshire, just to the east of the Church Stretton Fault, and lying on the western margin of the Midlands Microcraton, there are outcrops of rhyolites and shaley sandstones and siltstones of Caradoc age (Greig et al., 1968) that unconformably overlie Longmyndian, Uriconian and Cambrian rocks.

The subsurface distribution of Ordovician rocks outside the Midlands Microcraton is poorly known. The only provings in the postulated Anglian Basin in the region are the Tremadoc rocks of the Ironville 5 Borehole and the early Arenig siltstone and shale proved in the Eyam

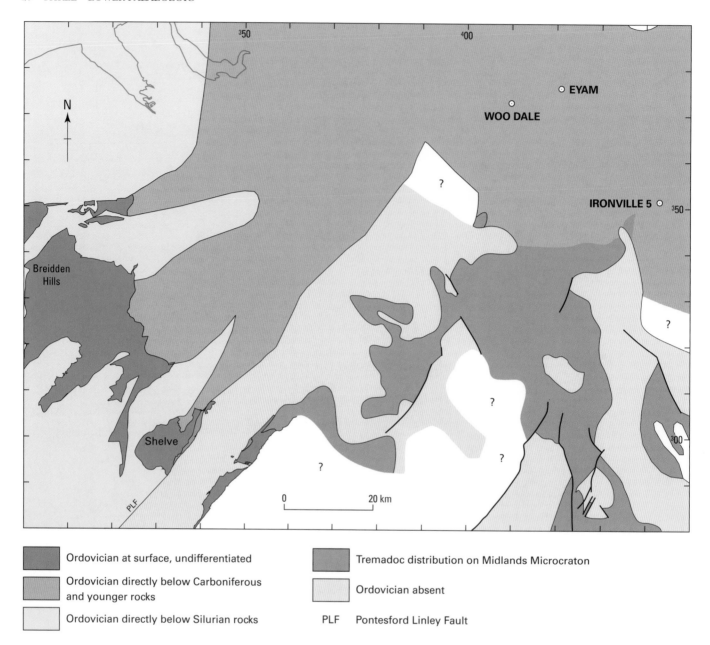

Figure 9b   Distribution of Ordovician strata in the region.

Borehole in Derbyshire. High amplitude reflectors in the north-east of Derbyshire, of a similar character to those originating from Caradoc strata seen on the BGS Longmynd seismic profile, may also indicate the presence of post-Tremadoc strata here. Llanvirn basinal sedimentary rocks were also proved in the Great Paxton Borehole in East Anglia to the south-east of the region.

Ordovician calc-alkaline volcanic and plutonic rocks are thought to be widespread and are believed to be the cause of the Derby–St Ives aeromagnetic anomaly (Lee et al., 1990; Pharaoh et al., 1993). The outcrop of grano-diorite with high magnetic susceptibility in the Mount-sorrel intrusion lies on this anomaly, emplacement of which is dated at 452 ± 10 Ma (Caradoc) using the U-Pb zircon method (Pidgeon and Aftalion, 1978; Noble et al.,

1993). Magnetic rocks have also been proved by borehole core, for example in the Rempstone and Kirby Lane boreholes, just outside the region. The Woo Dale Borehole in Derbyshire also proved felsic and intermedi-ate lavas and tuffs, although less magnetic than at the occurrences described above. These lavas yielded a Rb-Sr whole-rock isochron age of 399 ± 9 Ma (Pharaoh et al., 1991). However, the lavas have calc-alkaline affinities, comparable to the other rocks of proved Ordovician age, and this date is therefore interpreted as being indicative of Acadian hydrothermal resetting rather than the crys-tallisation age.

These plutonic and volcanic Ordovician rocks are thought to result from subduction of Iapetus–Tornquist oceanic lithosphere to the south beneath Avalonia

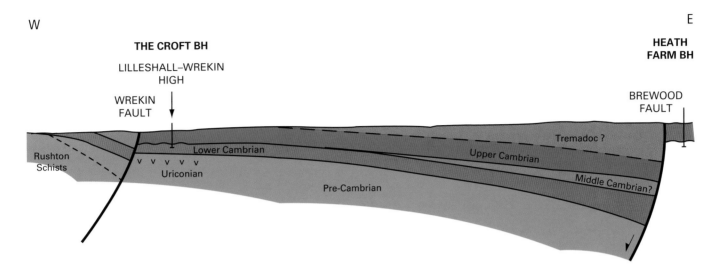

Figure 10 Schematic cross-section illustrating the development of possible Cambro-Ordovician basin between the Croft Borehole on the Lilleshall–Wrekin High and the Heath Farm Borehole in the footwall block to the Brewood Fault. Location of profile is indicated on Figure 9a.

(Pharaoh et al., 1993; Noble et al., 1993). It is likely that the geometry of this volcanic arc was controlled by the north-west-trending margin of the Midlands Microcraton.

Silurian

Silurian rocks of the Welsh Basin are exposed in the west of the region (Figure 11; Table 2), and comprise a thick basinal succession of Lower and Middle Llandovery rocks overlain by Upper Llandovery and Wenlock flysch deposits derived from the south-west, indicative of early Caledonian orogenesis (Wilson et al., 1992).

The Welsh Borderland lies in the western part of the region. It is a classic area of British geology and lies on the western margin of the Midlands Microcraton. Strata range from Llandovery to latest Přídolí in age, resting unconformably on rocks of Caradoc age and are overlain by early Devonian strata. The Much Wenlock Limestone of Wenlock Edge, trends north-east and dips to the south-east with prominent north-west-facing scarps, and passes south of the region into the Ludlow Anticline. Within the region, a few other inliers are present and show different trends, for example within the South Staffordshire Coalfield along the Russell's Hall Fault, near Sedgeley and near the Lickey Hills, just to the south of the region. A small Silurian (Přídolí) outcrop lies to the south of this fault at Lye.

The distribution of Silurian strata in the subsurface in the region and the age of the topmost preserved strata is presented in Figure 11. This is based on information from outcrops, boreholes, mine shafts and seismic data, and on the interpolation of possible sources of the fossiliferous clasts found in younger strata. In most cases there is an unconformable relationship between the topmost Silurian and overlying rocks, indicating a period of erosion prior to deposition of the Carboniferous succession. Elsewhere, such as under the Needwood and Stafford basins, the main unconformity appears to lie at the base of the Devonian. A correlation of Silurian strata proved in the Heath Farm, Codsall, Church Stretton 1 and 5 boreholes is presented in Figure 12. These show comparable wireline log characteristics and thicknesses of Wenlock to Přídolí strata to those of the Collington Borehole located just south of the region.

On the Midlands Microcraton, Silurian rocks were deposited following the Shelveian deformational phase and unconformably overlie Ordovician and older rocks. Silurian rocks are absent from a large area to the east of the Birmingham Fault (Figure 11), extending into East Anglia and the East Midlands (Smith, 1987). In the north of the Midlands Microcraton, available seismic data suggest that there is probably a subsurface continuation of the Silurian of the Welsh Borderland with the Silurian inliers of the South Staffordshire Coalfield, but this has not been proved by borehole evidence. Silurian rocks are thought to underlie large areas of the Needwood Basin

Table 2 Silurian strata of the Welsh Borderland.

Age	Formation
Přídolí	Ledbury/Raglan Mudstone Temeside Shale/Raglan Mudstone Downton Castle Sandstone
Ludlow	Aymestry (Sedgley) Limestone Elton (Lower Ludlow) Much Wenlock Limestone
Wenlock	Coalbrookdale Buildwas (Woolhope Limestone)
Llandovery	Hughley Purple Shale (Rubery) Pentamerus Sandstone Formation

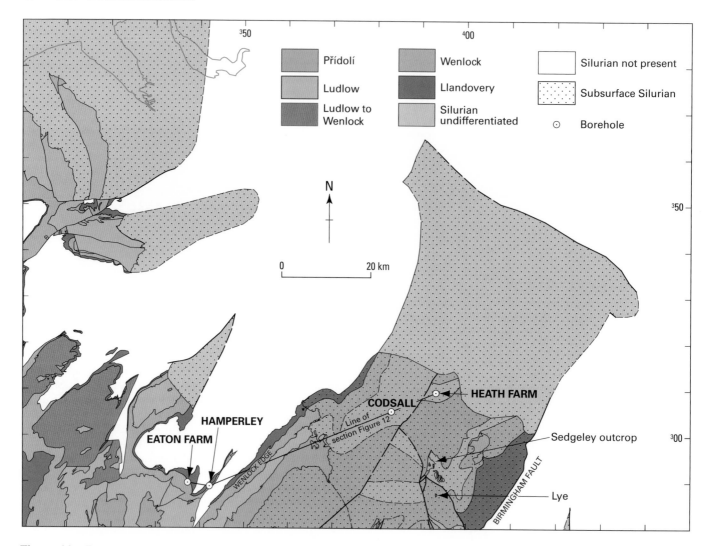

Figure 11   Distribution of Silurian strata across the region.

and Caldon Low district, and are traceable onto the BGS Duffield seismic profile from the Stafford area into the Needwood Basin, as far as the Derby High. The characteristic reflectors can be also be matched on seismic profiles in the Loughborough district, beneath the Hathern Shelf, where a clear basal Carboniferous unconformity overlies folded Silurian rocks.

Silurian pebbles are known from some breccias of late Carboniferous to Triassic age, overlying the strata of the South Staffordshire and Warwickshire coalfields (Shotton, 1927). Clasts have been found at several levels in the Warwickshire Coalfield but no Silurian rocks are present beneath this coalfield. Clasts have been found in the Hopwas and Clent breccias of the South Staffordshire Coalfield and surrounding area. Shotton (1927) hypothesised that the Warwickshire clasts had been derived from the Lickey area of the South Staffordshire Coalfield, just to the south of the region. However, the large pebble size (over 20 cm), which is greater in the west, and the distance of over 27 km (16 miles) to the postulated source, make it likely that they had a more local derivation from the Knowle basement. Combined with the

evidence of Cambrian and Dinantian clast derivation, Smith and Rushton (1993) have followed Wills (1956) in interpreting an uplifted Variscan block (Knowle Block) between the two coalfields.

Devonian

Lower Devonian rocks occupy the syncline to the north of the Ludlow Anticline in the Welsh Borderland with small outcrops of Upper Devonian rocks at Clee Hill and Merevale. Within the Welsh Basin, Lower Devonian strata are restricted to small areas just west of the Church Stretton Fault. They rest conformably on strata of Přídolí age and were folded and faulted during the last Caledonian (Acadian) deformation phase. Upper Devonian strata are thinner than the Lower Devonian succession, and in terms of tectonostratigraphy are considered to be part of the Dinantian rift phase (see Chapter 4).

Subsurface evidence suggests that the Lower Devonian rocks are generally absent due to post-'Caledonian' erosion, suggesting a greater degree of uplift over the main part of the Midlands Microcraton.

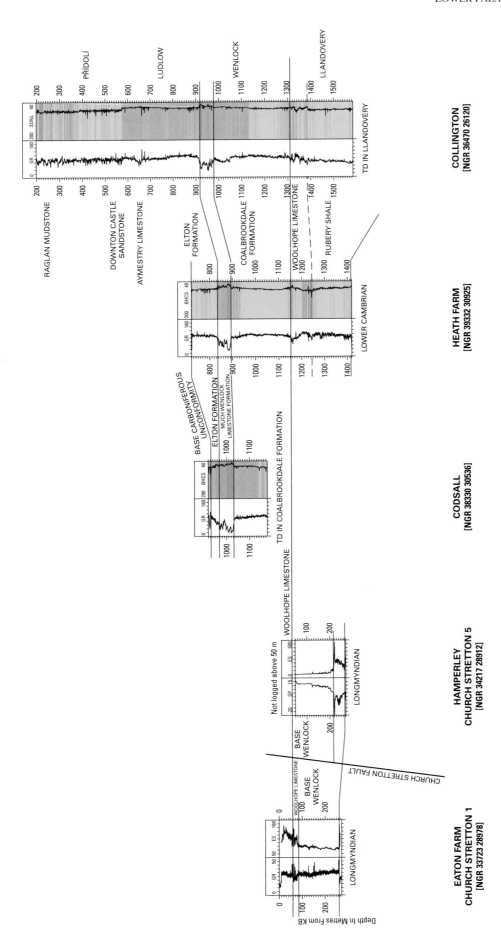

Figure 12 Geophysical log correlation of Silurian strata across the region. Location of profile is indicated on Figure 11.

Identification of rocks of this age is problematical in boreholes, and drilling is commonly terminated in this facies. Dating is not often precise owing to the lack of fossils (e.g. the Caldon Low and Alrewas boreholes in the Lichfield–Coalville area), and it is not always possible to distinguish Upper from Lower Devonian unless fish or palynological remains are found in the red beds. Lower Devonian strata have been proved only in the Highley Borehole beneath the Wyre Coalfield. They are thought to be present beneath Upper Devonian–Westphalian strata in the Clee Hills and at Brown Clee. Although the youngest rocks under the South Staffordshire Coalfield are generally considered to be Přídolí in age (King, 1921), some of the red beds may also include Lower Devonian strata.

FOUR

Late Devonian and Dinantian: extensional phase of upper Palaeozoic Basin development

In early Devonian times, the continents of Armorica and other Gondwana-derived terranes collided with Laurussia during the Acadian to Bretonian deformation phases (Figure 5). This region lay within the southern margins of the Laurussian continent that formed part of the Variscan Foreland. Erosion had reduced much of the land area to generally low relief, but there is evidence of some topographical relief (Aitkenhead and Chisholm, 1982; Aitkenhead et al., 1985; Chisholm et al., 1988). A tensional regime was established in the Variscan Foreland in late Devonian (Frasnian–Fammenian) times and the development of a series of linked half-graben was initiated. These formed part of a basin that extended at least from Ireland, eastwards through northern England, the East Midlands and North Yorkshire, the southern North Sea, Holland, Germany, Poland and ultimately to the Donets Basin of the Ukraine. These structures were to have a profound effect upon subsequent patterns of deposition and were the precursors of the main Dinantian Northumberland–Solway, Stainmore, Craven and Cleveland basins of Britain. The depocentres continued to grow as a result of pulsed rifting events into late Dinantian times resulting in strongly asymmetric rift basins, which were infilled largely with clastic sediments.

The late Devonian and Dinantian stratigraphy is known from outcrop and from boreholes across the region. The principal outcrops are in the Flint and Wrexham areas in the west and the Derbyshire Peak District in the east, with inliers to the south around Much and Little Wenlock. Late Devonian rocks are present in the south west of the region, notably around Clee Hill, although their development is restricted and poorly understood. The Dinantian strata comprise significantly less than 10 per cent of the outcrop, but are thought to exist at depth beneath more than half of the region (Map 2). Published information on the distribution and nature of the concealed Dinantian strata has been based largely on the 63 boreholes proving strata of Dinantian age. All are important in defining the extent of the Dinantian in the subcrop but are in the main of limited penetration and poorly constrained in terms of age. It is the hydrocarbon exploration wells such as the Milton Green, Blacon East, Ternhill, Stoke-on-Tern, Bowsey Wood, Bosley, Ironville 5, Erbistock, North Stafford and Ranton boreholes along with the Duffield and Eyam boreholes drilled by the BGS that have proved significant thicknesses of Dinantian strata, and in some cases complete successions. The boreholes provide lithological and age determinations, and important velocity data for depth conversion of the seismic reflection data. However, there are still significant areas in the subsurface where the detail is not known, seismic imaging is poor, or the isolated provings are difficult to relate to outcrop

sections. For example, the distribution of Carboniferous strata remains poorly understood beneath the southern part of the Cheshire Basin.

Geophysical investigations aimed at elucidating Dinantian structure and stratigraphy have, to date, relied mainly on an analysis of potential fields (gravity and magnetic), and are limited almost entirely to the areas in the north of the region, away from the areas of thick Permo-Triassic strata (for example Lee, 1988). There is a large dataset of reflection seismic data for the region, which is largely unpublished. This account utilises these data, in conjunction with the deep borehole data, to investigate the concealed Devonian and Dinantian strata.

The Dinantian succession, traditionally known as *Carboniferous Limestone*, comprises limestones of both shallow and deep-water origin, interbedded with mudstone and siltstone. Sandstones are not common. The exposed thickness of the Dinantian section ranges from a few metres to over 3200 m. In contrast to the Craven Basin where rocks of Tournaisian age are exposed (Charsley, 1984; Kirby et al., 2000), the oldest reliably dated strata exposed in the region are of late Chadian to Arundian age in Derbyshire and north Wales. The principal Dinantian depocentres of the region (Figure 13) are the Blacon Basin, with about 2000 m of Dinantian rocks, the Manchester–Winsford Sub-basin with a fill of up to 3000 m, the Alport Basin (4000 m), the Edale Basin with about 2000 m of platform carbonates, and the Widmerpool Gulf. In the Widmerpool Gulf, the Long Eaton Borehole proved the thickest (unbottomed) basinal Dinantian sequence of 2600 m; the full thickness may be up to 3200 m.

PRINCIPAL STRUCTURAL FEATURES

Structurally the region is subdivided into three domains. Each of these contains a series of fault-bounded highs and sub-basins that controlled the deposition of the Carboniferous strata, and were controlled by pre-existing basement structures (Figure 13). The **Iapetus (Cheshire) Domain** lies in the north-west, and faults trend predominantly north-east with downthrow to the north-west. The **Tornquist (East Midlands) Domain** lies in the north-east, and is separated from the Iapetus Domain by the Wem–Bridgemere–Red Rock Fault Zone, to the north of the Wales–London–Brabant Massif; the faults trend predominantly north-west with downthrow to the north-east. The **Midlands Microcraton Domain** lies on the northern flank of the Wales–London–Brabant Massif; fault trends range from north-west to north-east. The basin-margin faults are commonly several tens of kilometres in length and faults on opposed basin margins are generally not of

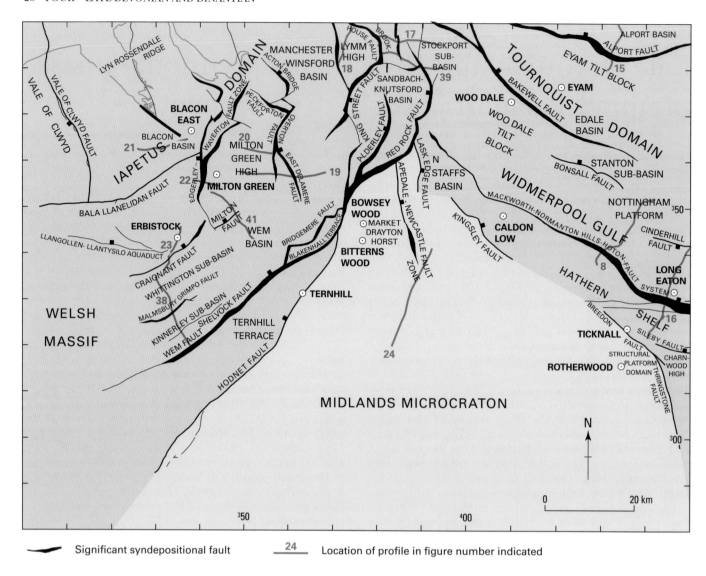

⬛ Significant syndepositional fault	24 Location of profile in figure number indicated

Figure 13 Principal early Carboniferous (synextensional) structures of the region.

equal magnitude, giving the basins a markedly asymmetrical profile.

The principal features of the Carboniferous basin-block system were fully formed by the end of the synextensional phase of basin development at end Dinantian times. In northern England, large, partially or wholly fault-bounded highs, referred to as *blocks*, include the Askrigg Block and Alston Block. These blocks are commonly underpinned by rigid, buoyant, basement granites and are characterised by thin, incomplete, synextensional sedimentary successions. However, in this region no granite-cored blocks have been identified, and structures fall into two basic categories:

- *high or shelf* These may be partially fault-bounded, and are characterised by thin, incomplete, synextensional sedimentary sequences. They generally form the crestal regions of tilted fault blocks

- *basin or sub-basin* These are characterised by thick, relatively complete, synextensional sedimentary

sequences. They are largely fault-bounded, and the major basin-margin faults show syndepositional normal displacement

Tornquist (East Midlands) Domain

This section describes structures from the Derbyshire, Staffordshire and East Midlands areas that reflect the influence of the underlying north-west-trending Caledonian basement fabric of the Tornquist Domain. The Thringstone Fault is a reverse fault that together with the Breedon, Kingsley and Lask Edge faults defines the south-west limit of the this domain and marks the southern limits of the Eastern Caledonides.

This area includes the Dinantian outcrops of the Peak District that lie at the core of the Pennine anticline, extending over an area of about 35 by 25 km. The surface folds and structures of this area have been known since the early 19th century (Farey, 1811; Watson, 1811), but interpretation of seismic borehole, gravity and magnetic data provide an insight into the relationships between basement structure and sedimentation. It is now recognised that the structure of the pre-Dinantian basement in north Derbyshire played a significant role in Dinantian sedimentation over the Derbyshire Dome and in the Edale Basin, (Aitkenhead et al., 1985; Gutteridge, 1987, 1991; Evans and Kirby, 1999; Ford, 1999; Kirby et al., 2000). Most models involve tilt blocks, but there are widely differing interpretations of the positions, trend and amount of throw on the buried faults, based upon the same information. There are very little seismic data over the Dinantian outcrop, and it must therefore be stressed that all these models are to some extent speculative. Proposed, but conflicting, models include:

- northerly tilted fault blocks controlled by faults that downthrow to the west or south-west, underlying the reefs at East Sterndale (Miller and Grayson, 1982)
- faults downthrowing to the north-east, producing the southerly dipping Eyam and Woo Dale tilt blocks (Smith et al., 1985)
- a more complex three tilt-block model beneath the Peak District, controlled by concealed northerly dipping, syndepositional faults and southerly dipping fault blocks (proposed by Gutteridge, 1987)

The model of Smith et al. (1985) is broadly followed in this account (Figure 14).

Alport Fault and Alport Basin

The Alport Basin is a half-graben that developed in the hanging-wall block of the Alport Fault and is thought to pass into the Gainsborough Trough to the east of the region. It contains up to 4000 m of Dinantian strata, most of which must be Arundian or older (as suggested by the Alport Borehole which terminated in strata of probable Arundian age); the strata thicken towards the Alport Fault. The Alport Fault is developed between the Alport and Edale boreholes (Evans and Kirby, 1999; Kirby et al., 2000) and has a downthrow to the north of up to 4 km. It is well constrained by seismic data and mapped as a large east- to east-south-east-trending fault extending into the north-east of the region (Figure 15). Much of the sedimentary fill within the Alport Basin was probably supplied from the contemporaneous carbonate platform developed over the Holme High to the north (Gutteridge, 1991; Evans and Kirby, 1999; Kirby et al., 2000). Strata of Arundian age in the Alport Borehole are overlain by about 126 m of shallow-water carbonates of Holkerian to early Asbian age. From mid-Asbian times, basinal mud and distal carbonates (about 200 m thick) become increasingly dominant, indicating a progressive starvation of the basin. This may have been related to the development of accretionary rimmed carbonate shelves (the Castleton Reef Belt) on the northern margin of the Derbyshire carbonate platform (Gutteridge, 1991). The subsequent Namurian basin (depocentre) was probably restricted to the area north of the Castleton Reef Belt.

Eyam Tilt Block: Bakewell Fault and Edale Basin

The Edale Basin is a half-graben that developed to the south of the Alport Fault, with the succession thickening towards the south-west. The Woo Dale and Eyam boreholes both penetrate the base of the Dinantian limestones, but there is a marked difference in the nature and thickness of successions proved in the boreholes. It is suggested that the southern bounding fault to the basin is the Bakewell Fault that trends west-north-west and downthrows to the north. This fault is largely concealed beneath late Dinantian shelf sedimentary rocks, but is likely to extend for over 50 km and underlie the Taddington–Bakewell Anticline (Gutteridge, 1987). The Woo Dale Borehole is interpreted as having proved the footwall block to the fault (marking the culmination of the Woo Dale tilt block to the south), which consists of pre-Carboniferous volcanic rocks beneath a thin cover of Dinantian strata at a depth of about 45 m below OD (Cope, 1979; Smith et al., 1985). To the north, the Eyam Borehole proved a varied Dinantian carbonate succession, 1800 m thick, within the hanging-wall block, and the succession may exceed 2200 m adjacent to the Bakewell Fault. This suggests that the basement of the Edale Basin is at great depth beneath the Castleton Reef Belt and that this Asbian reef belt built out northwards into the former basinal area. In contrast, Gutteridge (1991) proposed a more complicated basement structure for this area, suggesting that the Castleton Reef Belt is underlain and controlled by a major, concealed, down-to-the-north, syndepositional fault to the north of the Eyam Borehole. However, the limited seismic data from this area do not appear to support its presence.

Woo Dale Tilt Block

This forms part of the south-westerly dipping fault block that is bounded in the north by the Bakewell Fault, and in the south by the Mackworth–Normanton Hills–Hoton Fault System (Figure 13). The Dinantian succession thickens irregularly southwards. The Woo Dale Borehole proved a thin and incomplete succession, and the Bosley Borehole proved a thick basinal sequence. In the Caldon Low Borehole, a thick (over 170 m) succession of pebbly sandstone, siltstone and mudstone of possible Dinantian or Devonian age is overlain by Dinantian limestone and dolomite (Aitkenhead and Chisholm, 1982), and these were thought to lie in the hanging wall of the Mackworth–Normanton Hills–Hoton Fault System (Smith et al., 1985). Subsequently, a new interpretation suggests that they lie on the footwall block (Ebdon et al., 1990).

Bonsall Fault and Stanton Sub-basin

Towards the south-east of the Woo Dale tilt block, there is a fault terrace developed that is controlled by the Bonsall Fault, which trends parallel to the Bakewell Fault over a distance of 20 km. It is mapped as a down-to-the-north fault at basement level, but at outcrop the throw is to the south. This and its association with the Matlock

Figure 14 Schematic cross-section showing the development of Dinantian tilt blocks beneath Derbyshire Peak District. The location and relationships of carbonate reefs with respect to the underlying tilt blocks and controlling syndepositional faults is shown (based on Smith et al., 1985).

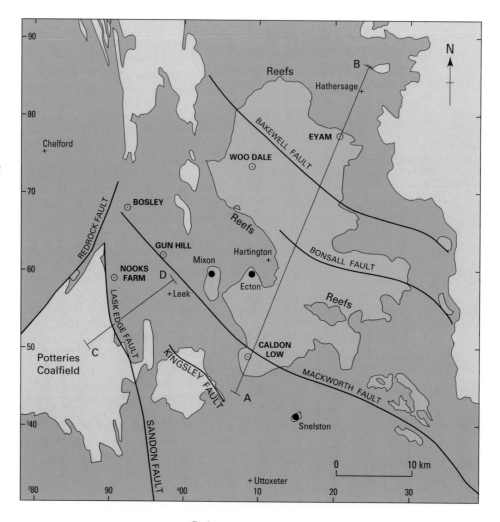

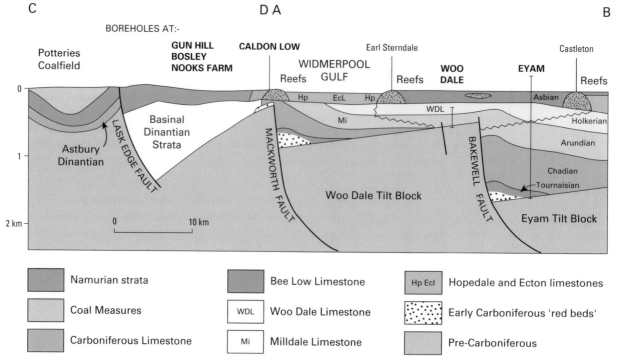

Namurian strata	Bee Low Limestone	Hp Ecl — Hopedale and Ecton limestones
Coal Measures	WDL — Woo Dale Limestone	Early Carboniferous 'red beds'
Carboniferous Limestone	Mi — Milldale Limestone	Pre-Carboniferous

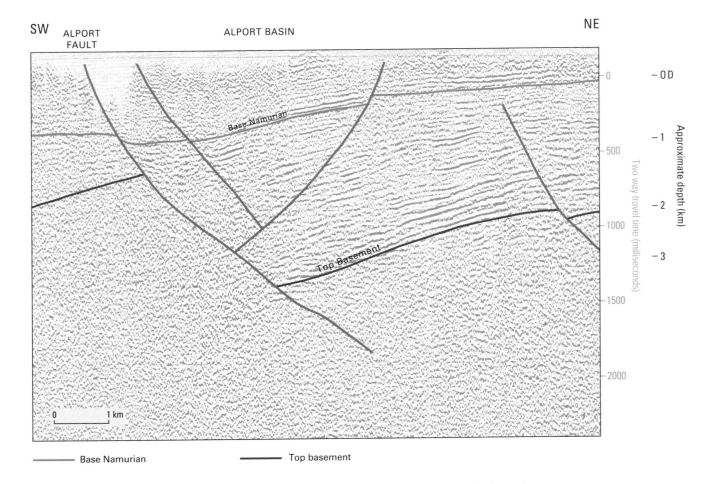

SW ALPORT FAULT   ALPORT BASIN   NE

Base Namurian

Top Basement

— 0 D

Approximate depth (km)

Two way travel time (milliseconds)

0

500

1000

1500

2000

0 — 1 — 2 — 3 —

0   1 km

‑‑‑‑‑‑‑‑‑ Base Namurian   ———— Top basement

Figure 15 Seismic reflection profile across the southern margin of the Alport Basin and the Alport Fault. Location of profile is indicated on Figure 13.

Anticline, and farther south-east with the Crich Anticline, indicates Variscan inversion. The Bonsall Fault controls the Stanton Sub-basin in which Dinantian strata are concealed mainly beneath Namurian strata within the Stanton Syncline. Gutteridge (1987) suggested that an easterly dipping carbonate ramp developed hereabouts during Brigantian times and that there was syndepositional movement on the Bonsall Fault.

Nottingham Platform and Cinderhill Fault

The Nottingham Platform is a narrow horst, bound to the north by the Bonsall Fault and to the south by the Cinderhill Fault that downthrows to the south and defines the north-east edge of the Widmerpool Half-graben. The pre-Dinantian basement lies at a relatively uniform depth of about 1500 m over the Nottingham Platform, and it is overlain by thin Dinantian strata of shallow-water origin. The Cinderhill Fault, mapped from surface exposure and mine records, forms a hinge zone that was reactivated during Permo-Triassic extension. Seismic sections and boreholes show that the hinge zone was a focus of Dinantian volcanic activity: an elongate pillow of basaltic lavas and tuffs extends from south-west of Matlock, via the Strelley 1 Borehole (which proved

some 380 m of volcanic rocks) into the Vale of Belvoir, where it continues as the Fosse Bridge Fault.

Mackworth–Normanton Hills–Hoton Fault System and Widmerpool Half-graben

The Mackworth–Normanton Hills–Hoton Fault System formed a major Dinantian syndepositional down-to-the-north extensional fault system that controlled the development of the southern boundary to the Widmerpool Half-graben and marks the northern margin of the Hathern Shelf area (Ebdon et al., 1990; Carney et al., 2001). The magnitude of late Dinantian downthrow on the fault system was reduced by subsequent (Variscan) inversion.

The *Mackworth Fault* is a north-north-west-trending, down-to-the-east, normal fault mapped from Chellaston in the outskirts of Derby, where it splays northwards off the Normanton Hills–Hoton Fault, via Osmaston to Mackworth (Figure 13). The *Normanton Hills–Hoton Fault* crosses the southern outskirts of Derby extending some distance to the east of the region; the total mappable length is 50 km, of which the western third is within the region. This fault was first recognised in the Mesozoic cover and named by Fox-Strangeways (1905); it is a normal fault, trending west-north-west and downthrows to the north. The dip of the fault plane appears to decrease with depth into the pre-Dinantian basement, eventually becoming a planar detachment with a relatively low dip of about 40º to north-north-east.

The west-north-west-trending *Widmerpool Half-graben*, also known as the Widmerpool Gulf (Falcon and Kent, 1960), is up to 17 km wide and lies partly within the region. It was controlled to the south by the Mackworth–Normanton Hills–Hoton Fault System and to the north by the Cinderhill Fault that downthrows to the south and breaks up the simple southerly dip of the tilt block, forming the southern margin of the Nottingham Platform (Fraser et al., 1990; Ebdon et al., 1990; Fraser and Gawthorpe, 1990). The seismic data (Figure 16) shows that the Widmerpool Half-graben contains over 3000 m of Dinantian strata (syn-rift sequence of Fraser et al., 1990, Ebdon et al., 1990), and up to 2500 m of later Carboniferous strata (post-rift). These thicknesses are considerably reduced up the dip-slope of the half-graben towards the north-east. Most of the syndepositional subsidence and deposition had already occurred by late Arundian times, and a prominent rollover anticline that was subsequently tightened during the Variscan inversion developed above the gently dipping detachment on the southern margin of the half-graben. The thickest sequences were proved in Long Eaton 1 Borehole (2596 m of Dinantian, terminating in late Tournaisian; Riley, 1997) and Ratcliffe on Soar 1 Borehole (1417 m of Dinantian strata up to early Asbian strata are overlain by 173 m of Namurian strata). A deep-water facies, the Widmerpool Formation, crops out in the area between Brailsford and Duffield, to the north-west of Derby, as a consequence of strong inversion in the vicinity of the Mackworth Fault. Shallow boreholes proved strata of a similar facies in the Trent valley, just north of Kings Newton.

Lask Edge Fault System, Kingsley Fault and North Staffordshire Basin

The north-north-west-trending North Staffordshire Basin and the Lask Edge Fault system form important Dinantian structures located near the northern apex of the Midlands Microcraton, to the west and south-west of the exposed Derbyshire Carbonate Platform. In this account we describe them within the Tornquist Domain, whereas Corfield et al. (1996) assign these structures to the Midlands Microcraton Domain.

The *Lask Edge Fault* was originally inferred from gravity data (Lee, 1988). It is a major north-north-west-trending Dinantian syndepositional fault that downthrows to the east and controls part of the south-western margin of the North Staffordshire Basin. East of Apedale in the Stoke-on-Trent district, it is concealed beneath a thick Carboniferous succession. Poor data quality makes it difficult to trace southwards. It seems likely that it is linked to the north-west-trending *Kingsley Fault* just to the south-east (Figure 13), across which there is a considerable thickening of the Dinantian succession, on the seismic data. However, it may continue *en échelon* as one offset of the Swynnerton Fault into the Sandon Fault, an important east-dipping fault that defines the western margin of the Permo-Triassic Needwood Basin. The *Market Drayton Horst* forms the footwall to the Lask Edge Fault and here 2500 m of Westphalian sedimentary strata are preserved in the north-north-east-trending Potteries Syncline. In the hanging wall of these faults the Carboniferous succession is deformed into a series of north-trending folds (the Eastern Folds of Rees and Wilson, 1998), which were formed during Variscan compression.

The North Staffordshire Basin is a westerly dipping half-graben, and the western margin is controlled by the Lask Edge Fault (Trewin and Holdsworth, 1973; Lee, 1988). It is also referred to as the Goyt Trough (Lee, 1988) or Goyt Low (Ebdon et al., 1990).

Sileby–Thringstone Faults, Hathern Shelf and Charnwood High

This series of structures lies on the complex boundary of the Wales–London–Brabant Massif and the Eastern Caledonides, although previous authors have placed this area within or on the Midlands Massif of the Wales–London–Brabant Massif (Corfield et al., 1996; Rees and Wilson, 1998). However, cleaved Caledonian basement of an Acadian (late Caledonian) age is present in the Ticknall Borehole on the Hathern Shelf and the basement rocks of the Charnwood High. The presence of cleaved rocks and the grade of metamorphism suggest that the Hathern Shelf and Charnwood Massif lie within the Caledonides domain. It is here suggested that this domain and thus the limit of the Caledonides, is defined by the north-west-trending Thringstone Fault to the south-west.

The *Hathern Shelf* is floored by Caledonian basement of Cambrian–Tremadoc age and locally intruded by stocks of granodiorite and granite of the Mountsorrel type. It forms an intermediate terrace, juxtaposed between the Wales–London–Brabant Massif and Charnwood High, and the Widmerpool Half-Graben. The Hathern Shelf is a southerly tilted block, bounded on the north-east by the Mackworth–Normanton Hills–Hoton Fault System, and to the south by the Sileby and Thringstone faults. The variation in the thickness and facies of Dinantian strata indicate that syndepositional faulting occurred at various times on the Hathern Shelf. The Hathern 1 Borehole, located towards the top of the tilt-block, proved 357 m of Dinantian strata and terminated in anhydrite of Tournaisian age. Controlled by early faulting along the Sileby Fault, subsidence continued until late Chadian times, when the main extension appears to have been transferred onto the Mackworth– Normanton Hills–Hoton Fault System and the deepening of the Widmerpool Half-graben occurred (Ebdon et al., 1990; Carney et al., 2001). Thereafter, the rate of subsidence was slower on the Hathern Shelf, and extensive uplift and erosion of the footwall occurred during rifting in Chadian–Holkerian times (EC3 rift phase of Ebdon et al., 1990). This is reflected by the prominent intra-Dinantian angular unconformities recorded in Cloud Hill Quarry, Breedon, where the Milldale Limestone Formation (Early Chadian)

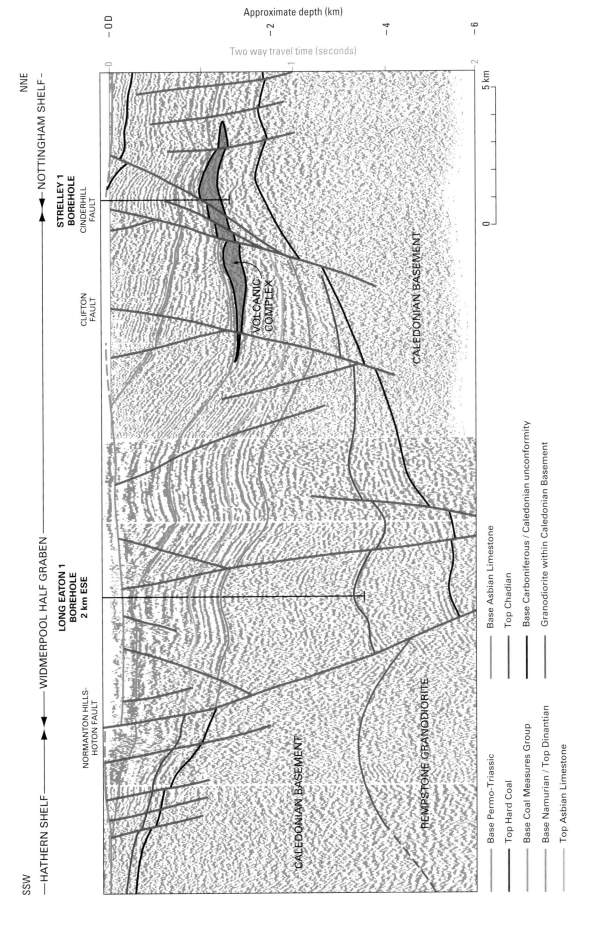

Figure 16 Seismic reflection profile across the southern margin of the Widmerpool half-graben, the Normanton–Mackworth Fault Zone and the Hathern Shelf. Location of profile is indicated on Figure 13.

is unconformably overlain by the Cloud Hill Dolostone Formation, of ?Holkierian to early Asbian age (Ambrose and Carney, 1997). Slump-induced folding in upper Asbian strata indicates continued tectonic instability. Further uplift in early Namurian times has resulted in the preservation of the Edale Shale Group (Pendleian) only in the north-east part of the shelf (Carney et al., 2001).

The *Sileby Fault* trends east-south-east in the southern outskirts of Loughborough, passing to the east of the region, subparallel with the Normanton Hills Fault (Figure 13). It defines the southern limit of the Hathern Shelf and is displaced by north-north-west-trending faults associated with the uplift of the Charnian basement in the Charnian Anticline (Carney et al., 2001). Up to 1650 m of downthrow to the north-east is suggested by the preserved stratigraphical thicknesses observed on seismic sections, and some of these Dinantian sequences encountered in the deeper boreholes have been tentatively identified as the attenuated equivalents of the Widmerpool Formation (for example Carney et al., 2001).

On the *Charnwood High*, Carboniferous strata are thin or absent. The high is bounded to the north by the Sileby Fault and to the south-west by the north-west-trending Thringstone Fault. Dinantian carbonate strata locally overstep onto the high, for example at Grace Dieu (Carney et al., 2001). The CHARM seismic reflection line acquired by Leicester University (Maguire, 1987) crosses the Charnwood High, but the complex internal structure is not well imaged by this profile; north-east-dipping planar reflectors image a basement shear zone, which is correlated with the Thringstone Fault.

The *Thringstone Fault* is a north-west-trending reverse fault. It can be traced from near Ticknall in the north, where its influence is considerably diminished and it is presumed offset by east–west-trending structures (Carney et al., 2001), south-eastwards to where it joins the Sileby Fault, and beyond this it forms the southern margin of the Charnwood High. The Thringstone Fault is a major Variscan inversion structure of the Variscan Foreland. It delimits that part of the Anglo-Brabant Massif dominated by Charnian rocks from the part underlying the Leicestershire Coalfield in which Cambrian–Tremadoc strata (proved in Rotherwood Borehole) are preserved. In Merry Lees Drift, near Coalville, a hade of 40° to the north-east was recorded (Butterley and Mitchell, 1946; Worssam and Old, 1988). Downthrow to the west along the fault ranges from about 500 m near Thringstone to about 300 m just south of Ticknall.

The *Breedon Fault* is a north-west-trending, down-to-the-west reverse fault that is largely concealed by Permo–Triassic cover. It is an important Variscan inversion structure linked to the Charnwood Anticline, and controls the present-day distribution of Namurian and Dinantian strata across the Hathern Shelf. Evidence for its presence is found at Breedon Hill and Cloud Hill quarries where, contrary to earlier interpretations of diapirism (Spink, 1965), it can be shown to be linked to basement faulting (Carney et al., 2001).

Iapetus (Cheshire) Domain

The Iapetus Domain includes the Welsh Massif and Cheshire plain areas of the region. The structure reflects the influence of the underlying north-east-trending Caledonian basement. Here we take the Wem–Bridgemere–Red Rock Fault System to define the south-east limit of the Iapetus Domain and thus to mark the southern limit of the Western 'Welsh' Caledonides.

Wem Basin and associated structures

Perhaps the most important structure within this domain is the *Wem–Bridgemere–Red Rock Fault System* that extends for over 110 km in a north-east–south-west direction (Figure 17). It comprises a series of large north-westerly dipping, down-to-the-west normal faults that lie along a major lineament in the Precambrian to Lower Palaeozoic basement, which has a long history of reactivation; it includes the *Pontesford–Linley Fault* and the *Clun Forest Disturbance*, to the south-west of the region (Wills, 1978; Woodcock, 1984b; Soper et al., 1987). Small east to north-east-trending transfer faults are also present along the fault zone, most notably defining the northern boundary of the *Blakenhall Terrace*. The constituent faults of the Wem–Bridgemere–Red Rock Fault System have a planar or subplanar geometry, and show a systematic variation in dip along the length of the fault system. The Red Rock Fault has moderate westerly dips (45° to 60°). To the south, the Wem and Bridgemere faults show significantly steeper north-westerly dips (60° to 70°). The observed total throw across the fault zone is in excess of 4000 m at the base of the Permo-Triassic strata in the south-central section, with throws on the Wem and Bridgemere faults locally in excess of 2500 m (Evans et al., 1993; Chadwick, 1997). The basement lineament has a long history of movement dating from the mid-Ordovician and possibly Proterozoic times onwards. Details of movement on the Wem–Bridgemere–Red Rock Fault System during the Carboniferous are sketchy owing to the poor quality data across the fault zone. However, isopachs (Map 2), outcrop and borehole data suggest that the *Pontesford–Linley–Wem–Hodnet* faults acted as down-to-the-west, syndepositional, normal faults in Dinantian times. The *Ternhill Terrace* forms the footwall block to the southern regions of the main Wem–Bridgemere–Red Rock Fault System and is itself, controlled by the Hodnet Fault to the east. The Ternhill Borehole proved some 100 m of Dinantian strata over this structure. However seismic reflection data in the area are of poor quality and limited extent, and provide little convincing evidence of the nature of the basement structure or the thickness of strata across the terrace.

The *Wem Basin* (Figure 13) is located in the hanging-wall block to the Wem Red Rock Fault System and is entirely concealed beneath the Silesian and Permo-Triassic rocks of the Cheshire Basin. Its development in Dinantian times can be interpreted from changes in the thickness of strata in the *Milton Green High* and across the Wem–Red Rock Fault system. Dinantian strata appear to thicken from the crest of the fault block forming the footwall block to the Craignant–Edgerley–Waverton Fault Zone south-eastwards into the controlling Wem–Bridgemere–Red-Rock Fault System. However, Dinantian isopachs reflect only the preserved thickness

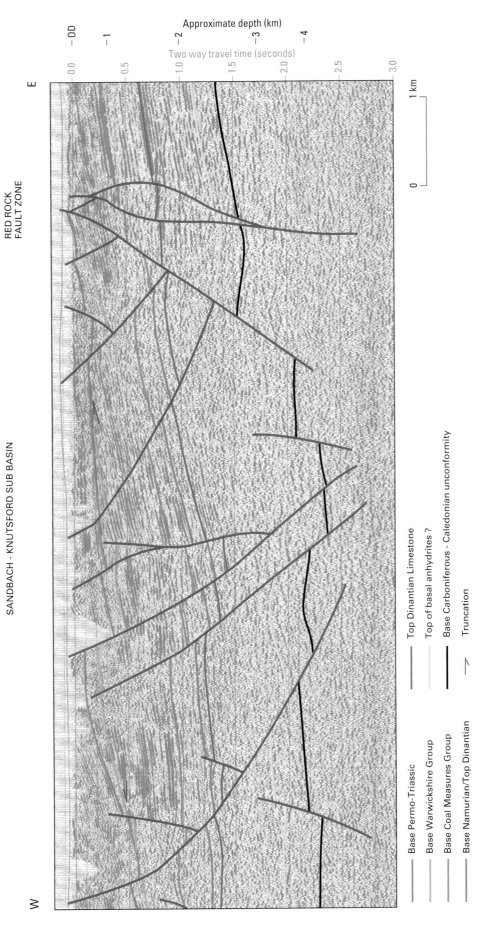

Figure 17 Seismic reflection profile across the Red Rock Fault Zone. Illustrates the seismic character of the Silesian section and the truncational unconformities at the base Permo-Triassic and the Warwickshire Group (Symon unconformity) that is itself removed by the inversion and erosion adjacent to the fault zone. Location of profile is indicated on Figure 13.

of the strata, and depositional thickening is not apparent. Subsequent Variscan compressional movements led to reactivation of the Wem–Bridgemere–Red Rock Fault System and basin inversion with uplift and erosion of the Dinantian basinal sequences, such that in the south-west, Lower Palaeozoic strata subcrop at the base Permo-Triassic unconformity (Figure 38).

The Wem Basin is divided into two sub-basins by the Maesbury Marsh–Grimpo Fault that has a curved north-east trend and down throws to the north-west (Figure 13). This fault is linked to one which has an offset of 5 km in the Dinantian strata south-west of Oswestry. Dinantian syndepositional movements produced the *Whittington Sub-basin* to the north and the *Kinnerley Sub-basin* to the south. The estimated thickness of Dinantian strata over the footwall block is around 275 m, although it is possible that the full succession is not preserved due to erosion associated with the base Permo-Triassic unconformity. The base of the Carboniferous in the Whittington Sub-basin is not well constrained, although up to 900 m of Dinantian strata may be preserved. The northern limit of the Whittington Sub-basin is controlled by the *Craignant Fault* that marks the southern limit (and footwall block) of the *Erbistock Basin*.

A smaller east–west trending fault, the *Shelvock Fault* (Figure 39) bisects the Kinnerley Sub-basin, but variations in the thickness of Dinantian strata across this fault are not pronounced. It is thought to be related to the change in orientation of the Dinantian outcrop to the south of Pant, and also by reactivation to the east–west faults mapped between West Felton and Shelvock (Wedd et al., 1929; GSGB, 1972).

The Maesbury Marsh–Grimpo and Shelvock faults perhaps indicate that the Dinantian carbonate platform, and with it the northern edge of the Wales–London–Brabant Massif in north Wales, was defined by a series of *en échelon* faults and associated transfer or relay ramps.

Sandbach–Knutsford Basin and associated structures

The *Brook House–King Street Fault Zone* is a complex, sinuous down-to-the-east structure comprising a number of segments. A near-vertical north-east-trending segment that may be a transfer fault, links two north-west-trending segments. Over 35 km in length, the fault zone is one of the most important structures in the northern part of the region (Figure 18). During Dinantian times it controlled the development of a generally westerly tilted fault block that formed the *Sandbach–Knutsford Basin*. The footwall block forms the Lymm High, the up-dip crestal region of the westerly dipping tilt block that controlled the development of the Manchester–Winsford Basin to the west (see below). Dinantian thicknesses changes across the fault zone may be up to 600 m.

To the west of Astbury, Dinantian strata thicken across the central regions of the Wem–Bridgemere–Red Rock Fault System into the Sandbach–Knutsford Basin (Figure 13). In contrast to the Wem Basin, the fault block containing this basin dips westwards. It is controlled by the down-to-the-east *Brook House–King Street Fault System* against which the Dinantian reaches thicknesses of up to 1600 m. This is compared to the estimated thickness of 1400 m at

crop in the footwall block around Astbury, where the Asbian–Brigantian section is estimated to be up to 110 m thick, and consists of reefal limestone passing upwards into interlayered mudstone, limestone and volcanic material (Evans et al., 1968). In the north-eastern reaches of the Sandbach–Knutsford Basin, the *Stockport Sub-Basin* is defined by a significant thickening of the Dinantian strata to over 2000 m in a narrow north-south-trending graben adjacent to the Red Rock Fault. The basin appears to be a narrow faulted terrace developed between two splays of this fault zone. Failure on the fault led to a rapid northerly deepening and the deposition of a thicker Dinantian sequence. The eastern margin is controlled by the Red Rock Fault, and the western margin by a north–south-trending fault that downthrows to the east.

The *Alderley Fault* splays north-north-east and lies in the hanging-wall block of the Red Rock Fault, cutting across the Sandbach–Knutsford Basin for some 30 km. It formed an important down-to-the-west structure in Permo-Triassic times, separating the *Alderley High* from the much deeper *Sandbach Basin* to the west (Chadwick et al., 1999). Earlier syndepositional movements on the fault can be interpreted by the change in thickness of the Dinantian sequence in the hanging-wall block.

Manchester–Winsford Basin and associated faults

The form of the *Acton Bridge–Overton–East Delamere Fault Zone* mirrors that of the Brook House–King Street Fault Zone 15 km to the east (Figure 13). It constitutes a complex major down-to-the-east north–south-trending structure 35 to 40 km long; individual faults are planar and of moderate dip, but become steeper in the south. Seismic reflection data indicate that Dinantian strata are over 1000 m thicker to the east of the fault, which suggests early Carboniferous syndepositional movement. This thickening defines the *Manchester–Winsford Basin* to the north of and *en échelon* with the Wem Sub-basin (Figure 13). Seismic data suggest that Dinantian strata may be up to 1800 m thick in the deepest parts of the basin, against the Acton Bridge Fault (Figure 19), but the strata have not been proved in boreholes.

Clotton and Peckforton Faults

The *Clotton Fault*, mapped at surface 4 km to the west of the Acton Bridge–Overton-East Delamere Fault Zone, is a normal fault downthrowing to the east and trending north-south; it displaces Permo-Triassic strata by about 300 m (Earp and Taylor, 1986). Seismic reflection data show a gradual thickening of the Dinantian strata eastwards over the footwall block with marked changes across the fault, indicating early Carboniferous syndepositional movements (Figure 20). To the south it is mapped swinging to the south-west and, traced northwards, it appears to coalesce with the Acton Bridge–Overton–East Delamere Fault Zone at basement levels. The *Peckforton Fault* is a complex down-to-the east fault developed between the Clotton and Acton Bridge–Overton–East Delamere Fault Zone (Figure 13). In the south it is developed in the hanging-wall block of the Clotton Fault where it appears as a short-cut fault,

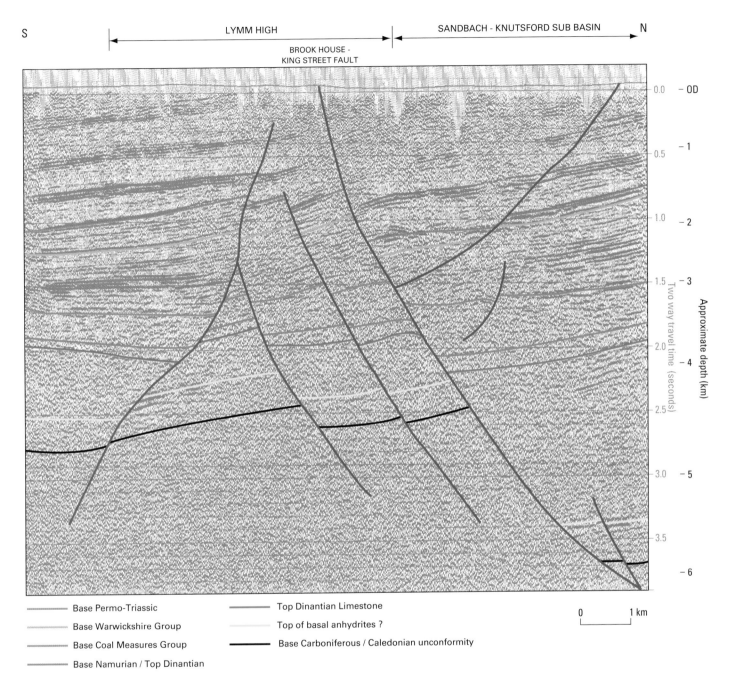

Figure 18 Seismic reflection profile across the Brookhouse–King Street Fault Zone, illustrating the Lymm High and the possible eastwards (syndepositional) thickening of the Dinantian across the fault into the Sandbach–Knutsford Sub-basin. Location of profile is indicated on Figure 13.

detaching on the Clotton Fault and having little effect upon Carboniferous strata.

Vale of Clwyd and Clwyd Fault System

The Vale of Clwyd Fault System (Anderson, 1951) defines the eastern side of the Vale of Clwyd. To the west, Silurian, Carboniferous and Triassic strata are cut by a series of more northerly trending *en échelon* faults (Denbigh, Llanrhaiadr, Rhewl and Llanfair faults), antithetic to the Vale of Clwyd Fault System. Gravity and resistivity studies indicate that these antithetic faults probably cut across the vale. They intersect the *Vale of Clwyd Fault* (Wilson, 1959; Collar, 1974), which downthrows to the west and has a displacement of around 450 m north-west of Tremeirchion, juxtaposing Triassic

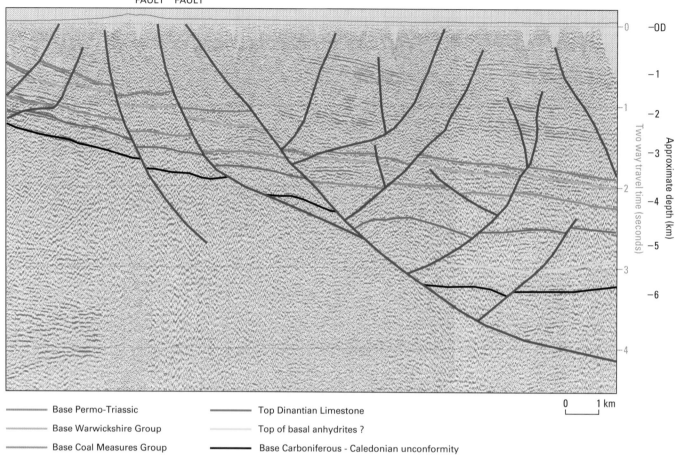

Figure 19 Seismic reflection profile across the southern reaches of the Peckforton–East Delamere–Overton Fault Zone. Illustrates the down-dip regions of the Milton Green High and the possible eastwards (syndepositional) thickening of the Dinantian across the fault into the Manchester–Winsford Sub-basin. Location of profile is indicated on Figure 13.

rocks against Carboniferous Limestone and Silurian (Elwy Group) strata. The fault extends offshore along the east of the Rhyll Sub-basin (BGS, 1994; Jackson et al., 1987) and traced southwards the throw decreases. In the Wrexham district, displacement is taken up on a series of subparallel fractures forming an anastomosing network enclosing inliers of various Westphalian and Dinantian formations. The main subsidiary structures include a fault near Bodfari that has a downthrow to the east of around 180 m and juxtaposes Carboniferous Limestone against Silurian strata (Elwy Group; Warren et al., 1984), and to the north the subparallel Marian Ffrith Fault shows a normal downthrow to the east.

The Vale of Clwyd half-graben and the displacement on related faults are indicative of dextral wrenching, consistent with east–west Permo-Triassic extension (Collar, 1974; Davies et al., 2004). The effects of this period of extension are widely recognised in the East Irish Sea Basin and northern England (Jackson et al., 1987;

Jackson and Mulholland, 1993; Evans et al., 1993; Chadwick and Evans, 1995). The pre-Triassic history of movement on the faults of the Vale of Clwyd is poorly understood. Most geophysical models show little or no change in the thickness of the Carboniferous strata across the basin into the Vale of Clwyd Fault (Powell, 1956; Wilson, 1959; Collar, 1974). However, interpretations of the offshore seismic profiles indicates that changes in thickness seen in the Dinantian and Silesian strata also pass onshore into the Vale of Clwyd Fault, thus suggesting some syndepositional movement (Jackson and Mulholland, 1993; BGS, 1994). Documented thickness changes in the Basement Beds across many faults (Warren et al., 1984) supports syndepositional movement on the Vale of Clwyd and associated faults during Carboniferous times. The distribution and thickness of late Chadian and early Arundian facies also suggest that a Clwydian Horst, bounded by the Vale of Clwyd Fault on the west existed at those times (Davies et al., 2004).

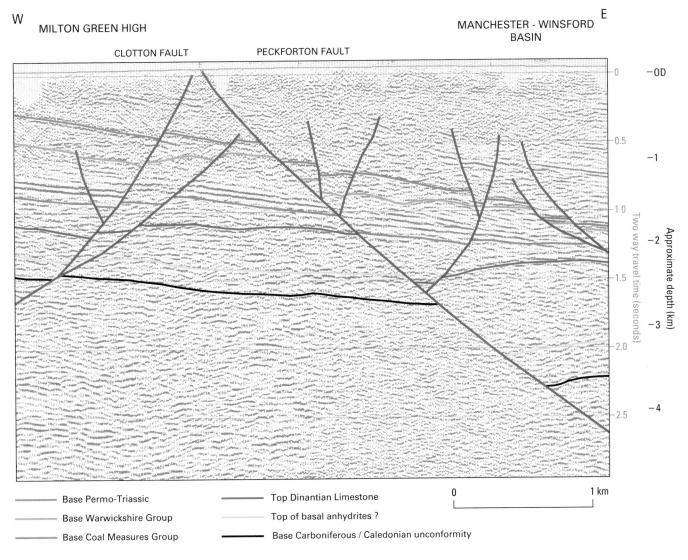

W   MILTON GREEN HIGH

CLOTTON FAULT   PECKFORTON FAULT

MANCHESTER - WINSFORD
BASIN   E

─────── Base Permo-Triassic   ─────── Top Dinantian Limestone

─────── Base Warwickshire Group   ─────── Top of basal anhydrites ?

─────── Base Coal Measures Group   ─────── Base Carboniferous / Caledonian unconformity

0   1 km

Figure 20   Seismic reflection profile across the northern part of the Peckforton–East
Delamere–Overton Fault Zone, where the Peckforton Fault is subordinate to the Clotton Fault.
The East Delamere Fault is east of the section shown. Illustrates the down-dip regions of the
Milton Green High and the possible eastwards (syndepositional) thickening of the Dinantian
across the fault into the Manchester–Winsford Sub-basin. Location of profile is indicated on
Figure 13.

Bala–Bryneglwys–Llanelidan Fault Zone

Dinantian thickness and facies changes noted in the area
were initially ascribed to posthumous folding (Smith and
George, 1961). However, evidence for the Blacon Basin
can be seen in borehole and seismic data (Figure 21).
The thicker Dinantian successions to the north (hanging
wall) of the Bala–Llanelidan Fault Zone and the west of
the Edgerley–Waverton Fault are interpreted as
synsedimentary.

The structure of the Bala Lineament and the
Bala–Bryneglwys–Llanelidan Fault Zone and its
movement history is fundamental to the understanding
of the sedimentary and tectonic evolution of north
Wales. Controlling the position of the Dinantian Corwen

outlier, it stretches from Cardigan Bay through north
Wales and extends beneath the Permo-Triassic crop of
the Cheshire Basin (Figure 2). Within the region at crop,
it comprises a series of north-east-trending, *en échelon*
faults that include the Tal-y-Lyn, Bala and Bryneglwys
faults (Fitches and Campbell, 1987). The easterly
trending Llanelidan Fault is also included, and towards
the southern end of the Vale of Clwyd, intersects and
appears to truncate the Bryneglwys Fault (Wedd et al.,
1928). Typically, the dominant sense of throw on the
lineament is northwards, juxtaposing Lower Palaeozoic
rocks against Carboniferous strata deposited in what is
recognised as the Blacon Basin: a Dinantian depocentre
developed to the north of the fault zone. To the north-
east of the intersection with the Minera Fault, the

lineament becomes a complex, anastomosing fault belt, across which, in general, the sense of downthrow appears to be southerly (Davies et al., 2004).

The Dinantian *Blacon Basin* is formed within the hanging-wall blocks of the Bala–Bryneglwys–Llanelidan Fault Zone and Edgerley–Waverton Fault Zone; locally, adjacent to the fault, the Dinantian succession is thought to be over 2000 m thick. Although late Asbian and Brigantian rocks thicken on the downthrown side of the fault zone (Somerville and Strank, 1984), most of the displacement appears to have occurred early in Dinantian times. Undated Basement Beds, and Arundian to early Asbian rocks and older rocks are thick to the north of the faults, yet absent to the south over their footwall-blocks. This basin lies in an area formerly recognised as part of the North Wales Platform and Lancashire Shelf: Asbian reef knolls overlain by proximal turbidite limestones of Brigantian age proved by the Croxteth Borehole in the Liverpool district (Magraw and Ramsbottom, 1956) just north of the region, were seen as the eastwards and northwards extension of the north Wales platform margin (for example Ramsbottom, 1969; Warren et al., 1984; Strank, 1985; Fraser et al., 1990).

Almost entirely concealed beneath Silesian and Permo-Triassic rocks, the *Llŷn–Rossendale Ridge* (Jackson and Mulholland, 1993) forms a tilted fault block dipping south-eastwards from an area of high basement on the Wirral. However, poor quality seismic reflection data hereabouts mean that the basin architecture it is not well constrained. To the west, the shallow-water Dinantian successions cropping out around Minera are 260 m thick developed on the up-dip margins of the tilted fault block. The succession proved in the Blacon East Borehole to the south-east, proved 402 m of Asbian and Brigantian strata of deep-water basinal facies, including thick limestone turbidites and hemipelagic mudstones equivalent to the Lower Bowland Shale. It is argued (Davies et al., 2004), that this demonstrates that the margin of the North Wales Platform must have curved southwards, parallel to the crop as originally suggested by George (1958). Within this basin, perhaps 600 m or more of Dinantian strata may be present below the terminal depth in the Blacon East Borehole. The reefs at Croxteth probably therefore relate to a quite separate carbonate platform described over the Central Lancashire High (Fraser and Gawthorpe, 1990; Riley, 1990; Evans and Kirby, 1999; Kirby et al., 2000).

The Bala–Bryneglwys–Llanelidan Fault Zone extends to the north-east in the subsurface beneath the Permo-Triassic cover of the Cheshire Basin, where it appears to truncate against the major down-to-the-west *Edgerley–Waverton Fault Zone* (contrary to the interpretation by Smith, 1999). This is a poorly understood north–south-trending structure over 60 km long, and the Dinantian strata thicken to the west across the fault (Figure 22). During Dinantian times, this curving fault zone formed the eastern boundary to both the Erbistock and Blacon basins, and it is perhaps linked to other faults of similar trend, which extend into the Liverpool district. The hanging-wall succession and this fault subsequently underwent Variscan inversion. The Milton Green

Carboniferous inlier lies in the footwall block; the Milton Green Borehole proved 320 m of Dinantian strata on the crest of the block. The downthrow across the fault at the base of the Carboniferous may be up to 2000 m.

Erbistock Sub-basin and associated structures

The northern limit of the southerly-tilted Erbistock Sub-basin is defined by the Bala–Bryneglwys–Llanelidan Fault Zone and up 2000 m of Dinantian strata are believed to be preserved. The southern margin appears to have been controlled by two largely concealed major faults, the Craignant Fault and a westward extension of the complex *Llangollen–Llantysillo–Aqueduct Fault* zone (Figure 13). The *Craignant Fault* trends east-north-east and downthrows to the north. About 1 km north-west of Selattyn in the Oswestry district, it splays into a series of faults with a westerly offset of about 1 km in the Dinantian crop of the hanging-wall block.

The *Aqueduct Fault* in the Dee valley curves west-north-west to north-west (Wedd et al., 1928), downthrows to the north and displaces the Carboniferous Limestone crop by some 6.5 km to the north-west. To the east, it merges with the *Llantysillo Fault* and ultimately, with the more east–west-trending *Llangollen Fault* within the Coal Measures crop. It may continue eastwards to meet the Craignant Fault, but both poor data quality and coverage do not provide conclusive proof of this. The Basement Beds are preserved at the base of the Dinantian succession within its hanging wall, and they appear to thicken southwards into the fault, thus suggesting some syndepositional movement during Dinantian times. The location of the Aqueduct Fault may have been controlled by a basement structure that appears as a weak image on the seismic profiles. These data indicate that at depth, beneath the reflector picked to mark the base of the Carboniferous, a zone of reflections, 300 ms thick appear to be gently folded and displaced across a reverse fault that dips to the north and downthrows to the south. There is however, a northerly downthrow at Dinantian and later levels, with associated thickening towards the fault that demonstrates that it formed an important syndepositional fault during Dinantian times (Figure 23). This would have reduced the total pre-Carboniferous reverse displacement. The Erbistock Borehole penetrates part of the hanging wall block succession, reaching a terminal depth of 1797.2 m in dark grey to black cryptocrystalline, argillaceous limestones referred to the Basement Beds. The identification of Basement Beds is at variance, however, with the seismic data, as below the terminal depth of the borehole and developed to around 1.5 secs TWTT, there are a series of moderate- to high-amplitude reflections of moderate continuity, which resemble the 'stripy' seismic facies recognised from more basinal sequences in the Craven Basin (Evans and Kirby, 1999). This may indicate that an earlier and basinal Dinantian succession lies at depth, which was not penetrated by the borehole. It may be that the borehole, which is 250 m off the seismic line, commenced in the hanging wall block succession, but passed through a

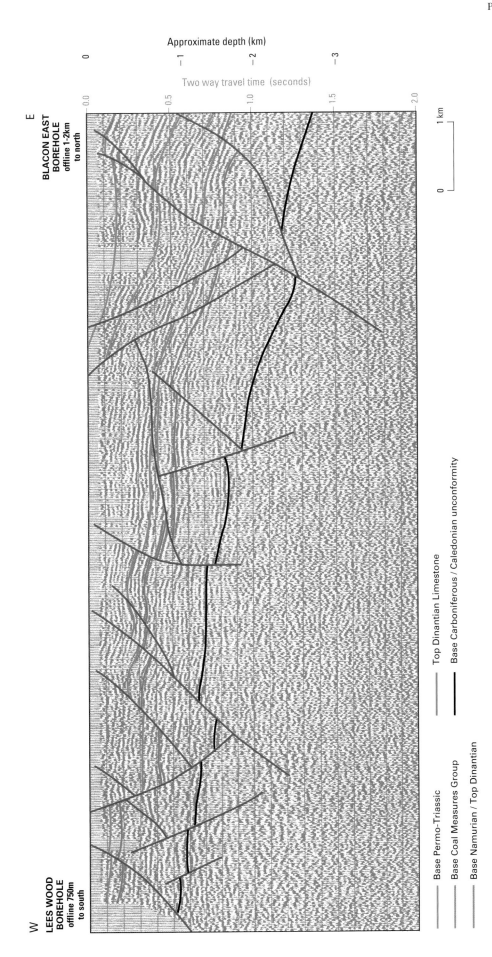

Figure 21 Seismic reflection profile from the Lees Wood Borehole eastwards across the Blacon Basin illustrating the structure and nature of the Carboniferous fill. Location of profile is indicated on Figure 13.

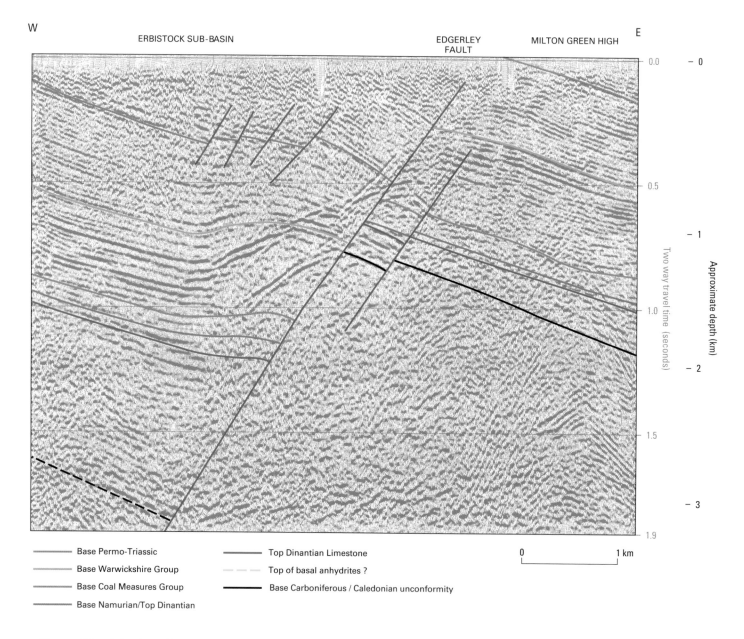

W
ERBISTOCK SUB-BASIN
EDGERLEY FAULT
MILTON GREEN HIGH
E

——— Base Permo-Triassic	——— Top Dinantian Limestone
——— Base Warwickshire Group	- - - Top of basal anhydrites ?
——— Base Coal Measures Group	——— Base Carboniferous / Caledonian unconformity
——— Base Namurian/Top Dinantian	

0   1 km

Figure 22   Seismic reflection profile across the Edgerley Fault that defines the eastern margin of the Erbistock Sub-basin and the Milton Green High. Syndepositional movement during Dinantian times is evidenced by the rapid westwards change in thicknesses across the fault. Development of an anticline in late Dinantian and Silesian strata is suggestive of inversion along the fault. Folding of Permo-Triassic strata means that post-Triassic inversion (?Tertiary) cannot be ruled out. Location of profile is indicated on Figure 13.

concealed fault to prove the basement beds in the footwall block, thereby missing the remaining basinal succession.

A distinct change in the seismic character occurs southwards across this fault zone, indicating that in the footwall block, the Dinantian sequences are both significantly thinner, and probably of a different facies and depositional setting. Reflections are of poor continuity, giving rise to a seismic facies similar to the seismically transparent facies recognised as being associated with carbonate platforms in the Craven Basin (Evans and Kirby, 1999). The base of the succession is not well imaged, being tentatively placed some 300 ms TWTT below the top Carboniferous Limestone.

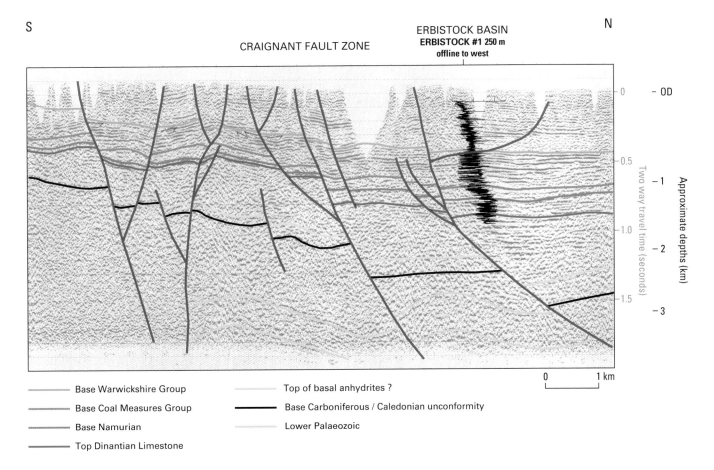

S   N

CRAIGNANT FAULT ZONE

ERBISTOCK BASIN
ERBISTOCK #1 250 m
offline to west

——— Base Warwickshire Group   ——— Top of basal anhydrites ?

——— Base Coal Measures Group   ——— Base Carboniferous / Caledonian unconformity

——— Base Namurian   ········ Lower Palaeozoic

——— Top Dinantian Limestone

Figure 23   Seismic reflection profile across the Craignant Fault Zone that defines the
southern margin of the Erbistock Sub-basin. The seismic tie to the Erbistock Borehole
indicates that a considerable thickness of Dinantian strata exists beneath the terminal
depth of the borehole. Reflections at depth indicate that an earlier Palaeozoic reverse fault
may exist and have been reactivated in extension, thereby controlling the development of
the overlying fault zone. Location of profile is indicated on Figure 13.

Midlands Microcraton Domain and the Wales–London–Brabant Massif

Lying to the south of the Iapetus and Tornquist domains,
the Wales–London–Brabant Massif was tectonically a
more stable area. The Midlands Microcraton formed a
triangular shaped northern promontory (Rees and
Wilson, 1998), and has no clearly demonstrable and
significant extensional features. Dinantian strata are
currently absent or very thin over much of this area. The
northern margins may have been onlapped by generally
thin Dinantian strata and subsequently by later Carboniferous and younger sediments. The presence of Carboniferous Limestone clasts in the Triassic Hopwas breccias
next to the Birmingham and Hints Faults however, may
suggest local derivation from the area underlying the
Permo-Triassic Knowle Basin. It is possible therefore, that
these faults acted as Dinantian syndepositional faults,
with deposition occuring in a narrow fault bounded
graben.

FIVE

Late Devonian and Dinantian stratigraphy

LATE DEVONIAN

In late Devonian times following the Acadian deformation, the continent on which the Old Red Sandstone facies had been deposited was subjected to a prolonged period of subaerial denudation with intermittent marine transgressions. The upper Devonian strata of the region record local deposition within intermontane basins, of continental red-beds, such as the arenaceous Redhouse Sandstones of the Ashbourne district (Chisholm et al., 1988). The Upper Old Red Sandstone of the Anglo-Welsh area is generally thin in comparison with the Lower Old Red Sandstone, and dating is imprecise. Evidence of fluvial and lacustrine deposition has been recorded in the mudstone and siltstone of the Merevale 2 Borehole and a series of 23 cyclothems have been identified (Taylor and Rushton, 1971). They are interpreted as fluviatile deposits that accumulated on a delta plain subjected to intermittent flooding. Concretionary limestones may indicate the development of lagoons on the delta top, or alternatively caliches; shrinkage cracks indicate that the mudflats dried out as the floods waned. Marine incursions are marked by intensely burrowed mudstone and the occurrence of lingulids and other bivalves, phyllocarids and articulate brachiopods. Shallow marine carbonates and evaporites indicate that marine conditions existed to the south and in areas of the North Sea from Mid Devonian times onwards (Glennie, 1986; Ziegler, 1990). The marine incursions perhaps indicate early fault-controlled subsidence of the Old Red Sandstone landmass and sedimentation linked to the crustal extension is evident to the south and east. Possible tilt block formation and early basin development during the late Devonian may be supported by the Ranton Borehole and nearby seismic reflection data, which shows a northwards thickening of Dinantian, late Devonian and perhaps earlier strata (Figure 24). In the Midlands, the Merevale 2 Borehole yielded marine fossils from red sandstone (Taylor and Rushton, 1971; Bluck et al., 1992) and the Caldon Low Borehole, in the Weaver Hills of Staffordshire, proved 170 m of early Dinantian and possibly late Devonian sandstone beneath a sequence of carbonates (Aitkenhead and Chisholm, 1982).

DINANTIAN

Major crustal stretching and basin subsidence continued into the Dinantian as pulsed rifting episodes increased structural differentiation across the region. Rifting was accompanied by sea-level changes, as a marine transgression inundated a landscape of variable relief (Cope et al., 1992). Palaeomagnetic studies indicate that northern

England at this time lay in low tropical latitudes, either just to the north of the Equator (Dewey, 1982) or, during the Courceyan–Arundian period, at a palaeolatitude of 4°S (Scotese and McKerrow, 1990; Falcon-Lang, 1999b). The climate varied from arid to monsoonal (Besly, 1988), the monsoonal conditions finally breaking down towards the end of the Namurian (Falcon-Lang, 1999a).

The division between structural and stratigraphical highs and lows during Carboniferous times was to a large extent controlled by the distribution of structural units within the basement resulting from the Caledonian orogeny. These structures determined the location of the major basin-bounding faults that controlled the development of Dinantian basins and highs discussed in Chapter 4. In the Peak District, the largest Dinantian outcrop in the region, there are only limited seismic data and the relationship between lithofacies and deep structure is speculative, relying on gravity, magnetic and sparse borehole data. Elsewhere, there is good seismic coverage, but borehole provings are sparse and Dinantian successions are commonly not bottomed; generally the strata are poorly constrained biostratigraphically. An understanding of the stratigraphical development of the region relies, in part, on analogy with similar structures, successions and lithologies developed in Dinantian basins elsewhere to the north (for example Gawthorpe, 1987; Gutteridge, 1987, 1991; Chadwick et al., 1993, 1995; Kirby et al., 2000). With these limitations in mind, generalised and locally somewhat speculative facies maps for early, mid and late Dinantian successions have been constructed (Figures 25; 26; 27). These are, in general, best constrained in the Tornquist Domain, parts of the Midlands Microcraton and the western part of the Iapetus Domain. For other areas there is very little direct evidence, and interpretations rely on seismic facies and inferences regarding deposition on the highs and lows. In common with much of northern England, shallow-water carbonates accumulated on highs, away from the Wales–London–Brabant Massif, and thicker, generally complete and argillaceous successions accumulated in deeper water basinal areas adjacent to controlling faults. Basal Dinantian successions where proved are generally of marginal siliciclastic or evaporitic facies, and range in age from Courceyan in basinal areas to Arundian on highs, indicating progressive inundation of the area during Dinantian times. However, coarse clastic material is sparse, indicating that these highs were of low relief (Chisholm et al., 1988).

The southern and western parts of the region lay on the northern margin of an upland region of folded Caledonian rocks (Wales–London–Brabant Massif; Ramsbottom, 1973), which was progressively drowned during Dinantian times (Worssam and Old, 1988; Somerville et al., 1989; Davies et al., 1989). Marginal nearshore clastic facies are recorded

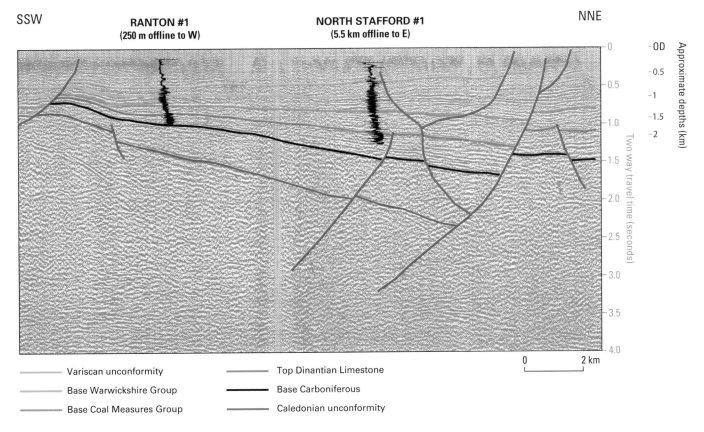

SSW

RANTON #1
(250 m offline to W)

NORTH STAFFORD #1
(5.5 km offline to E)

NNE

———— Variscan unconformity

············· Base Warwickshire Group

═══════ Base Coal Measures Group

———— Top Dinantian Limestone

━━━━━ Base Carboniferous

———— Caledonian unconformity

0   2 km

Figure 24   Seismic reflection profile illustrating the tilted fault block that controlled the structure, development and sedimentary fill of the Ranton Basin during Dinantian times. The two boreholes indicated provide stratigraphical calibration of the seismic line. Deeper reflections are suggestive of a thickening of earlier sequences towards the eastern fault and might therefore indicate a long history of syndepositional movement on the fault dating from early Palaeozoic times. Location of profile is indicated on Figure 13.

and these are overstepped to the south by shallow-water carbonates. Namurian rocks resting directly upon Cambrian around Merevale (Worssam and Old, 1988) illustrate that Dinantian rocks are ultimately overstepped southwards.

EARLY DINANTIAN: COURCEYAN–EARLY CHADIAN

The Tournaisian is the oldest and least well documented of the Dinantian stages across the region. Rocks are, in general, more siliciclastic than in later stages of the Dinantian, with the earliest rocks generally of continental facies 'Old Red Sandstone' (Bluck et al., 1992). A speculative palaeogeographical and facies map is presented in Figure 25.

Among the earliest sequences are the Basement Beds of north Wales (Somerville et al., 1989), the Middleton Dale Anhydrite Series in the Eyam Borehole in the Peak District (Strank, 1985; Dunham, 1973) and the Redhouse Sandstones, Rue Hill Dolomites and Milldale Limestones encountered in the Caldon Low Borehole and at crop (Aitkenhead and Chisholm, 1982; Welsh and Owens, 1983; Chisholm et al., 1988). Similar lithologies encountered in the Woo Dale Borehole, some 18 km to the north, comprise basal breccia overlain by grey to dark grey

limestone, 33 m thick. These were also initially assigned Tournaisian (Chadian) ages (Cope, 1979), with the remaining succession assigned to the Woo Dale Dolomites of Chadian–Holkerian age (George et al., 1976). However, Strank (1986, 1987) subsequently questioned these ages, suggesting that the basal sequences are no older than Arundian, thus implying a Chadian high within the carbonate platform, over which sedimentation did not commence until Arundian times.

Iapetus Domain

There are no borehole provings of rocks of this age in the Iapetus domain and therefore an understanding of stratigraphical development relies on the outcrops of Dinantian strata in north Wales and inferences from seismic facies. The oldest rocks, the Basement Beds, rest with marked unconformity on folded Lower Palaeozoic (Silurian) rocks (Strahan, 1885, 1890; Warren et al., 1984). They range up to 75 m thick in the Vale of Clwyd (Davies et al., 2004), and are unfossiliferous. However, overlying strata are of early Arundian and late Chadian age and provide both an upper age limit and demonstrate the diachronous nature of these beds. They comprise reddened and variegated

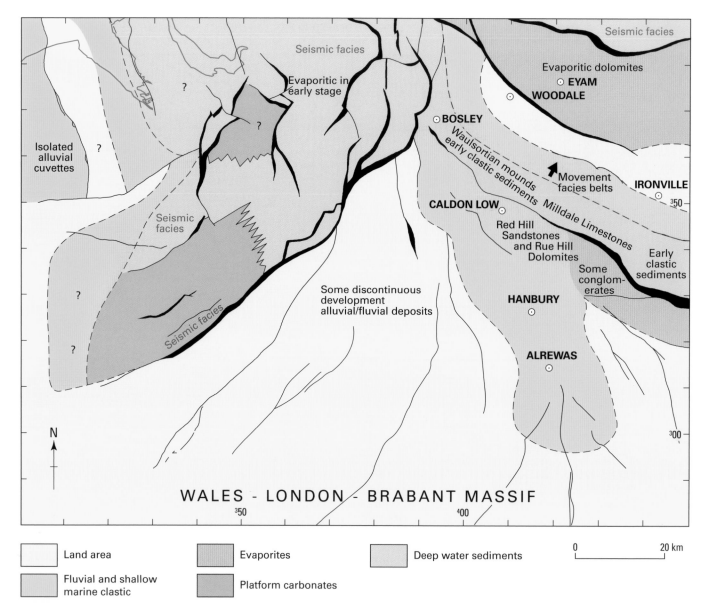

Figure 25 Generalised early Dinantian (Courceyan–early Chadian) palaeogeography and facies distribution across the region.

breccia, conglomerate, sandstone and silty mudstone with scattered calcretes, and comprise a suite of alluvial facies that probably accumulated under strongly oxidising, terrestrial conditions. They record the infilling of an irregular terrain, their source lying in the Welsh upland areas to the immediate south and west. Because of their lithofacies they were originally thought to be Devonian Old Red Sandstone (Ramsey, 1881), but are now considered to be early Carboniferous in age (Strahan and Walker, 1879; Morton, 1898; Neaverson, 1945; George, 1958; Warren et al., 1984; Somerville et al., 1989; Davies et al., 2004).

Subsurface evidence for facies distribution is limited, but seismic facies do suggest a basinal succession in the Erbistock Sub-basin (Figure 22) and shallow-water carbonates to the south across the Craignant Fault. Similarly, it is likely that

basinal successions existed at this time in the Blacon and Manchester Winsford Basins, with shallow-water carbonates deposited over depositional highs. Two deep and fairly continuous, moderate- to high-amplitude reflections are patchily developed in parts of this domain (Figure 17). Presently interpreted as originating from successions of early Carboniferous age, they may be equivalent to other early Dinantian anhydrite-dominated sequences developed near the base of the Dinantian succession, for example on the Hathern Shelf to the south-east. This would imply rapid drowning of the initial evaporitic facies.

Tornquist Domain

Rocks of Tournaisian age in this domain outcrop in the southern parts of the Peak District and have been proved in

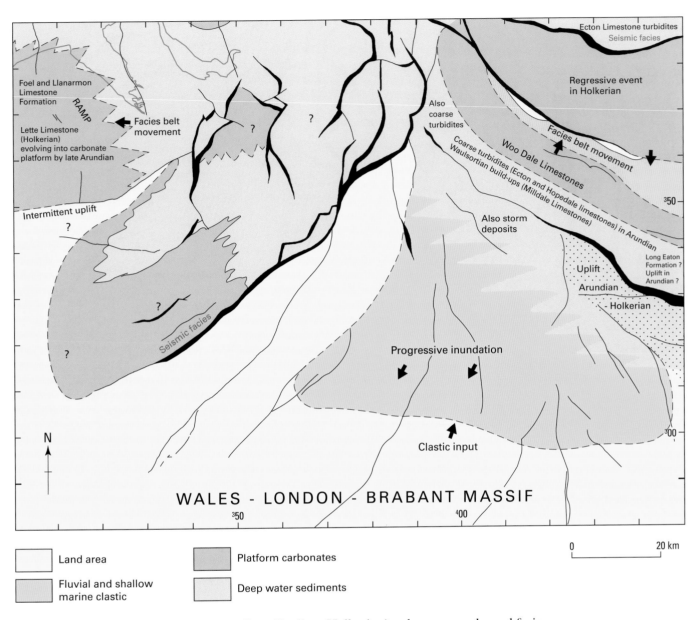

Figure 26   Generalised mid Dinantian (late Chadian–Holkerian) palaeogeography and facies distribution across the region.

the subsurface by the Caldon Low, Eyam, and Bosley boreholes. The structural framework of tilt blocks is based to a large extent on borehole provings, gravity and magnetic data, with limited input from seismic data. The known occurrences of rocks of this age with respect to this structural framework are analysed and a suggested synthesis of the distribution of the facies is shown (Figure 25).

The oldest Dinantian rocks, the continental fluviatile Redhouse Sandstone are proved in the Caldon Low Borehole, which lies on the crest of the foot wall block to the Mackworth–Normanton Hills–Hoton fault zone. Similar facies are encountered at the base of the Ironville Borehole and the Alrewas Borehole on the Midlands Microcraton to the south. They are similar to basal strata of indeterminate age encountered outside the region in the boreholes on the Central Lancashire and Holme

highs, from crop on the margins of the Southern Lake District High (Adams et al., 1990), in the Raydale and Beckermonds Scar boreholes on the northern part of the Askrigg Block (Dunham and Wilson, 1985; Evans and Kirby, 1999; Kirby et al., 2000) and in the Cominco boreholes immediately to the south in the Askrigg Terrace (Kirby et al., 2000). It is likely that this facies formed as a diachronous sandy and conglomeratic fluviatile and marginal shallow marine or supratidal sabkha facies on largely emergent areas during the earliest Dinantian times, and may be quite extensive although discontinuous in the subsurface.

The succeeding Rue Hill Dolomites in the Caldon Low Borehole consist of an alternation of grey, fine-grained dolomite, dark grey limestone and mudstone with penecontemporaneous evaporitic breccia, indicating

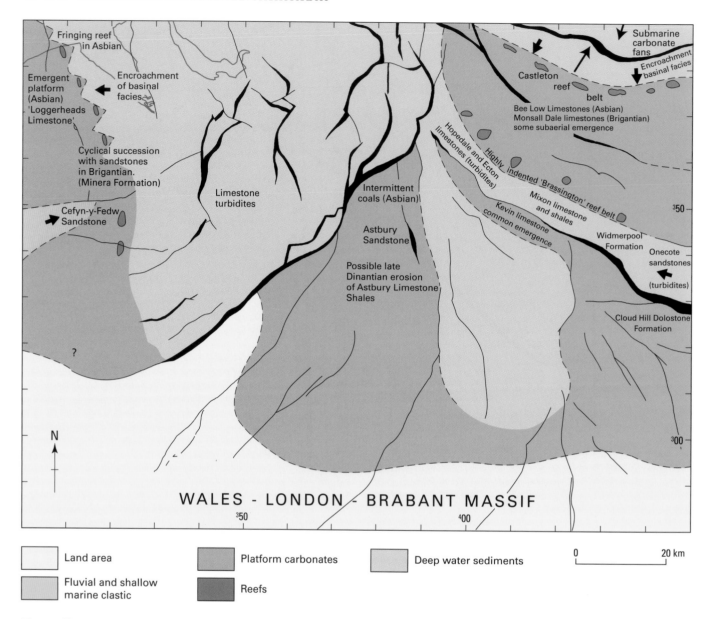

Land area

Fluvial and shallow marine clastic

Platform carbonates

Reefs

Deep water sediments

0   20 km

Figure 27 Generalised late Dinantian (Asbian–Brigantian) palaeogeography and facies distribution across the region.

deposition in shallow-water marine subtidal, intertidal or supratidal environments. A similar succession was encountered in the Eyam Borehole (Llewellyn and Stabbins; 1968, 1970) and it is possible that this facies was widespread on the Eyam tilt block, although this has not been proved. Anhydrites of this age were also found in the Hathern Borehole (Chisholm et al., 1988) on the Hathern Shelf to the south of the Widmerpool Gulf, indicating that these could be provings of a sabkha environment of wide extent (Dunham, 1973).

In the south of the Peak District, over the southern parts of the Woo Dale tilt block, and extending south across the controlling fault, the Milldale Limestones overlie these basal deposits. They comprise a series of dark grey medium- to fine-grained limestones and are the oldest rocks at crop. The base is proved only in the Caldon Low Borehole where the lowest bed is Courceyan in age (Welsh and Owens, 1983). They accumulated mainly in relatively deep water, although local thin coals attest to temporary emergent conditions (Chilsholm et al., 1988). This change to dominantly deep-water conditions indicates rapidly rising sea levels. In the Dovedale area, they form an inter-reef facies to large composite knoll-reefs (Aitkenhead et al., 1985; Chisholm et al., 1988). Similar Chadian basinal facies of interbedded mudstone, siltstone and detrital limestone are recorded in the Bosley Borehole in the North Staffordshire Basin, and although not dated, log correlation with the Long Eaton Borehole suggests similar facies were developed in the Widmerpool Gulf at the same time. The up-dip regions of the Woo Dale tilt block are thought to have been emergent at this time.

There are no borehole provings of rocks of this age in the Alport Basin to the north. However younger Dinantian rocks of basinal facies are proved and have a similar seismic facies to the deeper and much expanded succession, suggesting that this area accumulated a basinal succession at this time.

Midlands Microcraton

The only dated rocks of this age are in the Hanbury Borehole where there is a succession of interbedded sandstone, mudstone and minor limestone. Similar, although undated, successions are encountered in other boreholes, and this marginal marine facies, with clastic input probably from the south, was probably widespread.

MID DINANTIAN: LATE CHADIAN AND ARUNDIAN–HOLKERIAN

Sea level continued to rise with the progressive inundation of the Wales–London–Brabant Massif and the up-dip areas of tilt blocks. Evaporitic sedimentation ceased and clastic facies became much less widespread during this time. The Arundian in northern Britain generally marks a period of fault reactivation and rifting, accompanied by a rapid drowning of carbonate platform self margins as sea level rise outpaced carbonate production (Fraser et al., 1990; Fraser and Gawthorpe, 1990). The Arundian also marks the disappearance of the previously developed knoll-reef facies of Courceyan to Chadian times (Cope et al., 1992). A speculative and generalised facies and palaeogeographical map is presented in Figure 26.

LATE CHADIAN–ARUNDIAN

Iapetus Domain

The Basement Beds are succeeded and locally overstepped by limestones of the Foel Formation; this is up to 88 m thick and of dominantly shallow-water origin. Originally thought to be early Asbian in age (Warren et al., 1984), it is now known to be entirely late Chadian (early Visean) (Davies et al., 2004). At the base is a poorly exposed, but persistent heterolithic unit that includes a lithologically varied bedded sequence of porcellaneous calcite mudstone and wackestone, argillaceous packestone, peloidal and ooidal grainstone, cryptalgal laminite and oncolitic floatstone with intercalated mudstone, plant-bearing siltstone and calcareous sandstone. These lithologies form an aggradational peritidal and lagoonal facies that record the initiation and growth of a Lower Carboniferous carbonate platform on the northern margins of the Wales–London–Brabant Massif, with facies belts thought to parallel the outcrop along the Vale of Clwyd. They pass northwards and eastwards into offshore deeper water deposits of the East Irish Sea and Craven basins. Fault-bounded embayments defined by the Dinorwic, Bala and Craignant faults (Somerville and Strank; 1984b) are likely to have controlled both the rate and nature of early sedimentation and inundation of the Clwydian region. The absence of Chadian rocks to the west of the Vale of Clwyd

(Somerville and Strank, 1984a; Somerville et al., 1986) constrains the limits of this initial advance that was perhaps controlled by movement on the Vale of Clwyd Fault (Davies et al., 1989). The overlapping of Chadian strata by Arundian platform carbonates south of Gelligynan suggests southwards-directed onlap on the southern side of the Bala–Lanelidan–Bryneglwys Fault System, forming a carbonate ramp-to-platform transition with widespread deposition of shallow-water carbonates. The northward thinning of Dinantian strata to the south of the fault also supports intra-Dinantian uplift along the fault (Davies et al., 1989).

The initial transgression continued and in early to mid-Arundian times inundated large areas, introducing an eastward dipping shallow-water carbonate ramp facies (lower part of Llanarmon Limestone; Davies et al., 2004). Steadily rising sea level in late Arundian times led to shoal facies progradation and aggradation eventually forming a low-gradient platform. Arundian limestones overlapped earlier Carboniferous sequences and in places overstepped farther onto the Lower Palaeozoic of the northern margin of St George's Land (Davies et al., 1989; Somerville et al., 1989). The preservation of Arundian strata within a tract presently defined by the Bala and Menai Straits lineaments may reflect the form of an original marine embayment (Somerville and Strank, 1984b; Davies et al., 2004). However the original distribution may have been greater as intraclasts of Arundian grainstones associated with terrigenous deposits attest to a period of uplift and erosion along the embayment margins and perhaps beyond. This is coeval with a rifting event recognised elsewhere (Riley, 1990; Barclay et al., 1994).

Limited seismic facies evidence suggests that platform carbonates may have accumulated in the south-west of this region and perhaps on the Milton Green high. Basinal sediments accumulated elsewhere.

Tornquist Domain

Up-dip on the Woo Dale tilt block, a shelf facies, the Woo Dale Limestones Formation, started to accumulate in late Chadian times and continued developing into early Asbian times. These limestones outcrop in the southern part of the Peak District. However, the earliest dated shelfal succession in the Woo Dale and Ironville boreholes on the highest part of the Woo Dale tilt block and the Nottingham platform, are Arundian in age, suggesting that during late Chadian times these 'crestal areas' may still have been accumulating sediments of marginal marine facies at the same time as areas immediately to the south were accumulating shelf facies deposits. Chadian shelf facies are also encountered to the north of the Bakewell Fault in the much thicker succession proved in the Eyam Borehole. Thus the Bakewell Fault appears to have been active at this time, separating an area of shelf limestone deposition to the north on the Eyam tilt block from an emergent area to the south on the crest of the Woo Dale tilt block where siliciclastic deposits accumulated. This crestal area was subsequently drowned in Arundian times. Facies belts on the Woo Dale tilt block pass southwards and down-dip from siliciclastic deposits to shelf limestones and finally into deep water limestones and mudstones. The facies distribution on the Eyam tilt block is unproved.

To the south of the Woo Dale Limestones, in the southern Peak District, basinal limestones of the Milldale Limestone Formation accumulated, with some knoll reefs. However, tectonic and eustatic events towards the end of Chadian times produced an influx of coarse carbonate turbiditic sediments of the Hopedale Limestones and Ecton Limestones that continued throughout the Arundian and into Holkerian and Asbian times (Chisholm et al., 1988) and progressively replaced the Milldale Limestone.

By Arundian times, the shelf facies of the Woo Dale Limestones accumulated both on the slope and on the crest of the Woo Dale tilt block. These limestones thicken substantially northwards across the Bakewell Fault indicating that although the fault was active during this time, carbonate production was able to fill the extra space that was generated. Although the distribution of Woo Dale Limestones on the Eyam tilt block is not known, they are assumed to have accumulated everywhere; if shelf carbonates accumulated on the down-dip areas it would be reasonable to expect a similar or perhaps more marginal facies up-dip to the north. A thick succession of basinal sediments however continued to accumulate to the north of the Alport Fault in the Alport Basin during late Chadian and Arundian times; there are no borehole provings of this, but the limited seismic facies evidence is consistent with such an interpretation.

In the Caldon Low Borehole on the crest of the Caldon Low tilt block, there is evidence of periods of erosion during Arundian and indeed Holkerian times. This area may have formed part of the 'Midland Barrier' at this time as pebbles above unconformities show affinities to those found at Lilleshall and Breedon Cloud to the south on the Midlands Microcraton (Hains and Horton, 1969; Mitchell and Stubblefield, 1941).

Basaltic lavas proved in the Gun Hill Borehole and a thin tuff in the Milldale Limestones attest to local volcanic activity in off-shelf provinces (North Staffordshire Basin).

During Arundian and Holkerian times, the Hathern Shelf experienced uplift and erosion, and the apparent absence of Arundian strata in the Long Eaton Borehole in the Widmerpool Gulf suggests uplift there also at this time.

Midlands Microcraton

Thin and incomplete successions of shelf limestones interbedded with sandstones continued to accumulate at this time, the area of deposition extending southwards. However, a large area in the west remained emergent and no sediments accumulated.

HOLKERIAN

During Holkerian times, the progressive onlap of the pre-Arundian topography continued, culminating in the maximum transgression of carbonate platforms in northern England (Strank, 1987; Fraser and Gawthorpe, 1990). In the East Midlands, it has been recognised that Late Holkerian times were a still-stand phase characterised by the development of carbonate ramps and rimmed shelf environments. An angular unconformity

has been identified in the Widmerpool Gulf, its development associated with a late Holkerian basin inversion event (Ebdon et al., 1990; Fraser and Gawthorpe, 1990).

Iapetus Domain

In north Wales, earlier structural barriers were inundated and shoal facies withdrew to the outer part of the platform (Llanarmon Limestone; upper part in north Wales), where they sheltered an embayed platform interior that became the site of rhythmic peritidal carbonate deposition (Leete Limestone; Davies et al., 2004). Facies distribution in the subsurface is poorly known, but is likely to have been similar to that envisaged for late Chadian and Arundian times.

Tornquist Domain

The extent and nature of Holkerian strata are not well known, particularly in the off-shelf provinces and the palaeogeography remains uncertain (Aitkenhead et al., 1985). The Holkerian is thought to have been a time of renewed transgression that was sustained throughout the period into early Asbian times (Davies et al., 2004) and introduced widespread changes to the pattern of carbonate sedimentation in the region. However, sections of the uppermost Woo Dale Limestone exposed in the type area contain birdseye structures and rare coals, suggesting a late Holkerian regressive phase when intertidal and supratidal conditions prevailed (Aitkenhead et al., 1985). In the southern Peak District, Ecton Limestones of Holkerian age crop out in the Manifold Valley and are encountered in a borehole at Grindon. They are predominantly grey-brown to dark grey, thinly bedded and poorly fossiliferous bioclastic limestones of deeper water slope or ramp facies. The bioclastic and conglomeritic beds were probably deposited by turbidity currents flowing from shelf areas to the east (Aitkenhead et al., 1985). Similar facies are encountered in boreholes in the Widmerpool Gulf and North Staffordshire Basin. They contrast markedly with, and are five times thicker than, beds of a similar age in the Woo Dale Limestones, which developed in up-dip areas on the Woo Dale tilt block in an environment varying from open shelf to restricted lagoon (Schofield and Adams, 1985; Chisholm et al., 1988). The margins of the shelf are neither exposed nor proved in boreholes, but the northern boundary certainly extended to a point north of the Eyam Borehole on the Eyam tilt block.

Midlands Microcraton

There is no precise age dating available, but log correlation of borehole successions suggests that this area continued to accumulate shelf sediments with some clastic input.

LATE DINANTIAN

This was a period of changing sea level and some renewed fault movements, and in Brigantian times the development of basin-wide subsidence. A simplified and in part speculative facies and palaeogeographical map is presented in Figure 27, but the stratigraphy in Asbian and Brigantian times is described separately.

ASBIAN

Late Holkerian to mid Asbian times have been interpreted as a stillstand or regressive phase characterised by carbonate ramp and rimmed shelf development in the East Midlands and the Craven Basin (Fraser and Gawthorpe, 1990). Shoaling-upwards cyclical shelf carbonates developed in sediment-starved shallow-water areas, and there was a general progradation of rimmed shelf areas. In the East Midlands, these carbonates pass basinwards through platform-margin facies into hemipelagic lime mudstones and calciturbidites of the foreslope. Erosion is inferred to have removed all but a few remnants of the shelf facies from the northern margin of the Midlands Microcraton (Chisholm et al., 1988).

Iapetus Domain

In north Wales, common karstic and pedogenic features capping abundant open marine, shoaling-upwards sequences of platform carbonates (Loggerheads Limestone), indicate frequent emergence of the platform caused by cyclical changes in sea level in late Asbian times (Davies et al., 2004). During this period, the platform margin was marked by knoll reefs, now exposed on the Little Orme, at Dyserth and at Axton Bridge in the adjacent Rhyl district. In north-east Wales the platform developed a rimmed margin, with build-ups forming a linear belt between platform and basin (Somerville et al., 1989). To the north, the late Asbian Prestatyn Limestone was formed as an apron of limestone turbidites, and may equate with limestones of this age in the Blacon East Borehole (Davies et al., 2004), indicating the development of deeper water in that area.

Tornquist Domain

In Derbyshire, a clear differentiation emerged between shelf areas delineated by fringing apron reef facies, and off-shelf areas beyond the reef belt. On the Woo Dale tilt block, the change from shelf to off-shelf areas occurs in a down-dip direction. Thickly bedded pale grey calcarenites developed on the shelf in shallow water (Bee Low Limestones), with numerous periods of subaerial emergence (Aitkenhead et al., 1985). Pale micritic fore-reef limestones have a depositional dip away from the shelf into deeper water. Off-shelf, inter reef sediments (Hopedale Limestones) were deposited between contemporaneous and older upstanding reef knolls on an irregular, southerly dipping ramp in water of variable depth. Limestone turbidites (Ecton Limestones) also accumulated in the deeper troughs. The transition from shelf to off-shelf, and marking the southern margin of the Derbyshire shelf, is clearly delineated by the Brassington apron reef belt between Parwich and Carsington. This belt is highly indented with embayments and promontories. The lateral passage southwards from the Hopedale Limestones into

the Ecton Limestones and Widmerpool Formation reflects the transition from ramp into a deeper water basinal facies, proved by the Widmerpool Borehole in the Widmerpool Gulf (Falcon and Kent, 1960; see below). This basinal area may have been linked to the North Staffordshire Basin, a suggestion supported by the Duffield Borehole that proved thick basinal facies. The distribution of shelf and off-shelf facies in Derbyshire by end-Asbian times is discussed in Aitkenhead and Chisholm (1982). Thick basinal successions of Asbian age were proved by the Edale Borehole on the northern up-dip margin of the Edale tilt block (Gutteridge, 1987, 1991; Strank, 1987). This apparently anomalous occurrence of deep water facies on the crest of the tilt block deposited while shallow water facies continued to accumulate on down slope areas may indicate cessation of movement of the Edale Fault at that time, such that the deep water facies to the north of this fault progressively encroached onto the Eyam tilt block, causing a retreat of the carbonate shelf margin.

In the south-east of this domain, the Cloud Hill Dolostone Formation of late Holkerian and Asbian age was deposited unconformably on Chadian strata. This passes north-westward into the Kevin Limestone, a fine to coarse-grained biosparite limestone with common palaeokarst surfaces, indicating periods of emergence.

Midlands Microcraton

Boreholes illustrate the progressive southerly overstep and development of shallow marine sedimentation over the Wales–London–Brabant Massif, the western and southernmost parts of which remained emergent until late Silesian times. The basal succession of the Rotherwood Borehole, lies with marked angular unconformity upon Cambrian rocks, and is of late Asbian (Riley, 1986) or Brigantian age (Worssam and Old, 1988). Shelf limestones with some coals accumulated over the Market Drayton Horst at this time, encountered at Astbury in outcrop and in the Bowsey Wood and Bittern's Wood boreholes (Earp and Calver, 1961; Evans et al., 1968; Rees and Wilson, 1998). The lowest beds are the Astbury Limestone Formation of Asbian age. They resemble closely the contemporaneous Bee Low and Kevin Limestones of the shelf areas to the east in Derbyshire. This would suggest that the three formations had a similar depositional environment, developed on blocks that were separated by the North Staffordshire Basin.

The overlying Astbury Limestone Shale Formation is known only from the Astbury inlier in the Macclesfield district where it is less than 10 m thick (Evans et al., 1968; Rees and Wilson, 1998). It is likely that it extended over most of the Market Drayton Horst, and its absence in the Bowsey Wood and Bittern's Wood boreholes probably reflects late Dinantian erosion related to a period of uplift (Gutteridge, 1987, 1991).

BRIGANTIAN

From late Asbian to early Brigantian times, Britain continued to lie in equatorial regions (Scotese et al.,

1979; Smith et al., 1981). Pulsed rifting continued to affect northern England, but this was gradually replaced by post-extensional regional subsidence. The severity of extension varied, with the Widmerpool Gulf showing a greater effect than seen in, for example, the Gainsborough Trough (Fraser and Gawthorpe, 1990). Renewed fault block rotation resulted in strong erosional unconformities on the footwall block to the Hoton Fault with the development of boulder beds in the hanging-wall blocks. Volcanic rocks of late Asbian to early Brigantian age are related to the renewed extensional activity, having been erupted both subaerially and subaqueously.

Iapetus Domain

In north Wales, renewed rifting in latest Asbian and early Brigantian times is reflected in a noticeable thickness change across the Bala Lineament and the associated Nercwys–Nant–Figillt Fault Zone. From the early Brigantian onwards, regional subsidence and eustatic oscillations in sea level led to transgressions that were individually more extensive and more rapid than those during Asbian times. During these inundations, platform facies of deeper water aspect were deposited (Cefn Mawr Limestone). At this time, the marginal reefs were abandoned and the platform margin retreated south-westwards as platform carbonate facies in north Wales achieved their greatest geographical extent (Davies et al., 2004). The Blacon East and Milton Green boreholes prove Brigantian strata of basinal aspect comprising limestone turbidite and hemipelagic mudstone (Riley, 1988) that are equivalent to the Telia Formation of the Prestatyn area, lying on shelf limestones. This demonstrates the progressive rise in relative sea level and also that the margin of the north Wales platform, contrary to most models (for example Warren et al., 1984; Fraser et al., 1990; Fraser and Gawthorpe, 1990; Somerville et al., 1989), must have curved southwards at this time, parallel to the central crop along a line through Flint and Hawarden as originally suggested by George (1958) and supported by Davies et al. (2004).

A widespread basin inversion event and regressive phase is recognised in early to mid Brigantian times (Fraser and Gawthorpe, 1990) and may have been coincident with climatic changes promoted by plate collision in southern Europe as well as the Gondwanan glaciation (Leeder, 1988). Following this regressive phase, post-rift (regional) subsidence and sedimentation resumed and led to the drowning and submergence of the majority of platform shelf and off-shelf areas. This was accompanied by an increase in the volume and grade of terrigenous material supplied to carbonate platform areas, as reflected in the Minera Formation of north Wales. From latest Brigantian times, the encroachment of deltaic facies (Cefn-y-Fedw Sandstone) caused the cessation of widespread carbonate deposition in the west of the region and brought a major episode of carbonate sedimentation to an end.

Tornquist Domain

The shelf provinces established during the Asbian in Derbyshire persisted into the Brigantian, although the growth of fringing apron reefs diminished or ceased. The Monsal Dale Limestones are in the main, pale grey shallow water limestones with emergent surfaces. Some darker argillaceous limestones deposited in deeper water are found. The shelf margins were eroded during late Asbian or early Brigantian times with the lowest of the Monsal Dale Limestones, comprising shelly limestones of shelf facies, resting on the remnants of Asbian apron reefs (Aitkenhead et al., 1985). Shelf margin bioclastic grainstone shoals in the north of the Derbyshire shelf fed detritus into the Edale basin to the north to form a submarine fan that passes up into a mudstone-dominated succession. Siliciclastic input into the off-shelf or basinal areas increased during the Brigantian with deeper water deposition and accumulation of clastic material. Within the North Staffordshire Basin and Widmerpool Gulf areas, mudstones are interbedded with limestone turbidites (Ecton Limestones and Mixon Limestone-shales), with some sandstone turbidites (Onecote Sandstones; Aitkenhead et al., 1985).

The early–mid Brigantian inversion event marked the onset of widespread deposition of dark, terrigenous, basinal turbiditic mud and silty sand that affected former ramp and shelf areas over the whole of the south Pennine region. In Derbyshire, a well-marked emergence and resubmergence of the shelf in late Brigantian times was followed by a short-lived knoll-reef development unrelated to the shelf margin (knoll reefs in Eyam Limestones; Aitkenhead and Chisholm, 1982; Strank, 1987). The margins of both the Staffordshire and Derbyshire shelves were, it seems, in places subjected to further erosion during late Brigantian or early Namurian times as limestones of Asbian or Brigantian age are now overstepped by Namurian mudstones (Strank, 1987).

Midlands Microcraton

Sedimentation on the Midlands Microcraton was dominated by the argillaceous Widmerpool Formation, thought to indicate deposition in moderate water depths, although it is possible that a marginal shelf limestone facies was developed. On the 'Structural Platform Domain' that lies on the eastern margin of the Midlands Microcraton to the south-west of the Thringstone Fault (Carney et al., 2001) the nature of Dinantian strata present is largely unknown. However, the Rotherwood Borehole in the Coalville district to the south proved 114 m of strata of Brigantian age with an association typical of the Ticknall Limestone Formation proved in the Ticknall and Worthington boreholes (Carney et al., 2001). They are of shallow-water or subaerial origin, deposited on a karstic surface developed on underlying early Asbian strata (Riley 1997). Dinantian carbonate strata locally overstep onto the high, for example at Grace Dieu (Carney et al., 2001).

DINANTIAN IGNEOUS ACTIVITY

Dinantian successions within the region contain contemporaneous extrusive igneous rocks first described by Arnold-Bemrose (1894b, 1907) and Geike (1897). A wide range of igneous and related rocks have been penetrated in boreholes or are known at crop, including lava flows, tuffs, bentonites, vents, sills and dykes (Walkden, 1977; Walters and Ineson, 1981); they indicate that there were a number of centres of volcanism. Basaltic lavas and tuffs, may in areas, make up the bulk of the Asbian and Brigantian sequence (Aitkenhead et al., 1985). The main borehole provings and areas of crop are illustrated in Figure 28.

Basic volcanic activity occurred from Holkerian to early Brigantian times in the Peak District culminating around the Asbian–Brigantian boundary (Stevenson and Gaunt, 1971; Walters and Ineson, 1981), coincident with a significant phase of synsedimentary tectonism (Ebdon et al., 1990; Gawthorpe et al., 1989). The distribution of lavas suggests the existence of four distinct centres (Walters and Ineson, 1981; Aitkenhead et al., 1985). These centres correlate with comparatively large amplitude, east-south-east-trending aeromagnetic anomalies, which indicate that further igneous rocks lie concealed at depth elsewhere (Aitkenhead et al., 1985). The Matlock lavas were extruded from a centre near Bonsall. The Lees Bottom, Shacklow Wood, Lathkill Lodge, Conksbury Bridge lavas and a group of flows at the north end of the Millclose Mine workings are linked to a centre near Alport. These two centres formed the most active eruptive sites. A series of hyaloclastites, tuffs and lavas relate to a third centre located near Longstone Edge. The distribution of the Miller's Dale lavas indicates a fourth centre near Tunstead.

Individual volcanic units generally referred to as lavas, comprise a series of flows and may contain interbedded tuffs. There is a close association of lavas (olivine-basalts) that were extruded subaerially on a periodically emergent platform with pillow lavas and hyaloclastites, which were produced during submarine eruptions, perhaps marginal to the emergent platform (Walkden, 1977; Walters and Ineson, 1981). Eruptions from the various centres were not contemporaneous and it is thus impossible to correlate flows from one centre to another. Nor did the volcanic centres comprise single volcanic vents or fissures, but perhaps more local concentrations of eruptive sources (Aitkenhead et al., 1985). It is not clear whether vents or fissures predominated, although Stevenson and Gaunt (1971) favoured fissures as there seems to be little relationship between lavas and the vents.

Dinantian volcanic rocks may be traced off the platform to the south (Falcon and Kent, 1960) and to the north in the Alport Basin (Gutteridge, 1991) and are present at crop elsewhere across the region. To the south within the Widmerpool Gulf, the Tissington Volcanic Member within the Widmerpool Formation (late Asbian to Brigantian) forms a continuous elongate outcrop extending over 3 km south-east of Tissington (Chisholm et al., 1988). A highly amygdaloidal hyaloclastite basalt, it was probably erupted in a submarine environment. Basaltic lavas are also known (Arnold-Bemrose, 1899) notably at two small outcrops near Brookhouse Farm, Kniveton and Shaw's Farm. Similar material has been penetrated in boreholes at Rusheycliffe Barn, Lees Farm

and Tissington No. 2 (Chisholm et al., 1988). Their stratigraphical positions within the marine turbiditic carbonate mudstones of the Widmerpool Formation suggests they form part of the Tissington Volcanic Member. As such, they were probably erupted into relatively deep water, although the member does extend farther north-westwards into a shallower water facies (Hopedale Limestones) suggesting a southward-orientated palaeoslope in this vicinity at this time. Along the Cinderhill Fault, a series of volcanic centres were active during late Asbian to early Brigantian times (Ebdon et al., 1990). Their stratigraphical equivalents are the basaltic Lower and Upper Miller's Dale lavas of the Peak District (Ebdon et al., 1990; Macdonald et al., 1984).

Volcaniclastic facies of early Holkerian and Asbian to Brigantian age are described from the Alport Borehole in the Alport Basin (Edale Basin of Gutteridge, 1991). They comprise tuffaceous material including bedded tuffs and dispersed volcaniclastic material within limestone sediments. The nature of the tuffs and fragments appear to indicate submarine, phreatomagmatic eruptions of magma. Elongate vesicles indicate degassing of cooling lavas that were still flowing. The sedimentary textures and structures of the bedded tuffs indicate subaqueous deposition, probably from a waning flow (Gutteridge, 1991).

Elsewhere, volcanic rocks are exposed on the Market Drayton Horst–West Midlands Shelf to the south-west at Little Wenlock, and farther north at Astbury. The Little Wenlock exposures comprise a 'conglomerate of decomposed basalt' within the basal Lydebrook Sandstones and a microporphyritic olivine-basalt lava lying between the Lower and Upper limestones (Pocock et al., 1938; GSGB, 1978). The volcanic rocks encountered at crop around Astbury comprise late Asbian tuff-breccias, tuffs and fragments of highly vesicular lavas interbedded with limestones (Gibson and Hind, 1899; Hind, 1904; Evans et al., 1968; Rees et al., 1996). Interbedded limestones and shell debris indicate they most probably originated in subaqueous eruptions. Three levels of volcanic rocks (or volcaniclastic debris), thought to be representatives of the Astbury successions, are proved in the Dinantian by the Caldon Low, Gun Hill, Nooks Farm and Apedale boreholes (Rees et al., 1996). The oldest volcanic rocks in the boreholes are the thin pre-Holkerian lavas interbedded with limestones in Gun Hill (Hudson and Cotton, 1945; Rees et al., 1996). Lack of associated tuffs suggests they are unlikely to be correlatives of the Astbury Tuffs, probably sourced from a small volcanic centre near Gun Hill. Also in Gun Hill are over 60 m of Holkerian tuffs, equivalents of which are thought to be present in the Nooks Farm and, to the north-east, in the Alport Borehole (Hudson and Cotton, 1945). The Gun Hill and Nooks Farm boreholes also encountered the tuffs of late Asbian/early Brigantian age exposed at Astbury. The succession at Apedale probably remained above sea level until early Chokierian times with the accumulated thickness of volcanic rocks being greater than in any other Dinantian volcanic centre in England (Rees et al., 1996). The thickness of the tuffs and the paucity of nonvolcanic rocks, in particular limestones, indicate that the volcanic complex was largely subaerial,

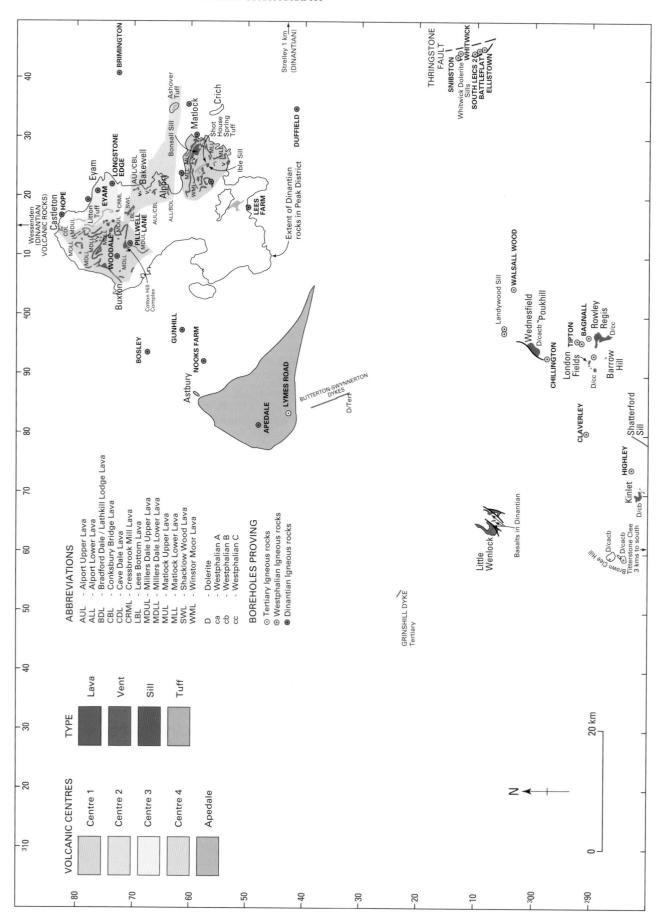

Figure 28   Distribution of Carboniferous volcanic rocks across the region.

the tuffaceous material suggesting that the volcanic activity was phreatomagmatic or hydromagmatic in origin. Estimating the former extent of the volcanic centre is made difficult by possible uplift and erosion in Brigantian times (Ebdon et al., 1990; Fraser et al., 1990; Fraser and Gawthorpe, 1990) and Silesian to Permian (Variscan) inversion and erosion that may have removed volcanic rocks from some areas. However, it is likely that much of the Apedale centre and its products were uplifted and eroded (Rees et al., 1996). The volcanic rocks at Apedale, Astbury and Little Wenlock, perhaps form remnants of a formerly extensive volcanic province developed along the Wem–Bridgemere–Red Rock Fault System (Rees et al., 1996).

In general, therefore, the volcanism seen across the region throughout Dinantian times was synchronous with, and probably caused by phases of active rifting over much of north-western Europe, particularly during late Asbian to early Brigantian times. Trace element geochemistry of the basalt lavas has been used to assess the tectonic setting of both the British Isles and the volcanism during Dinantian times and is wholly consistent with the view that they lay well within the Laurasian continent. The Derbyshire basalts indicate volcanism was of within-plate type and were mainly tholeiitic magmas, generated by varying degrees of partial melting of heterogeneous mantle sources followed by fractional crystallisation and final equilibration mainly within the lower crust (Macdonald et al., 1984). Similarly, the geochemistry of the basaltic magmatism of the Gun Hill, Astbury and Apedale volcanic rocks support such a tectonic setting. Volcanism at Apedale and Astbury appears to be indicative of 'within-plate' alkaline basalts erupted at broadly the same time and with the same source, whereas the Gun Hill tuffs are interpreted as more limited volumes of within-plate continental tholeiites (Rees et al., 1996).

54

SIX

Silesian: post-rift phase of Carboniferous basin development

By Silesian times, the Dinantian 'syn-rift' subsidence had given way to a broadly passive, regional and thermally driven post-rift subsidence (sag) phase (Leeder, 1982). All Silesian strata are included in the post-rift megasequence of Fraser and Gawthorpe (1990) and Fraser et al. (1990). The region therefore inherited a pronounced end-Dinantian basin topography and bathymetric basin floor relief that was progressively infilled by siliciclastic sediments in Silesian times; hence Silesian lithofacies and depositional patterns differ markedly from those of the Dinantian (Fraser and Gawthorpe, 1990; Fraser et al., 1990; Chadwick et al., 1995; Kirby et al., 2000). The differences are attributed to uplift of the source areas and to climate change (Besly, 1988; Cope et al., 1992). Deposition took place within the internally draining Pennine Basin (Figure 29) that lay to the north of the Wales–Brabant Massif and extended northwards towards the Southern Uplands of Scotland (Collinson, 1988; Martinsen et al., 1995).

Silesian rocks record the infilling of this basin as sediment supply exceeded subsidence rates (Guion and Fielding, 1988). They consist dominantly of alternations of sandstone and mudstone, and include subordinate chert, coal and seatearth. These were deposited in a major fluvio-deltaic system that developed across the whole of northern England and the Pennine Basin. Deep water conditions were widespread in Namurian times, but in late Namurian to early Westphalian times delta progradation led to a transition to emergent, coal swamp conditions, which covered most of northern England by late Langsettian to late Bolsovian times (Westphalian A to Westphalian C; Guion and Fielding, 1988). The Namurian progradational succession, formed during falling or low relative sea level, was punctuated by marine transgressions during highstands of sea level. The highstands led to the deposition of ammonoid (goniatite) bearing marine bands. These occur throughout the succession and record periodic transgressions over the delta system. Thus, Silesian strata show a strong cyclic pattern of sedimentation (cyclothems). Although there was probably significant variation, the average duration of a cyclothem in the Namurian Millstone Grit Group is estimated at approximately 180 000 years (Maynard and Leeder, 1982). Cyclothems are also strongly developed in the Westphalian strata, but coal and soil horizons are more abundant and trangression events are relatively rarer than in the Namurian. The Westphalian Epoch has been divided into four stages, Westphalian A to D; the lower three stages have now been formalised as Langsettian, Duckmantian and Bolsovian.

There is some evidence of a progressive change in climate, particularly in later Silesian times. At the beginning of the Silesian, the region lay in equatorial latitudes (Scotese et al., 1979; Smith et al., 1981; Cope et al., 1992) and the climate was humid, but later during the closing stages of the Variscan Orogeny semi-arid conditions prevailed, and it has been suggested that the northerly migrating Variscan deformation front contributed to the change to arid conditions. The deposition of extensive red beds of the Warwickshire Group has been attributed to the development of a rain shadow in the lee of the emerging Variscan mountains to the south (Besly, 1983, 1987).

Silesian strata reach a maximum thickness of 3000 m in the north, and underlie the Permo-Triassic rocks of the major rift basins that developed subsequently (Maps 4, 6).

NAMURIAN

Namurian strata crop out extensively around and to the north of the Derbyshire Dome, and around the synclines of the Potteries and Cheadle coalfields (Figure 2). In north Wales, they occupy a tract of land east of the Carboniferous Limestone crop, running from Prestatyn, southwards by Flint and Mold, to Ruabon Mountain and Oswestry, and may lie at depth below the northern part of the Vale of Clwyd (Warren et al., 1984). Namurian strata are absent in the Welsh Borderland (Earp and Hains, 1971).

In the subsurface in northern and central parts of the region Namurian rocks are widely distributed and have been proved by a number of boreholes (Maps 3 to 5). Thickness varies markedly, due partly to the infilling of a remnant Dinantian topography with onlap onto positive areas such as intrabasinal highs, and partly to syndepositional fault movement, for example Namurian strata thin and onlap the Milton Green High (Figure 30). In general, the succession thins southwards onto the Wales–London–Brabant Massif, and Namurian strata are overstepped by Westphalian strata. In places there is a minor unconformity at the top of the Namurian succession. Lower Namurian rocks are absent on the Market Drayton Horst where they have been overlapped by later Namurian strata (Rees and Wilson, 1998); latest Namurian strata are absent locally due to erosion in the early Westphalian and also a later period prior to the deposition of the Warwickshire Group.

A late Brigantian to earliest Namurian inversion event in central England is thought to have uplifted basin margins and led to intra-Carboniferous erosion (Strank, 1987; Coward, 1990; Fraser and Gawthorpe, 1990; Fraser et al., 1990). Supporting evidence is provided by the folding of Dinantian strata in the hanging-wall blocks of some earlier Dinantian syndepositional faults (e.g. Kirby

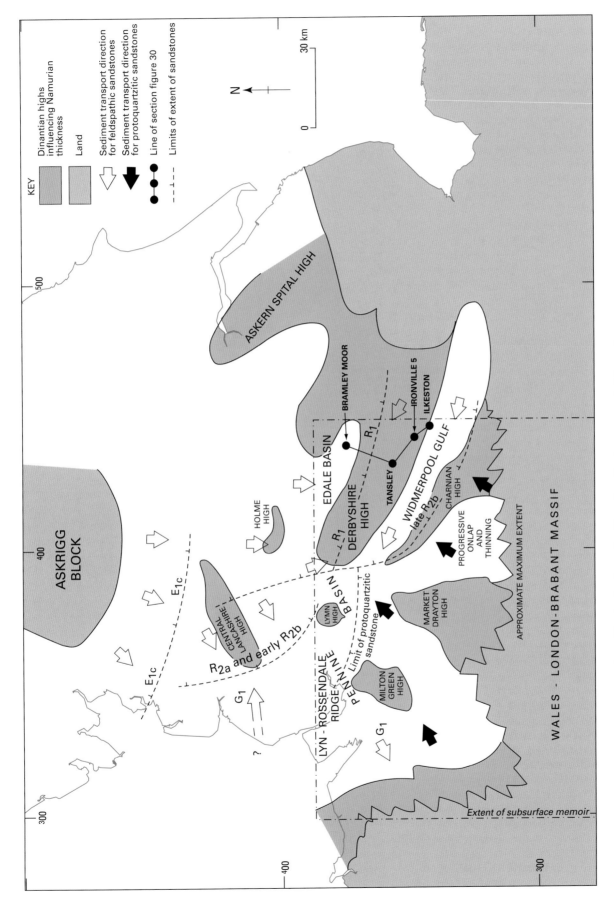

KEY

Dinantian highs influencing Namurian thickness

Land

Sediment transport direction for feldspathic sandstones

Sediment transport direction for protoquartzitic sandstones

Line of section figure 30

Limits of extent of sandstones

N

0   30 km

ASKRIGG BLOCK

ASKERN SPITAL HIGH

HOLME HIGH

CENTRAL LANCASHIRE HIGH

E_{1c}

E_{1c}

G_1

R_{2a} and early R_{2b}

LYMN HIGH

LYN - ROSSENDALE RIDGE

PENNINE BASIN

Limit of protoquartzitic sandstone

G_1

?

MILTON GREEN HIGH

MARKET DRAYTON HIGH

CHARNIAN HIGH

late R_{2b}

WIDMERPOOL GULF

PROGRESSIVE ONLAP AND THINNING

APPROXIMATE MAXIMUM EXTENT

WALES - LONDON - BRABANT MASSIF

Extent of subsurface memoir

EDALE BASIN

DERBYSHIRE HIGH

R_1

R_1

BRAMLEY MOOR

IRONVILLE 5 ILKESTON

TANSLEY

500

400

400

300

300

Figure 29   Namurian palaeogeography of both the broader Pennine Basin area and this region.

et al., 2000), the possible absence of strata of Brigantian to early Namurian age on the Holme High just to the north of the region (Evans and Kirby, 1999) and a locally pronounced disconformity at the base of the Pentre Chert Formation in north Wales. This disconformity may owe its origin to both localised dissolution and foundering of the Dinantian platform margin and tectonic uplift leading to subaerial erosion (Davies et al., 2004). The inversion is however relatively minor and perhaps correlates with collision events associated with nappe emplacement to the south of the region (Sellwood and Thomas, 1986; Fraser et al., 1990).

Postextensional subsidence progressively came to dominate during Namurian times. Basin floor relief thus resulted from a combination of factors including postextensional regional thermal relaxation subsidence, inherited relief due to incomplete infilling of basins during the Dinantian, local active faulting along basin-margin faults, distance from the sediment source and differential compaction of underlying platform and basinal rocks. Variations in thickness of the Namurian succession due to this relief are illustrated by the borehole correlation (Figure 30). Initially, tilted fault blocks formed a series of starved rifts, and basinal mud was deposited in the central parts of these rifts, which included the Edale, Pennine and Staffordshire basins and the Widmerpool Gulf, lying between the highs of the Wales–London–Brabant Massif and Derbyshire (Figure 29).

The basin floor relief was gradually infilled as deltas, fed from two main source areas, built farther into the basin (Figure 29). The largest sediment source lay to the north of the region where a major river system draining southwards from Greenland and Scandinavia supplied vast quantities of feldspathic detritus (Jones, 1980). A second, more local source, supplied sediment (notably the protoquartzitic sand found in the Minn Sandstones) into the basin in the south and west of the region (Holdsworth, 1963; Aitkenhead, 1973; Trewin and Holdsworth, 1973; Aitkenhead et al., 1985; Chisholm et al., 1988; Fulton and Williams, 1988; Martinsen et al., 1995). Additionally, a possible source to the west or north-west has been postulated for successions both of early Pendleian age (within the Lask Edge Shales) and later Yeadonian age (for example the Haslingden Flags of south-east Lancashire). This shows progradation from west to east and significantly different characteristics to the sequences above and below (Collinson, 1988; McLean and Chisholm, 1996; Hallsworth and Chisholm, 2000).

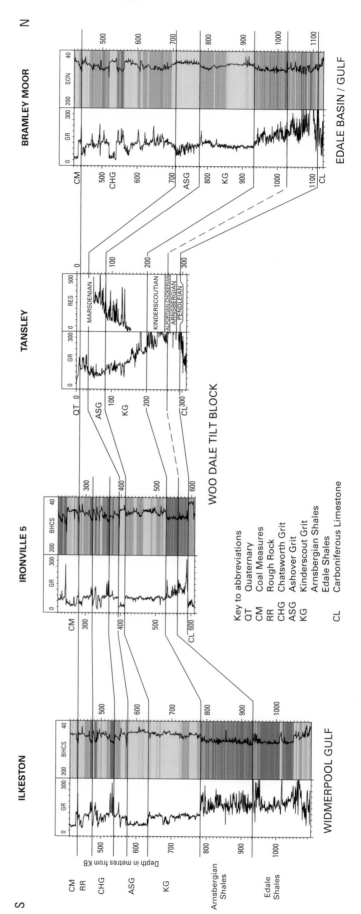

Figure 30   Geophysical log signature, lithostratigraphical correlation and chronostratigraphy of the Millstone Grit from the Edale Gulf to the Widmerpool Gulf. Location of profile is indicated on Figure 29.

The northerly derived deltas had already reached the Midland Valley of Scotland and northern England during Dinantian times and progressively built southwards across the Pennine Basin during the Namurian, eventually to overwhelm the basin and the subordinate western and southern sources in late Namurian times (Collinson, 1988; Guion and Fielding, 1988). Consequently, the rifts in the central and distal parts of the basin (Staffordshire Basin, Edale Basin and Widmerpool Gulf) were initially starved of clastic material, and the earliest Namurian sediments were basinal silt and mud. As the basin filled, the supply of turbiditic and prodelta sands increased progressively, and characteristic coarse-grained delta-slope and delta-top sands dominated late Namurian deposition.

The nature and distribution of early Namurian rocks shows that the course of the deltas prograding from the north was strongly influenced by the inherited bathymetric and topographic relief. The evidence indicates that the sediments were deposited in increasingly shallower water during the Silesian (Kent, 1966; Aitkenhead et al., 1985; Fraser and Gawthorpe, 1990). Discrete basins were separated by generally submerged highs, which acted as barriers to turbidity currents, preventing the deltas and turbidites from reaching certain areas; thus the turbidites of the Widmerpool Gulf were deposited significantly later in Namurian times (Trewin and Holdsworth, 1973). This effect is well documented in Derbyshire, where the Ashover Grit delta (Marsdenian) which, with a source in the north-east, was deflected around an intrabasin high, arriving in Staffordshire via south-east Nottinghamshire (Jones, 1980; Jones and Chisholm, 1996).

The southward progradation of the deltas was interrupted by marine incursions, resulting in widespread marine bands that can be used to correlate the succession. To the north of the region, these marine incursions divide the succession into three main progradational phases, during the Pendleian, Kinderscoutian and Marsdenian stages, each with depocentres progressively farther south (Kirby et al., 2000).

The strongly cyclical nature of the alternating sandstone, siltstone and marine bands of the Silesian succession, and the apparent persistence of individual marine horizons over large areas has been recognised since the early part of the 20th century. Wright et al. (1927) were among the first to demonstrate a detailed understanding of how a particular Millstone Grit cycle developed in terms of depositional setting and relative sea level changes. Subsequently, it was suggested that the cyclicity was eustatic in origin (Ramsbottom, 1977). Continued development in stratigraphical methods, and in particular of sequence stratigraphy, led to the application of these techniques to the Namurian succession. Read (1991) suggested that the grits of the differing types of deltaic successions correspond to different types of 'sequence'; thus turbidite-fronted deltas were designated as single or multiple 'lowstand systems tracts' and many sheet deltas as 'highstand systems tracts'. While there are certain attractions with the simplicity of the scheme, closer examination of the sequences casts serious doubts on it. The cyclicity has been related to short-period glacio-eustatic sea-level changes, the main regressions and transgressions were attributed to glacio-eustatic draw-down and rise of sea-level respectively. No agreement however has been reached on the applicability of sequence stratigraphical concepts to the Silesian succession and in particular the Namurian deltas (Read 1991; Martinsen, 1991, 1993; Collinson et al., 1992; Maynard, 1992). Indeed, Martinsen et al. (1995) concluded that the major cycles of deposition known to exist in the Namurian show no systematic architecture. They cast doubt over whether the major Namurian cycles relate to significant changes of relative sea level, but suggest instead that they may result from major avulsive shifts of sediment depocentres. This study has not clarified matters further.

Six basic lithofacies associations are recognised (Collinson, 1988): basinal mudstone, basinal turbidite, turbidite-fronted deltas, sheet deltas, elongate deltas and sheet-like channel sandstones. Turbidite-fronted deltas constitute the dominant basin fill succession. The best examples are the Pendleian of the Craven Basin (Baines, in Collinson, 1988), the Kinderscoutian of the Central Pennine Basin (Walker, 1966; Collinson, 1969; McCabe, 1978) and in the Marsdenian of the Staffordshire Basin (Jones, 1980, Jones and Chisholm, 1996). Less well-exposed examples occur in the Marsdenian of Derbyshire (Mayhew, 1967; Chisholm, 1977, Jones and Chisholm, 1996). Within the region, sedimentation was initially dominated by basinal mudstone until mid-Namurian (Kinderscoutian) times. The mudstone was succeeded first by turbidite-fronted and then by shallow water deltas as the main river systems progressively prograded into the area from the north (Walker, 1966; Collinson, 1988). However, across the region, the picture is complicated by the influence of the Wales–London–Brabant Massif, which acted as a sediment source for smaller northerly prograding deltas.

Over the years the variable lithofacies developed across the region have given rise to a complex lithostratigraphical nomenclature. Originally 'Millstone Grit' was used to describe a coarse-grained sandstone in the Whaley Bridge area of the Derwent valley in north Derbyshire (Whitehurst, 1778), subsequently, the term acquired a time-stratigraphical connotation and, although inappropriate, was for some time extended to include all strata of Namurian age (e.g. Gibson, 1925) in the Pennine region. Following this, the fundamental distinction between the mudstone-dominated lower Namurian and the sandstone-dominated upper part was recognised, although many local formational names arose within both facies. The lithostratigraphical nomenclature of the Namurian is, at the time of writing this memoir, the subject of a research report (Waters et al., in prep.). The approach taken in this report is to simplify nomenclature by taking a facies-based approach. The lower mudstone-dominated succession is termed the Craven Group and the upper sandstone-dominated succession the Millstone Grit Group. However, the distinction between southerly derived sandstones, and the northerly derived Millstone Grit Group is also recognised, with the establishment of the

Cefn-y-fedw Sandstone Formation in north Wales and the Morridge Formation of the Widmerpool Gulf (*see inside front cover* summary of the geological succession).

Pendleian (E₁)

Strata of Pendleian age are proved in boreholes (see below) and found at crop around the region, most extensively around the Derbyshire High. They are also encountered at crop in north Wales, as the Pentre Cherts and the partly equivalent Cefn-y-fedw Sandstone Formation, the younger parts of which interfinger with the Holywell Shales. The strata consist mainly of dark grey mudstone deposited from suspension in quiet, relatively deep water, largely unaffected by coarser clastic supply in the major basins of Edale, Alport, Staffordshire and Widmerpool gulf. The sediments were banked against topographical slopes in the Dinantian limestone at basin margins (Broadhurst and Simpson, 1967). Boreholes at Ashover, Derbyshire prove a condensed sequence of mudstone above a Dinantian platform, suggesting that mud also draped the upstanding platform areas (Ramsbottom et al., 1962). Marine bands developed when basin waters were fully saline and connection to the open ocean was well established. Unfossiliferous mudstone accumulated when the water was brackish or fresh. The relative levels and changes in salinity have been discussed by Martinsen et al. (1995).

The earliest strata of Namurian age in the Staffordshire Basin are the Lask Edge Shales. They range in thickness from 173 m in the Gun Hill Borehole and around the Mixon–Morridge Anticline to 110 m in the Werrington Borehole and between 27 to 60 m thick farther east (Aitkenhead et al., 1985). The succession is dominated by mudstone and siltstone, but contains subordinate protoquartzitic sandstone, and interbedded calcareous siltstone derived from the west (Trewin and Holdsworth, 1973). The sandstone was deposited as thin sheets and is generally graded, with sole marks; the fauna indicates that most of the sandstone is non-marine in origin (Evans et al., 1968; Rees and Wilson, 1998). Clasts were derived from the weathered terrain of the Wales–London–Brabant Massif to the south and carried into the basin by turbidity currents flowing from deltas flanking the massif; these seldom prograded far into the basins (Trewin and Holdsworth, 1973; Aitkenhead et al., 1985; Bolton, in Collinson, 1988; Rees and Wilson, 1998). The distribution of the sandstones shows significant bathymetric control; the main accumulations occur along the north-south axis of the Staffordshire Basin, and they thin to the east and west margins, dying out 'down current' to the north. The first major protoquartzites, the Minn Sandstones, appear in late Pendleian times in the Macclesfield–Congleton area of north Staffordshire. Eastwards around Buxton and Bakewell, the most distal turbidites are referred to as Minn Mudstones-with-Sandstones (Aitkenhead et al., 1985). Farther east in the Widmerpool Gulf, unnamed sandstones of turbiditic origin occur at the same levels in the sequence (Aitkenhead 1977; Ramsbottom et al., 1978; Chisholm et al., 1988).

In north Derbyshire, Pendleian strata comprise the marine Edale Shales (Jackson, 1923) which crop out in Edale valley and were proved in the Alport and Edale boreholes; they range up to 150 m thick (Stevenson and Gaunt, 1971). The Edale Shales consist mainly of silty mudstone with thin siltstones, which become finer grained towards the top of the Pendleian and extend up into the Kinderscoutian. The top is marked by the appearance of sandy beds of R₁ age (Mam Tor Beds, Shale Grit and Kinderscout Grit; Stevenson and Gaunt, 1971). Despite their deep-water setting, basinal turbidites appear to be absent from Pendleian strata in the Edale and Alport basins to the north of the Derbyshire Platform (Collinson, 1988). This may be the result of energy loss of the turbidite currents in the more distal parts of the basin, as well as intrabasinal slopes and highs that separated the Staffordshire, Edale and Widmerpool gulfs into discrete basins and acted as barriers to turbidity currents (Trewin and Holdsworth, 1973; Collinson, 1988).

The succession of chert and cherty mudstone of the Pentre Chert Formation are the lowermost beds of Namurian age in north Wales. Considerable debate surrounds their age and it is thought that they may extend down into the Brigantian (see Jones and Lloyd, 1942; Warren et al., 1984; Davies et al., 2004). Comparable beds of chert are recorded from the uppermost Dinantian of the Great Orme on the north coast of Wales (Warren et al., 1984) and from south Wales (Woodland and Evans, 1964). Locally they rest with pronounced unconformity upon late Dinantian strata and are overlain by the Holywell Shales Formation. Both formations interfinger with and pass laterally into the Cefn-y-fedw Sandstone, informally divided into the Lower, Middle and Upper units (Davies et al., 2004), the main outcrop comprising the lower unit. The Cefn-y-fedw Sandstone is up to 600 m thick flanking the Flint Coalfield, thinning northwards to Pentre Halkyn. South of the Necwys–Nant-figillit Fault Zone, it succeeds the Dinantian Minera Formation. Borehole data suggests the formation extends beneath the thick drift deposits of the Alyn valley (Davies et al., 2004). The Holywell Shales Formation comprises marine, brackish and non-marine mudstone with subordinate thin sandstones, and is interpreted as a prodelta facies. The Cefn-y-fedw Sandstones are of fluvial-deltaic origin, with seatearths and thin coals locally at the top of some cycles indicating deposition in delta-top swamp conditions. Regional thickness variations suggest that deposition was largely centred on the Bala Lineament and that this complex fracture belt effectively controlled the course of the major fluvial system that discharged onto the delta. The greatest thickness of sediment accumulated along the northern side of the fault, suggesting that the area marked a depositional trough inherited from Dinantian times.

Arnsbergian (E₂)

Strata of Arnsbergian age crop out most extensively around the Derbyshire High area, and also occur in Staffordshire and north Wales. At this time the northerly sourced deltas retreated to the north of the region, forming the Sabden Shales (Kirby et al., 2001), and deposition of basinal mud with distal turbidites continued in this region, for example the upper part of the Edale Shales were deposited in the Edale Basin of north

Derbyshire. The mudstone sequence is up to 100 m thick (Stevenson and Gaunt, 1971), and spans Stages E_2, H and lower part of R_1, thus ranging from Arnsbergian to Kinderscoutian (Edwards and Trotter, 1954). Similar mudstone with E_2 ammonoids have been proved in boreholes at Hathern and Lawn Bridge (Edwards and Trotter, 1954).

In the North Staffordshire Basin, deposition of the Minn Sandstones continued into early Arnsbergian times. They are succeeded by the Hurdlow Sandstones (Lower Churnet Shales of Evans et al., 1968), a mudstone succession that contains protoquartzitic proximal sandstone turbidites (Hurdlow Sandstones) interbedded with more distal turbidites (Hurdlow Sandstones-with-Mudstones of Aitkenhead et al., 1985). As with the Minn Sandstones, these become more distal away from the Wales–London–Brabant Massif and thin against the Derbyshire Limestone Shelf.

In north Wales, deposition of the Holywell Shales continued into the Arnsbergian. They crop out on Hope Mountain where they overlie the Lower Cefn-y-fedw Sandstone (of late Pendleian to earliest Arnsbergian age).

Chokierian to Alportian (H_1 and H_2)

Rocks of this age are generally very thin or absent in the region. Elsewhere in northern England this stage coincides with a non-sequence or unconformity (Ramsbottom et al., 1978). In west Derbyshire and Staffordshire, however, there is an uninterupted succession of mudstone and protoquartzitic sandstone. In the north, the sequence consists mainly of mudstone (Middle Churnet Shales of Evans et al., 1968), but southwards the proportion of sandstone increases. In the Buxton area, the sandstones are turbiditic (Lum Edge Sandstones of Aitkenhead et al., 1985) but these pass southwards into shallow-water fluvial deposits (Cheddleton Sandstones of Chilsholm et al., 1988; Rees and Wilson, 1998). At Ipstones Edge, fluvial sandstones account for the whole succession, indicating deposition closer to the basin margin; they pass up into sandstones of Kinderscoutian (R_1) age.

At Hope Mountain in north Wales, a thick sequence of Middle Cefn-y-fedw Sandstone separates two leaves of the Holywell Shales; the lower leaf is Arnsbergian in age and the overlying leaf is of mid-Kinderscoutian (R_{1b}) age. The sandstone therefore appears to span the whole of the Chokierian to Alportian stages (Davies et al., 2004). Thin distal correlatives of the Middle Cefn-y-fedw Sandstone are found in the north of the Flint district, but no representatives were proved in either the Abbey Mills or Blacon East boreholes farther north.

Kinderscoutian (R_1)

Strata of Kinderscoutian age crop out around the Derbyshire High and in north Wales. The northerly sourced deltas advanced southwards once more as a great influx of feldspathic sands encroached upon and ultimately spread across the relatively thin Pendleian to early Kinderscoutian successions. The lowest sandstones are usually turbiditic, and the distribution indicates some control by basin floor relief. They are succeeded by coarser beds and ultimately by fluviatile deposits, as the basin was infilled. In the Peak District, rocks of this age are up to 450 m in thickness, and are referred to the Upper Churnet Shales or Kinderscout Grit Group (Edwards and Trotter, 1954; Stevenson and Gaunt, 1971).

Evidence of strong bathymetric control on currents and clastic supply occurs in the earlier Kinderscoutian rocks (Mam Tor Sandstones and the Shale Grit) in the south of the Pennine Basin, around Edale. A turbiditic succession, some 300 m thick, deposited just to the north of the Derbyshire High, is overlain by 150 m of slope and delta-top deposits. In the Staffordshire Basin, only 8 km to the south-west, equivalent sandstones are absent, suggesting that a barrier existed between the two basins at the north-west end of the Derbyshire High (Collinson, 1988). This barrier, perhaps related to an extension of the Bakewell Fault, was probably not obliterated until latest Kinderscoutian times when the turbiditic Longnor Sandstone (equivalent to the Kinderscout Grit deposited in the Pennine Basin to the north of the barrier region) was deposited in the Staffordshire Basin by currents flowing from the north (see below).

In west Derbyshire and north Staffordshire, rocks of this age are the Upper Churnet Shales of the Macclesfield district and equivalents (Evans et al., 1968). The lower part of the succession is mainly argillaceous but contains protoquartzitic sandstones of turbiditic origin, including the Blackstone Edge Sandstones and Kniveden Sandstones (Aitkenhead et al., 1985; Chisholm et al., 1988). The Kniveden Sandstones (of late R_{1c} age) are interpreted as prodelta turbidites. They thin and pinch out northwards from the Werrington Anticline (Evans et al., 1968; Rees and Wilson, 1998), and die out around Carsington, where deep-water conditions appear to have lasted throughout Kinderscoutian times (Chisholm et al., 1988). To the south they pass into the upper part of the Ipstones Edge Sandstones, which are of shallow-water facies and contain no marine bands. Originally thought to be entirely Kinderscoutian in age (Morris, 1969), Ipstones Edge Sandstones are now recognised to include sandstones of H_1, H_2 and R_1 age. They indicate deposition in a more proximal position in the basin, closer to the source area, and the protoquartzites of the distal sandstone units cannot be separated (Lum Edge, Stanley, Cheddleton, Blackstone Edge and Kniveden sandstones) (Chisholm et al., 1988). All are apparently of shallow-water origin, forming an assemblage of fluviodeltaic channel and mouth bar sandstones with overbank deposits.

The Lognor Sandstone and Kinderscout Grit of the Macclesfield–Buxton area illustrate a marked change in turbidite provenance in Kinderscoutian times, from the southerly derived protoquartzites to northerly derived feldspathic sandstones (Holdsworth, 1963; Aitkenhead et al., 1985). The Lognor Sandstones reach a maximum thickness of between 200 and 250 m, and are thickest some 5 km south-west of Buxton where variations indicate that the late Dinantian shelf persisted as a feature on the sea floor. They show a change from proximal turbidites in the north-west to distal turbidites in the south-east, and are interpreted as a turbidite fan that accumulated at the foot of a submarine prodelta slope, with sediment supplied via feeder channels (Collinson, 1968). In the region, the uppermost Lognor Sandstones pass laterally and upwards into the Kinderscout Grit. This thins southwards across the area from a maximum thickness in the Chapel-en-le-Frith district dying out near Bakewell. It comprises massive coarse, pebbly sandstones and is turbiditic in its more distal parts (Stevenson and Gaunt, 1971; Aitkenhead et al., 1985).

In north Wales, sandstones of the Upper Cefn-y-fedw Sandstone range from early Kinderscoutian to late Marsdenian in age (Davies et al., 2004). Thin correlative sandstones are interbedded with the Holywell Shales in the Flint district and were proved in the Abbey Mills No. 4 and Blacon East boreholes. The earliest sandstones are interpreted as delta sand that has been reworked into shoreface bars and beach deposits. They are followed by upward-coarsening cycles, recording the progradation and accretion of a complex of distributary channels and mouth bars over a sequence of interdistributary and prodelta deposits. Seatearths and thin coals at the top of some cycles result from the periodic development of delta-top swamp deposition. Unfossiliferous prodelta mudstone forms the base to most cycles.

Marsdenian (R_2)

In this region Marsdenian rocks are amongst the thickest in Britain (Ramsbottom et al., 1978). They form the main fluviodeltaic clastic infill to the Widmerpool Gulf and Staffordshire Basin (Jones, 1980; Collinson, 1988; Chisholm et al., 1988; Jones and Chilsholm, 1996; Rees and Wilson, 1998). In general, sandstones of Marsdenian and Yeadonian age (Millstone Grit Group; Rees and Wilson, 1998), were formed by the repeated progradation of deltaic systems across the Pennine Basin from a northerly source area, as they by-passed previously filled basins to the north-west (Jones, 1980). Growth faulting, which may have resulted from gravitational collapse of these deltaic sequences, is recorded in several places (Chisholm, 1977, 1981; Jones, 1980; Jones and Chilsholm, 1996).

Cropping-out on both flanks of the Goyt Syncline of the Staffordshire Basin, the Marsdenian succession consists of a lower mudstone-dominated and an upper deltaic sandstone succession. The latter includes the Roaches Grit in the western outcrop and the laterally equivalent Ashover Grit in the east. In the Ashbourne and Stoke-on-Trent districts, the succession also comprises a lower mudstone succession, but is here overlain by the last major occurrence of southerly derived protoquartzitic sandstones in the region. These are the Brockholes Sandstones of R_{2b} age (Chisholm et al., 1988; Rees and Wilson, 1998), which are of shallow-water facies. In the Widmerpool Gulf, mud deposition with only rare pulses of coarse sediment, continued until R_{2b} times when the main northern delta began to supply feldspathic clastic material into the region. Consequently, to the north and east the Brockholes Sandstones interdigitate with, and are

overlain by, easterly derived feldspathic sandstones of the Roaches Grit.

Successions developed across the Central Pennine Basin illustrate the progressive southerly or south-westerly migration of the depocentres. The basin topography was progressively infilled by south-easterly derived siliciclastic sediments during Kinderscoutian and Marsdenian times. The Roaches Grit in its type area is a thick succession of clastic rocks resulting from the infilling of the deepest remaining parts of the North Staffordshire Basin (Jones and Chisholm, 1996). The initial turbidite system entered the Widmerpool Gulf from the south-east and flowed axially along the Central Pennine Basin. In the Leek–Buxton district, the full Marsdenian sandstone succession (Sheen Sandstones, Five Clouds Sandstones, Corbar and Roaches Grits) indicates deposition in deep-water prodelta turbidite fan, delta-slope turbidite and delta-top environments (Jones, 1980; Aitkenhead et al., 1985; Jones and Chisholm, 1996). In places, coarse fluvial sandstones of the delta top are succeeded by post-abandonment facies (Jones, 1980; Jones and Chilsholm, 1996). To the south and west, turbidite-fronted delta deposits are the major basin-fill successions of the Staffordshire Basin and the last deep-water infill (Jones, 1980; Rees and Wilson, 1998). Less well-exposed examples of these facies also occur in Derbyshire (Mayhew, 1967; Chisholm, 1977; Jones and Chilsholm, 1996). In the Stoke-on-Trent and Ashover areas, the Roaches Grit is thin and fine grained at the south-west limit of its depositional area (Chisholm et al., 1988; Rees and Wilson, 1998). Succeeding sandstones comprise the shallower water, fluviatile, delta-top components of the delta systems.

The last major feldspathic sandstones of R_{2c} age are generally referred to as the Chatsworth Grit (Aitkenhead et al., 1985; Chisholm et al., 1988). They form part of a coarsening-upwards unit that represents a transition from transgressive marine to fluviatile conditions; the sandstones are channel deposits of rivers that flowed from the east or north-east.

In north Wales, sandstones of the Upper Cefn-y-fedw sandstone range from early Kinderscoutian to late Marsdenian in age (Davies et al., 2004). These interdigitate with the Holywell Shales and indicate the diachronous northwards progradation of a fluviodeltaic facies over the former Dinantian platform. Around Hawarden, the top of the local Cefn-y-fedw Sandstone succession is associated with either the late Marsdenian B. bilinguis (R_{2b2}) or B. superbilinguis (R_{2c1}) marine bands. Farther south around Warren Dingle, the highest levels of this sandstone occur above this marine band and perhaps only 20 m below the basal Yeadonian C. cancellatum (G_{1a}) marine band.

Yeadonian (G_1)

Strata of Yeadonian age crop out most extensively around the Staffordshire Basin and Derbyshire High but are also encountered in north Wales. As is the case with the earlier (Marsdenian) Chatsworth Grit cycle, the Yeadonian succession comprises a lower argillaceous unit and an upper sandstone unit, the Rough Rock, which indicates a transition from transgressive marine to fluviatile conditions. The

Rough Rock is the uppermost and most widespread Namurian sandstone in the Central Pennine Basin. It comprises major multistorey fluvial sheet sandstones, which are laterally persistent, medium to coarse grained, sub-arkosic and pebbly (Shackleton, 1962; Bristow, 1988). By late Yeadonian times, the Central Pennine Basin had essentially been filled by the southerly prograding delta front.

The Rough Rock, although derived from a northern source, shows pronounced regional changes in petrography and palaeocurrents (Shackleton, 1962; Bristow, 1988). Palaeocurrents are variable across the Pennine Basin, particularly in Staffordshire; this appears to suggest the establishment of a fluvial braidplain across the area, perhaps in response to a period of lower base levels, or to tectonic rejuvenation of source areas. Growth faulting that may be the result of gravitational collapse of the large-scale deltaic successions (Chisholm 1977, 1981) allied to synsedimentary faulting is intermittently recorded in the Rough Rock in several places (Bristow, 1988). Studies indicate that shallow braided rivers flowed into a brackish area of standing water in the centre of the basin. One braided stream prograded southwards as far as Sheffield, and can be traced laterally into the Gainsborough Trough (Bristow, 1988). South of this line, only fine-grained sandstones and siltstones were deposited in a prodelta or lacustrine environment. Some currents flowed in a westerly direction along the northern margin of the Derbyshire High. South of this high, braided rivers carrying sediment derived from the Wales–London–Brabant Massif flowed westwards along the axis of the Widmerpool Gulf towards the Red Rock Fault. In the Goyt Trough (northern end of Staffordshire Basin), current directions converge from all sides.

In north Wales, the Gwespyr Sandstone ranges from Yeadonian to early Westphalian (Langsettian), and crops out around the Flintshire Coalfield. It consists of feldspathic sandstone with subordinate thin sandstones and mudstones. The source is interpreted as igneous and metamorphic rocks of probable Archaean or Caledonian age (Drewery et al., 1987; Collinson, 1988; Davies et al., 2004). Deposited as detrital input from the southerly sourced deltas waned, the Gwespyr Sandstone records the first major incursion of northerly sourced deltaic sediments into north Wales and the ultimate 'drowning' of the southerly derived delta (Davies et al., 2004). Initially the delta built out into deep water, resulting in a series of relatively fine-grained stacked successions, reflecting deposition of mouthbar and distributary channel complexes some distance from the source in a pro-delta to delta-slope environment. However, a delta plain was rapidly established during the late Namurian as it continued to advance southwards. Thin coals were developed in delta-top swamp environments and marine influences were restricted; the *G. Subcrenatum* and *listeri* marine bands (of Westphalian age) provide the only preserved evidence of widespread marine inundation.

WESTPHALIAN

Conformably overlying Namurian strata, Westphalian rocks of the Pennine Coal Measures Group outcrop in a number of coalfields and are present beneath much of the younger rocks of the region (Maps 5–8). They comprise cyclical successions of mudstone, siltstone, sandstone, seatearth and coal (cyclothems). Allocyclic events (such as change in climate, subsidence rates, tectonics and glacio-eustacy) and autocyclic controls, (sediment compaction and sedimentary processes) were important influences in determining the sedimentation pattern. Tectonic events were locally important in controlling sedimentation and became progressively more important from late Bolsovian times onwards. Westphalian palaeogeography and thickness variations have been described by Wills (1948, 1951, 1973), Trueman (1946, 1947, 1954) and more recently by Cope et al., (1992), which form the basis of this account.

Sedimentation of the Langsettian to Bolsovian Coal Measures took place in delta and alluvial plain environments across the Pennine Basin. The southern margin of the basin was formed by the Wales–London–Brabant Massif, and small embayments extended south onto it. The massif had a subdued relief and supplied perhaps minimal amounts of sediment to the north. Sedimentary lithologies of the basin are characteristically laterally extensive and comprise claystone, siltstone and sandstone. Interbedded coal and seatearth indicate the development of swampy delta top environments. Marine incursions across the wide low-lying delta plains occurred, but rarely, and are marked by marine bands. Fossil plants are common throughout the Westphalian strata. The deposition of the Warwickshire Group marks the end of widespread coal-forming conditions in the region, which thereafter was characterised by the continued uplift and erosion of earlier, Dinantian, syn-rift basins and sediment accumulation occurred in smaller intermontane troughs.

Owing to subsequent earth movements, Westphalian strata of the Pennine Basin are now distributed within a number of separate areas that include the South Staffordshire, North Staffordshire (Potteries, Cheadle and Shaffalong coalfields), Warwickshire, Coalbrookdale, Lancashire and East Midlands coalfields (Figure 31). This geographical separation has resulted in the proliferation of local names and lithostratigraphical schemes for each coalfield, reflecting the local, but distinctive, sedimentary fill resulting from variable rates of basin subsidence, uplift and sediment flux (Ramsbottom et al., 1978). Westphalian strata are divided into the **Coal Measures Group** (formerly 'Productive', including Lower, Middle and part Upper Coal Measures; Powell et al., 2000) ranging in age from Langsettian to Bolsovian, and the **Warwickshire Group** (formerly part of the Upper Coal Measures, Barren or Red Measures) ranging in age from Bolsovian to Autunian (Table 3). This group is equivalent to the inversion megasequence of Fraser et al. (1990) and Fraser and Gawthorpe (1990) that are collectively referred to as the Westphalian C–D molasses by Corfield et al. (1996). The boundary between the two groups is more or less conformable in many parts of the basin. However, locally on the margins there is an unconformity, which in the Coalbrookdale Coalfield, miners referred to as the 'Symon Fault' (Hamblin and Coppack,

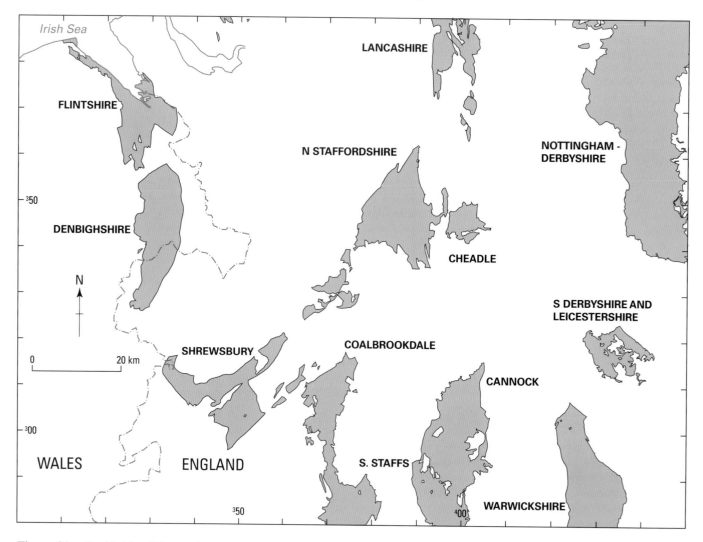

Figure 31 Coalfields of the region.

1995, p.35). This study retains the name Symon, but replaces 'fault' with 'unconformity'.

Westphalian strata of the region show a variation in thickness that broadly appears to support a 'thermal sag' model (Leeder, 1982). Strata of Namurian to Bolsovian age onlap southwards and thin towards the London–Brabant Massif (Fulton and Williams, 1988). To the north, the Coal Measures Group (Langsettian to Bolsovian) becomes thicker and individual coal seams split. A thickness of about 150 m is recorded in south Staffordshire with 450 m in the Cannock Coalfield (Beete-Jukes, 1859; Mitchell and Stubblefield, 1945; Hains and Horton, 1969), and in a depocentre centred in south Lancashire between Manchester and Stoke (Trueman, 1947; Fraser et al., 1990) the maximum preserved thickness of the group may be up to 2500 m (Smith et al., 1984; Map 6). However, by mid-Duckmantian times this simple picture was complicated by the first effects of the progressive northerly migration of the Variscan deformation front, such that in later Westphalian times depositional systems and the distribution of sequences were increasingly affected by faulting and uplift. The simple 'thermal sag' model does not account for many features

evident in central England over the southern part of the Pennine Basin (Besly, 1988; Waters et al., 1994). The Warwickshire Group records the initial basin-wide Variscan inversion events within the Variscan Foreland, that culminated in Westphalian D times with the onset of the second and strongest compressional pulse of the Variscan Orogeny.

Within the basin, there is evidence that deposition was controlled in places by a remnant topography, but the effects of synsedimentary folding and faulting was important and is well documented (Fielding, 1984a; Fielding and Johnson, 1987; Guion and Fielding, 1988; Read, 1988).

Pennine Coal Measures Group

The base of the Pennine Coal Measures Group is defined at the base of the Subcrenatum Marine Band, or where this is absent or not identified the base is taken at the lowest coal-bearing sequence. The Coal Measures Group extends up to the base of the lowest overlying red-bed formation of the Warwickshire Group (Table 3). The

Table 3 Stratigraphy of the Warwickshire Group in south Staffordshire, Warwickshire and north Staffordshire.

Group	Formation				Series/Stage
	South Staffordshire	Warwickshire		North Staffordshire	
WARWICKSHIRE GROUP (BARREN MEASURES)	*(hiatus)*	Ashow Formation		*(hiatus)*	AUTUNIAN†
	Clent Formation	Kenilworth Sandstone Formation			
	(hiatus)	Till Hill Mudstone Formation			STEPHANIAN
		Salop Formation (*Meriden Formation*)	Allesley Member		
			Keresley Member		
	Salop Formation		Whitacre Member	Salop Formation (*Radwood Formation*)	
	Enville Member (*Enville Fm*)				WESTPHALIAN D
	Alveley Member (*Keele Fm*)				
	Halesowen Formation	Dark Slade Member	red facies*	(*Keele Formation*)	
				(*Newcastle Formation*)	
	(hiatus)				
	Etruria Formation				BOLSOVIAN (WESTPHALIAN C)

Notes
* Local red lithofacies in Halesowen Formation
† Base Permian is assumed to be below the Clent and Kenilworth formations
Italicised names in brackets are superseded

vertical lines indicate a hiatus
shaded areas indicate predominantly red beds

boundary between the Lower and Middle Coal Measures is the Vanderbeckei Marine Band and the top of the Cambriense Marine Band marks the boundary between the Middle and Upper Coal Measures. In this area of the Pennine Basin, the Etruria Formation is seen as lying conformably upon the Coal Measures Group (Powell, et al., 2000), but this may not apply in all areas. A full development of the group, proved by numerous boreholes, shafts and exposures, exists in the North Staffordshire Coalfield within the Potteries Syncline (Rees and Wilson, 1998) where it may be up to 1600 m thick (Map 6).

The sedimentology of the Coal Measures has been described by Fielding (1984a, b, 1986) and Guion and Fielding (1988). The strata were deposited in upper and lower delta plain environments; most sediment was carried across the delta plains by major distributary channel complexes between 2 and 10 km wide. Many of the major sandstones of the coalfields were deposited in these channel systems that show patterns of regular switching. However, many thin sandstones with erosive bases form belts of minor channels. The channel systems were separated by extensive lakes where mud and cannel coal accumulated. The beds commonly coarsen upwards into fine-grained sandstone as a result of progradation of lacustrine deltas fed by minor channels that discharged into the lakes. Breaching of the channel banks resulted in the deposition of laterally variable overbank and crevasse-splay deposits. Such deposits show erosive bases near the source, becoming unconfined, non-erosive and sheet like away from the breach. Plants colonised many areas of the delta producing seatearths or siliciclastic palaeosols with numerous rootlet horizons. The environment is interpreted as a poorly drained swamp fed by groundwater. Coal formed from peat that accumulated on the floor of equatorial rain forests in extensive sheet-like mires. In contrast to seatearths and high-ash coals, most coal developed from rain-fed bogs above the water table. Marine bands, consisting of dark grey to black mudstone and extending for thousands of kilometres, formed during the flooding of the delta plain in periodic sea-level changes (Calver, 1968; Ramsbottom et al., 1978).

Facies associations of the lower part of the Langsettian include lower delta plain, shallow water and marine prodelta environments. There is an upward transition into upper delta plain successions that dominated during mid Langsettian to Duckmantian, with a possible return to lower delta plain environments later in Duckmantian times. Tectonic control on deposition at this time (Fielding, 1984b; Guion and Fielding, 1988) can best be illustrated by the Crawshaw Sandstone of lowermost Langsettian age, in the area of the Edale Basin. This sandstone is considerably thicker in the Edale Basin, and palaeocurrent data indicate that the delta lobes were deflected to flow westwards towards the basin depocentre. A similar increase in thickness of the Langsettian succession is also noted in the Widmerpool Gulf (Howitt and Brunstrom, 1966; Guion and Fielding, 1988). There is also evidence for active anticlinal structures having affected sedimentation in the east of the region at this time, for example the Crawshaw Sandstone in the Ashover Anticline (Ramsbottom et al., 1962).

Synsedimentary normal faulting in the region is indicated by coal seam splitting in the Coal Measures. The splitting of the Staffordshire Thick Coal across the Bentley Fault in the Warwickshire Coalfield perhaps best illustrates this (Waters et al., 1994; Powell et al., 2000). Deposition of major sandstones was also affected by anticlines that were rising at the time of sedimentation.

Due to erosion in post-Bolsovian times, the extent of Coal Measures Group deposition on the southern margins of the Pennine Basin can not be determined. However, Langsettian and Duckmantian strata are thought to have been deposited in embayments on the flanks of the Wales–London–Brabant Massif (Guion and Fielding, 1988) and alluvial facies of the same age at the extreme southern margins of the Midlands coalfields suggests that these areas lay close to the basin margin (Besly, 1983).

Alkaline basic igneous activity occurred in the central part of the Pennine Basin during early Carboniferous times, migrating to the south-eastern and south-western margins of the basin by late Carboniferous times. On seismic profiles the Coal Measures Group is characterised by a highly reflective and continuous package of reflectors (Figure 32). Alkaline igneous rocks of Namurian to Bolsovian age, occur in the Warwickshire Coalfield (Old et al., 1991; Bridge, 1991), in the East Midlands and Derbyshire (Burgess, 1982; Kirton, 1984), and the West Midlands. South of the region in Berkshire and south Oxfordshire, basic volcanic and intrusive rocks locally dominate the Langsettian to Duckmantian strata (Foster et al., 1989).

Warwickshire Group

Up to 1400 m of multicoloured beds (Maps 7, 8) containing only minor coal-bearing horizons overlies the Coal Measures Group. These are of late Bolsovian to Stephanian/Autunian age (Besly, 1988). Long known as the Upper or Barren Measures because of the general lack of coals, they have been renamed the Warwickshire Group (Powell, Chisholm et al., 2000) and a formal lithostratigraphical nomenclature has been established (Table 3). The revised name reflects the fact that the Warwickshire Coalfield has the thickest and most complete succession in the Pennine Basin. The group progressively oversteps southwards across Coal Measures, Namurian and Dinantian strata, to rest unconformably on Silurian and older rocks (Figure 33).

In areas of central England (North Staffordshire, Nottingham–Derbyshire), the base of the lowest division of the Warwickshire Group, the Etruria Formation, is conformable but shows a complex interfingering of coal measures and red beds over an estimated 150 m of strata (Besly, 1983, 1988; Bridge et al., 1998; Rees and Wilson, 1998; Powell et al., 2000). The change to red-bed strata is diachronous, with the transition occurring later in the north. In areas marginal to the basin, for example in the Coalbrookdale and Wyre Forest coalfields, the conformable relationship can be traced into an unconformity at the base of the Etruria Formation that is also seen on seismic profiles (Figures 32; 33). This unconformity was originally termed the 'Symon Fault' by coal miners, but was recognised and named as the **Symon unconformity** by Scott (1861), and attributed by Clarke (1901) to folding that occurred during deposition of the Coal Measures. Subsequent workers (Stonehouse, 1951; Hoare, 1959; Besly et al., 1993; Hamblin and Coppack, 1995) have supported the presence of an unconformity, which is well documented in the Madeley area where the Coal Measures ('Lower' and 'Middle') were gently folded and eroded prior to deposition of the Etruria-equivalent Hadley Formation. In the Flint Coalfield, the Etruria Formation (formerly Ruabon Marl) rests with marked unconformity upon older Westphalian sequences in areas around the Dee estuary and the town of Flint (Davies et al., 2004). An unconformity is also recognised on Coal Authority seismic profiles over the Arley Anticline in the Warwickshire Coalfield. The presence of 'espleys' (conglomeratic beds, some containing clasts of pre-Carboniferous basement rocks) in the Etruria Formation in the western part of this coalfield and the thickening of the Etruria Formation in

Figure 32 Seismic reflection profile illustrating the seismic response of the Westphalian rocks within the Manchester–Winsford Sub-basin. Stripy seismic character interpreted to arise from the coal-prone Westphalian A B and part B succession (Langsettian, Duckmantian and part Bolsovian), while the seismically quieter interval beneath the Base Permo-Triassic Unconformity represents the less coal-prone Warwickshire Group.
Note: South-west onlap and thinning of the Coal Measures, which perhaps reflects an early Westphalian inversion of an underlying structure displaying a transpressional character. Location of profile is indicated on Figure 13.

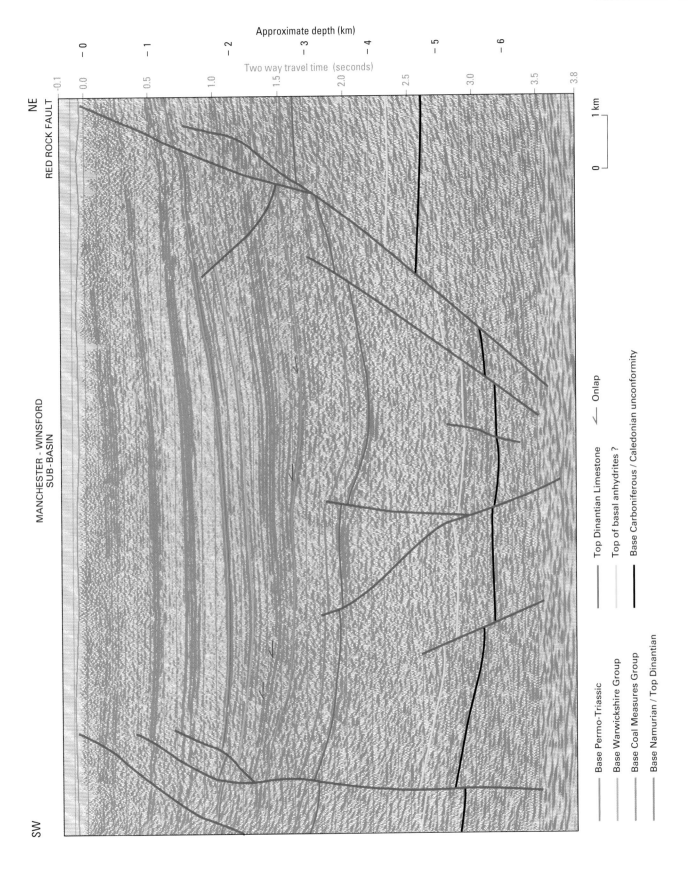

NE

RED ROCK FAULT

SW

MANCHESTER - WINSFORD
SUB-BASIN

Approximate depth (km)

- 0
- 1
- 2
- 3
- 4
- 5
- 6

Two way travel time (seconds)

-0.1
0.0
0.5
1.0
1.5
2.0
2.5
3.0
3.5
3.8

0   1 km

— Base Permo-Triassic

— Base Warwickshire Group

— Base Coal Measures Group

— Base Namurian / Top Dinantian

— Top Dinantian Limestone

— Top of basal anhydrites ?

— Base Carboniferous / Caledonian unconformity

↙ Onlap

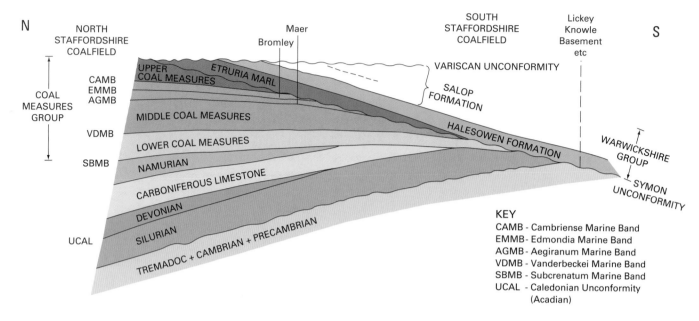

Figure 33   The Symon unconformity as developed and recognised from the relationships of the Coal Measures and Warwickshire Group in the North and South Staffordshire coalfields.

the opposite direction to the Coal Measures (Figure 34), also attests to movement of the Western Boundary Fault at this time. A similar pattern of thickening of the Etruria Formation together with the appearance of espleys occurs in a westerly direction towards the Coalbrookdale Boundary Fault, suggesting that this fault was also active at this time. Thus syndepositional fault movements and the development of the Symon unconformity appear to be quite widespread in marginal areas.

These earth movements provide the first widespread evidence of early Variscan inversion events. The migratation northwards of the Variscan deformation front culminated in the main phase of the Variscan Orogeny in Westphalian D to Stephanian times. These events were associated with a change from humid to arid conditions and hence the development of the red beds sequence. A mid-Bolsovian marine incursion, the Cambriense Marine Band, was followed by deposition of well-drained alluvial plain red-beds that form the Warwickshire Group. The initial uplift and denudation of the basin margins led to the spread of the alluvial fan and floodplain facies of the Etruria Formation into the basin. These rocks were derived from lateritic sources resulting from pedogenic reddening of waterlogged grey coal measure successions during intra-Westphalian uplift (Besly, 1988). Continued uplift and denudation of the margins at this time led to a rapid expansion of red-bed facies across the Pennine Basin. The overlying Halesowen Formation comprises a mixture of red-bed sandstones, grey green micaceous sandstones, grey green mudstones, Spirorbis limestones, caliches and intraformational breccias. Coals formed to the south of the region in the Oxfordshire and south Wales coalfields.

The Salop and Clent formations overlying the Halesowen Formation are red-bed facies, mainly derived from erosion of Variscan nappes and the continued uplift

of basin margins in the south of the British Isles and increasingly, intra-basinal areas. However, Besly (1988) has suggested that some of the earliest red beds in what he referred to as the Keele Formation (now part of the Halesowen and Salop formations), were derived from a northern Lower Palaeozoic terrane. The successions are interpreted as a series of stacked progradational alluvial fan systems, incorporating distal (argillaceous) and proximal arenaceous and conglomeritic beds. Uplifted fault blocks occupying the sites of what are now Triassic basins at Knowle and Hinckley were identified as the principal sources of coarse detritus (Wills, 1956; Besly, 1988).

On seismic profiles the Warwickshire Group is characterised by a package of reflectors that are generally of lower amplitude and poorer continuity than that of the Coal Measures Group (Figure 32).

Coalfields of the region

The region includes a number of coalfields and prospects, stretching from Wales to the east Midlands (Figures 31; 35). The concealed strata of Westphalian age beneath the Permo-Triassic Cheshire Basin form an important link between the many surrounding coalfields at crop. Only the general characteristics of the coalfields and prospects are given here with a correlation of the local marine bands (Table 4); a more detailed description can be found in Glover et al. (1993a).

Nottinghamshire–Derbyshire Coalfield

The Nottinghamshire–Derbyshire and the Yorkshire Coalfield occupies much of the north-eastern part of the region extending from Sheffield to Nottingham (Eden et al., 1957; Smith et al., 1967; Frost and Smart, 1979), and

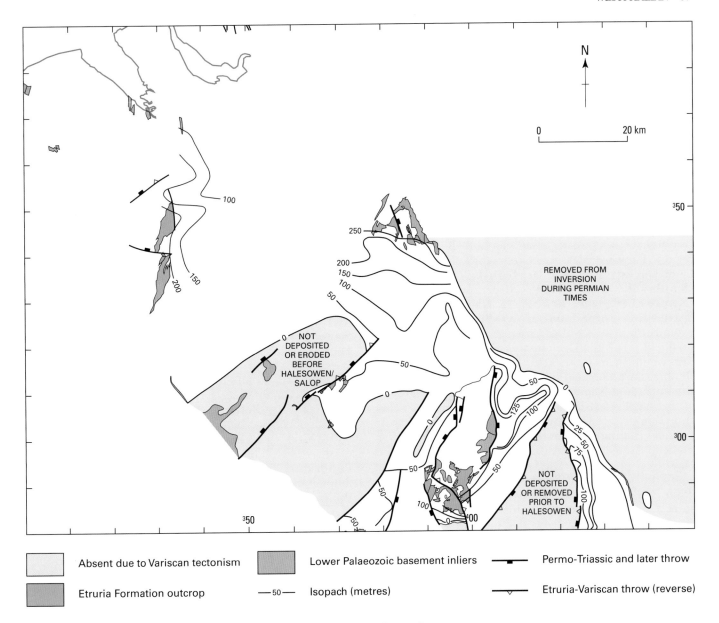

Figure 34 Distribution and thickness variation of the Etruria Formation.

the Westphalian successions have been taken as the standard for the coalfields of the Pennine Basin (Rams-bottom et al., 1978). The succession dips beneath Permian and Triassic rocks, and has been described by Edwards (1951, 1967) and Smith et al. (1968). Boreholes prove that it is generally absent between the exposed Nottinghamshire and Leicestershire coalfields, where Permo-Triassic strata overlie Namurian rocks.

Within the coalfield, up to 1500 m of grey Coal Measures rest conformably on Namurian strata and are overlain by red and varicoloured mudstone and sandstone of the Warwickshire Group. An unconformity is recognised within the Warwickshire Group (Edwards, 1951). Rocks of Langsettian to Bolsovian age contain up to 100 horizons at which coals are developed; lateral facies changes throughout the basin cause significant variations in coal seam thickness and abundance.

The exposed Coal Measures have been worked exten-sively with both old workings and modern opencast pits throughout the area. The concealed part of the coalfield is worked less towards the east. Intrusive and extrusive igneous rocks are found locally in Langsettian strata of the coalfield and have a detrimental effect on any future potential, for example on coalbed methane prospectivity (Creaney, 1980; Glover et al., 1993).

South Lancashire coalfield

Within the region, the coalfield is mainly concealed beneath the Permo-Triassic rocks of the Cheshire Basin between Liverpool and Manchester, but it extends well south of the southern limit of deep mining. Boreholes at Knutsford and Blacon and seismic reflection data here-abouts reveal Westphalian rocks are nearly continuous at depth between South Lancashire and the north Wales and north Staffordshire areas (Map 6). Strata of Langsettian to Westphalian to D age are present. The Coal Measures are about 1600 m thick, thickening towards the north-east to a maximum in the Burnley coalfield (Kirby et al., 2000). The facies is typical of that found throughout the Pennine Basin. At least 33 named coals are recognised within the succession which includes Lower and Middle Coal Measures 590 to 880 m thick. Reddened Middle and Upper Coal Measures are present in, for example, the St Helens area (Trotter, 1953, 1954).

North Wales coalfields

The Neston–Point of Ayr–Flintshire coalfield and the Denbighshire–Oswestry coalfield both lie within the region. The Coal Measures Group thickens northwards from Oswestry through Denbighshire to Flintshire (Smith and George, 1961; Calver and Smith, 1974; Campbell and Hains, 1988, fig.42; Hains, 1991). In the north, the Neston–Point of Ayr–Flintshire Coalfield extends from the southern part of the Neston (Wirral) Coalfield across the Dee estuary to the Point of Ayr and thence south to Caergwrle. It is separated from the Denbighshire Coalfield to the south by a narrow strip of Dinantian and Namurian strata that marks the position of the long-lived Bala (Llanelidan) Fault System (Fitches and Campbell, 1987). The Westphalian succession of the coalfield is around 650 m thick. It comprises 300–350 m of Coal Measures Group, and the overlying 'Red Measures' may exceed 300 m in the extension of the coalfield beneath the Permo-Triassic of the Cheshire Basin. The Red Measures are equivalent to the Warwickshire Group of other coalfields (Davies et al., 2004; Figure 33). Evidence suggests that the Lower and Middle Coal Measures are fairly uniform in thicknesses below the Main Coal in the two coalfields. However, above the Main Coal, in the upper part of the Middle Coal Measures, significant differences exist between the two coalfields indicating that contemporaneous movements on the Bala–Llanelidan Fault Zone were important after the deposition of the Main Coal. The number and thickness of coal seams increase in the Denbighshire Coalfield. Rocks of the Warwickshire Group appear at differing levels across the coalfield. This and the presence of only the late Duckmantian Ruabon Marl Formation in the Flintshire Coalfield, reflects the effects of local tectonic influences, related to Variscan events farther south, on the regional subsidence pattern of the Westphalian basin (Davies et al., 2004). In places to the north of the Bala (Llanelidan) Fault System, Coal Measures (Westphalian A–B) lie directly below the base Permo-Triassic strata. The coalfield is affected by a series of open folds and disrupted by faulting, creating an irregular 'basin and dome' structure. On the eastern side of the coalfield, the Coal Measures of Flintshire in general dip eastwards beneath Permo-Triassic strata of the Cheshire Basin.

The Denbighshire–Oswestry Coalfield lies to the south of the Bala (Llanelidan) Fault System, and deep mining has taken place from the Llay Main Colliery. All three formations of the Warwickshire Group are present, and

the succession ranges up to 1000 m thick. It rests on the Coal Measures Group that reach about 820 m thick in the north of the coalfield (Davies et al., 2004). Both successions dip eastwards and are overlain unconformably by Permo-Triassic rocks of the Cheshire Basin. The Lower to Middle Coal Measures (Westphalian A–B) vary in thickness from 85 m near Oswestry to 250 m east of the town on the edge of the Cheshire Basin. Strata of the Warwickshire Group also occur in the Milton Green inlier of the Cheshire Basin. At outcrop in the south these strata consist of red mudstones with subordinate more or less pebbly sandstones. To the north however, some parts of the red-beds succession passes laterally into grey beds of siltstone and mudstone.

North Staffordshire Coalfield

Most of the North Staffordshire Coalfield crops out at surface, but the southern limits are concealed beneath Triassic rocks of the Staffordshire and Needwood basins. To the south, the Swynnerton Fault separates it from the Staffordshire Basin. It is bounded to the west by the thick Permo-Triassic succession of the Cheshire Basin and the Wem–Bridgemere–Red Rock Fault Zone. The North Staffordshire Coalfield comprises three separate coalfields, each named after the syncline in which they are preserved: the **Potteries Coalfield** (Evans et al., 1968; Rees and Wilson, 1998), the **Shaffalong Coalfield** (Rees and Wilson, 1998) and the **Cheadle Coalfield** (Chisholm et al., 1988). The exposed parts of the Cheadle and Potteries coalfields have a long history of both deep mining and opencast extraction. The structural setting of the North Staffordshire coalfield is well known from workings, boreholes and seismic reflection surveys acquired across the area. There are thickness changes attributed to growth folds that continued to develop during the main phase of the Variscan Orogeny (Corfield, 1991). These structures are associated with reverse faulting along reactivated Proterozoic basement lineaments or lines of weakness.

The Coal Measures Group consists of a grey mudstone-dominated succession with numerous coal seams (Rees and Wilson, 1998) and it thickens northwards towards the Pennine depocentre to around 1500 m (Wilson et al., 1992b). It is overlain by Warwickshire Group strata reaching a thickness of 1600 m. The influence of the Market Drayton Horst on sedimentation diminished with time and, from Mid-Westphalian times onwards, Variscan compressive events played an increasingly important role.

Shrewsbury Coalfield

The Shrewsbury Coalfield comprises three small areas of Westphalian rocks forming the Hanwood and Leebotwood coalfields (Earp and Hains, 1971) and the Dryton coalfield. No Coal Measures Group rocks have been proved in the Shrewsbury Coalfield, but coal has been worked from the Warwickshire Group. The Warwickshire Group onlaps Precambrian and Lower Palaeozoic strata (Pocock et al., 1938; Pocock and Whitehead, 1948;

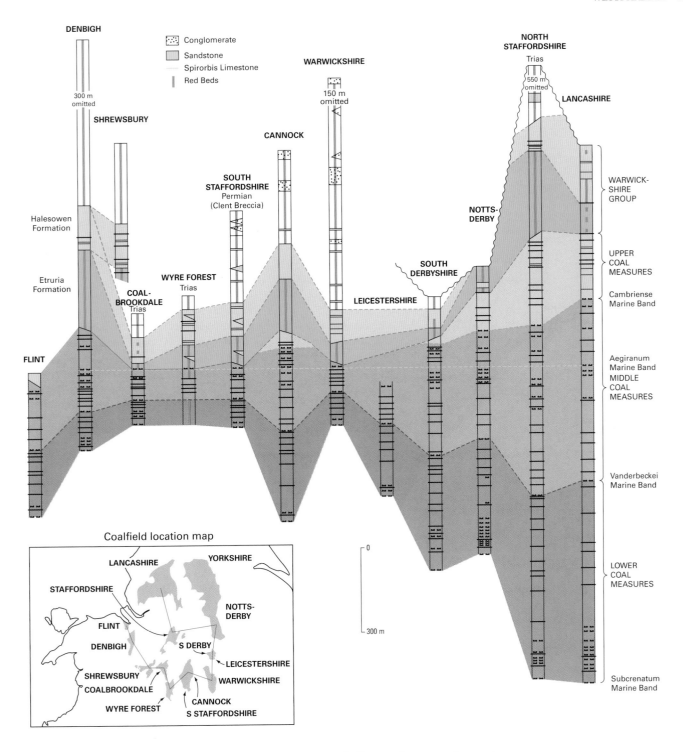

Figure 35 Lithostratigraphical correlation of the Westphalian rocks across the region.

Ramsbottom et al., 1978). In the Leebotwood Coalfield, located between Caer Caradoc and the River Severn, red-beds rest unconformably on Lower Palaeozoic and Precambrian (Longmyndian) rocks (Earp and Hains, 1971). The thinning and disappearance of the Coal Measures Group sequences beneath the unconformity is due to the close proximity of the Wales–Brabant Massif in the south.

The Halesowen Formation (formerly the Coed-yr-allt Formation) contains three workable coal seams totalling 2 m in thickness within a 70 m-thick sequence of grey mudstone, siltstone and sandstone with thin limestones. The coal seams are laterally persistent and are generally less than 200 m deep. The coalfield may continue to the north-east beneath Permian and Triassic strata, but to the south-west it is likely to be limited by the Market Drayton Horst.

Table 4   Correlation of local marine bands.

Standard Name	Flint and Den	Coalbrookdale	Wyre Forest	South Staffs	Warwick	Leicestershire	S Derby	Notts-Derby	N Staffs	Lancastershire
CAMBRIENSE				not named			Top	Top	Bay	Prestwich Top
SHAFTON				Silvesters Bridge			Shafton	Shafton	Priorsfield	Lower Sankey
EDMONDIA	Ty Cerryg			Kendrick			Edmondia	Edmondia	Rowhurst Rider	Manchester
AEGIRANUM	Warras Farm	Chance Pennystone	Eymore Farm	Charles	Nuneaton		Overseal	Mansfield	Gin Mine	Dukinfield
SUTTON							Sutton	Sutton	Clayton	Moston
HAUGHTON	Lower Stinking			not named		not named	Haughton	Haughton	Doctors Mine	Bradford
CLOWN	Garden Lodge						Clown	Clown	Longton Hall	
MALTBY	Powell	Blackstone		Sub Brooch			Two Foot	Two Foot	Moss Cannel	Ashclough
VANDERBECKEI	Llay	Pennystone		Stinking	Seven Feet	Bagworth	Molyneux	Clay Cross	Seven Feet Banbury	Sutton Manor
BURTON JOYCE								Burton Joyce		Ditton
LANGLEY								Upper Band		Pasture Mine
AMALIAE	not named	Crawstone					not named	Norton	Knypersley	Tonges
MEADOW FARM	not named						not named	Forty Yard	not named	Cannel Mine
PARKHOUSE								Parkhouse		Inch
LISTERI	not named	Lancashire Ladies		not named	not named	Alton	Alton	Alton	Crabtree	Bullion Mine
HONLEY						not named		First Smalley	Lower Foot	Lower Foot
SPRINGWOOD								Second Smalley	not named	Upper Bassy
HOLBROOK								Holbrook	not named	Upper Bassy
SUBCRENATUM	not named	Bottom		not named	not named	not named	not named	Pot Clay	not named	Six Inch

Wyre Forest, Mamble and Clee Hills coalfields

The Wyre Forest Coalfield lies between Bridgnorth in the north and the Abberley Hills in the south. There are no strata of Langsettian age in the coalfield and Coal Measures are rarely deeper than 300 m below ground level. The succession contains fewer coals and more sandstone beds than the South Staffordshire Coalfield. The Coal Measures Group is unconformably overlain by the Etruria and Halesowen (formerly Highley) formations that are in turn unconformably overlain by the Salop Formation.

A similar succession is present in the very small Mamble Coalfield, located south-west of the main Wyre Forest Coalfield. This coalfield is bounded to the west by Silurian rocks that are thrust south-westwards over Devonian strata (Mitchell and Taylor, 1961).

The Clee Hills Coalfield comprises two small outliers on Titterstone Clee and Brown Clee (Ramsbottom et al., 1978). At Titterstone Clee, Coal Measures Group are of late Langsettian to early Duckmantian age (Jones and Owen, 1961), but are now worked out. The small outlier of Brown Clee Hill is capped by dolerite, and in the past, locally, five coal seams of probable Duckmantian age have been worked.

Coalbrookdale Coalfield

The Coalbrookdale Coalfield (Hamblin and Coppack, 1995) is severely disrupted by faulting and folding. Strata range from Langsettian to possibly Stephanian in age. In addition to the Coal Measures Group, coal has been worked from the Halesowen Formation (Coalport Beds) of the Warwickshire Group (Glover et al., 1993a). The Coal Measures Group are over 200 m thick in the Lilleshall area, thinning to 75 m at Madeley in the south, where much of the higher strata have been removed by erosion associated with the Symon unconformity. The Coal Measures Group generally lies unconformably upon Lower Carboniferous and older rocks. Around Madeley, the Coal Measures Group rest unconformably upon Silurian rocks but uppermost Namurian strata may be present locally, illustrating southwards overlap of Dinantian rocks of the Lilleshall and Little Wenlock areas.

South Staffordshire and Cannock Coalfield

The South Staffordshire Coalfield lies on the southern limits of the region and passes northwards into the Cannock Coalfield, which shows a thicker succession of Langsettian to Westphalian D strata (Ramsbottom et al., 1978). The Coal Mesures of the South Staffordshire Coalfield have been mined extensively in the past. Generally they lie at depths of less than 200 m and are overlain by up to 500 m of Warwickshire Group (Whitehead and Eastwood, 1927; Glover, 1990; Powell et al., 1992). Dips within the Coal Measures Group are generally gentle and towards the south and south-west;

the south-eastern margin of the coalfield is marked by the Russell's Hall Fault, against which bedding appears to steepen (Glover, 1990). The western margin is probably formed by an extension of the Western Boundary Fault of the South Staffordshire Coalfield with a thick sequence of Permo-Triassic to the west. Several deep boreholes have penetrated beneath the Permo-Triassic proving Coal Measures, which appear to be thin and may have been eroded prior to the deposition of the Etruria and Halesowen formations (Glover, 1991). The Baggeridge and Smestow boreholes demonstrate that the Coal Measures thicken towards the south and east.

Warwickshire Coalfield

The coal is now largely worked out in the Warwickshire Coalfield, which forms a broad syncline that plunges southwards. The Coal Measures Group (250 m thick) rests conformably on Namurian strata, and is overlain by up to 1000 m of Warwickshire Group (Bridge et al., 1998). The coalfield is bounded to the west by the Western Boundary (or Maxstoke–Meriden) Fault System, to the east by the major Eastern Boundary (or Polesworth) Fault and to the north-east by outcrop. Movement on these faults was reversed in late Bolsovian or early Westphalian D times, associated with uplift of strata on both sides of the coalfield. Thus, the Langsettian and Duckmantian Coal Measures deposited in the Knowle and Hinckley basins on either side of the Warwickshire Coalfield were largely eroded. To the south, the coalfield passes beneath Triassic rocks, and in places the strata were folded and eroded prior to the deposition of the Triassic. Subsurface data show that both the Namurian succession and the Coal Measures Group thin and overstep to rest unconformably upon Cambrian and Tremadoc rocks. The thinning of the coals is associated with seam splitting (Old et al., 1989).

Within the grey mudstone and siltstone of the Coal Measures Group, individual coals are up to 8 m thick (averaging 2.5 m) and occur at a spacing of 2 to 25 m over some 70 m of strata. Coal extraction was concentrated mainly on the 'Thick Coal' of the Warwickshire Group. This coal splits into a group of seams, as a result of increased clastic input. In addition to the workings in the north (Old et al., 1989), mine workings are present at Binley Colliery, which was abandoned in 1963 (Old et al., 1987, 1989; Sumbler, 1985a, b).

South Derbyshire and Leicestershire coalfields

The South Derbyshire and Leicestershire coalfields lie within two north-west-trending synclines lying to the west and east, respectively, of the Ashby Anticline. The succession is similar in both coalfields, but more complete in the South Derbyshire Coalfield (Mitchell and Stubblefield, 1941; Greig and Mitchell, 1955) where higher parts of the sequence are preserved.

The north-west-trending Boothorpe Fault crosses the South Derbyshire Coalfield. To the east, only Lower Coal Measures are present, and they appear to be faulted against older strata of probable Namurian age (Jones, 1981; Smith, 1985). The Lower Coal Measures thicken northwards, and several coals are present below the Kilburn Coal, which marks the base of the 'Productive Measures'. The Lower, Middle and lower part of the Upper Coal Measures are present in this coalfield, which extends westwards beneath the Triassic of the Needwood Basin, to the west of the Netherseal Fault (Jones, 1981), and was proved in Grange Wood Borehole. The western part of the concealed extension forms part of the East Staffordshire prospect (see below).

To the east of the Ashby Anticline, the Leicestershire Coalfield lies in the western part of an asymmetrical syncline, with the western limb dipping gently (4°E) eastwards toward the Thringstone Fault, a reverse fault against which the strata dip steeply towards the west (Carney et al., 2001). The Lower Coal Measures and lower part of the Middle Coal Measures (Langsettian to Duckmantian) occur within the coalfield, generally at depths of less than 450 m, and are up to 240 m thick with some 18 named seams.

Vale of Clwyd Prospect

A number of outcrops of reddened Westphalian strata occur in the Vale of Clwyd, and were originally thought to be part of the Warwickshire Group with little coal potential. More recently, the Rhuddlan Borehole sunk during exploration for coalbed methane has proved Coal Measures of Langsettian age, at least in the north of the vale. Significant coals have been proved within the Coal Measures Group, which may extend offshore and connect with the Point of Ayr Colliery. It is overlain unconformably by the Warwickshire Group.

Bulkington Prospect

The concealed Bulkington Prospect lies to the east of the Warwickshire Coalfield and comprises Langsettian and Duckmantian strata, preserved in a small north–south-trending, fault-bounded syncline in the Hinckley Basin; the Coal Measures are overlain unconformably by Triassic strata (Boulton, 1926; Bridge, 1991, 1998) and have been proved in the Green Farm Borehole resting unconformably on Cambrian rocks. The grey measures were first discovered in a water well sunk in 1922, and since then have been proved in a number of other boreholes; the westward extent has been investigated by gravity surveys. The Coal Measures are over 100 m thick and dip to the west. Further, smaller, outliers of Coal Measures, directly analogous to the Bulkington Prospect, may subcrop beneath the Permo-Triassic in other areas of the Hinckley and Knowle basins.

East Staffordshire Prospect

The East Staffordshire Prospect is an area of Westphalian rocks concealed beneath younger strata, connecting the productive coalfields of South Staffordshire, the Potteries, Warwickshire and Leicestershire. Exploration indicates that the prospect is structurally complex, and that at least part of the area is underlain by strata which are not coal-bearing. The Coal Measures are not widely exploited here, with mining only along the boundary with the South Staffordshire Coalfield and at Lea Hall, close to the Cannock Chase Coalfield. Many areas around the margins remain untouched by coal mining.

The prospect is largely fault-bounded; the northern margin is partly defined by the Namurian subcrop beneath the Permo-Triassic cover of the Needwood Basin (Smith, 1985), and at the southern edge of the Potteries Coalfield by the Swynnerton Fault. Movement on this fault is postulated from Duckmantian (Besly, 1983) to Bolsovian and Westphalian D times (Corfield, 1991). The Duckmantian sequences thin by up to 40 per cent towards the fault, and many seams split north of the fault. The eastern limit of the coalfield is defined by the western margin of the South Derbyshire–Leicestershire coalfield along the Netherseal Fault, southwards to the Warwickshire Coalfield. The western margin adjoins the West Staffordshire Prospect (see below), with the boundary, in part, following the Sandon Fault. The southern margin is variously defined by the Western Boundary Fault of the Warwickshire Coalfield, the northern margin of the Knowle Basin, the Hints and (northern) parts of the Birmingham faults and the north and north-western margins of the exposed South Staffordshire Coalfield.

The Warwickshire Group, up to and including the Salop Formation, overlies the Coal Measures Group. It does not contain coal and northwards terminates against the base Permo-Triassic unconformity.

West Staffordshire Prospect

The West Staffordshire Prospect comprises Westphalian strata concealed beneath a variable thickness of Permo-Triassic strata in the Stafford Basin. The basin trends north–south and is bounded by faults. The Swynnerton Fault forms the northern boundary, and the north-eastern edge of the prospect adjoins the East Staffordshire Prospect, the boundary in part following the Sandon Fault. The Bushbury Fault marks the eastern boundary, this is a the normal north-north-east-trending fault (Whitehead et al., 1928). The western edge of the prospect approximates with the eastern margin of the Market Drayton Horst.

Numerous coal seams up to 2.5 m thick occur at 2 to 25 m intervals over some 250 to 300 m of strata, but towards the south, the Langsettian to Duckmantian sequence thins to less than 150 m, and coals become less common, generally thinner and laterally less persistent. On the flanks of the Stafford Basin, the Coal Measures Group is overlain by northward thickening red mudstone and thin coarse-grained sandstone of the Etruria Formation (Figure 34). These are succeeded conformably by the Westphalian D to Stephanian, Halesowen and Salop formations (formerly Keele and Enville formations), which are 250 to 300 m in total thickness. The increase in thickness of the Coal Measures Group to 559 m in the North Stafford Borehole reflects its position nearer to the Pennine Basin depocentre. The Heath Farm and Ranton boreholes prove approximately 263 m and 223 m, respectively. Boreholes at Brinsford and Codsall were located on a high, and proved 90 m and 53 m of Coal Measures Group, respectively. The Warwickshire Group rests unconformably on the Coal Measures the total thickness of which may be even less if sandstones interpreted to lie within the group are in fact a sandy facies at the base of the Etruria Formation.

SEVEN

Variscan structures and basin inversion

In latest Carboniferous times, the final closure of the 'Proto-Tethys' or Rheic Ocean that lay between Gondwanaland and Laurussia, culminated in the Variscan Orogeny. In detail, this probably involved the successive collision of a number of Gondwanan-derived microcontinents, and resulted in a major orogenic belt, the Variscides in the Iberian–Amorican–Massif Central region (Leeder, 1982, 1987, 1988), some 500 km to the south. North of this belt, large-scale thrusts and nappes were emplaced in northern France, Belgium, and in the south of England, Wales and Ireland. The northern limit of these northerly directed thrusts, known as the Variscan Front, lies to the south of this region. To the north of the Variscan Front, on the Variscan Foreland in which this region lies, deformation was less pervasive, and started in late Westphalian times with minor warping, culminating in the reactivation of pre-existing lines of weakness. This was affected principally by reversal of Dinantian normal faults and associated inversion of basins. There is a wide range in the orientation of the inversion structures, which is related to the trend of the underlying Dinantian extensional faults. There is also a range in the degree of inversion and fault reversal in the region, and this appears to be related to the angle of the pre-existing structures in relation to the dominant stress fields.

The propagation of thrusts, final nappe emplacement and the formation of the Variscan Front in southern Britain indicates that the final stages of the Variscan orogenic phase must have involved a significant north–south component (Williams and Chapman, 1986; Corfield et al., 1996). However, reverse displacements on north–south faults and the north-west vergence of inversion structures, such as the Pennine Monocline, indicate a component of east–west shortening (e.g. Critchley, 1984; Chadwick et al., 1993; Chadwick et al., 1995; Kirby et al., 2000). This, together with the variation in style of inversion, the sense of fault movement and the trend of structures led Corfield et al. (1996) to propose north-west- to north-north-west-directed compression.

Cope (1946) demonstrated substantial eastwards thinning of Langsettian and Duckmantian strata (Westphalian A and B) between the Potteries and Cheadle coalfields (Figure 31), and this may indicate the first stage of the growth of the Pennine Anticline. However, the appearance of exotic clasts in the espleys of the Etruria Formation (the basal division of the Westphalian to early Permian Warwickshire Group) is the first evidence of basin-wide Variscan movements. This change of facies was perhaps induced by a change in climate from damp to dominantly arid conditions in the rain shadow created by the rising Variscan Mountains to the south, which also acted as the source for the sediments. The development of the Symon unconformity in the south of the region provides evidence of local uplift, and the base of the Warwickshire Group oversteps onto older rocks, mostly on the Midlands Microcraton. Elsewhere in the region, there is evidence of gentle folding of the underlying Westphalian rocks, for example the Manchester–Winsford Sub-basin (Figure 32). Early reversal of movement along faults may have occurred locally and contributed to the formation of the Symon unconformity (e.g. the Craignant–Milton Fault Zone, and possibly along the Red Rock Fault in the north of the region). These initial phases were followed by the main phase of Variscan movements. Subsequently, further normal movement occurred during Permo-Triassic rifting on some of these reversed faults.

PRINCIPAL INVERSION STRUCTURES

Except where overlain by Permo-Triassic strata, the Variscan origin of many structures affecting Carboniferous strata cannot be proved. Variscan deformation and inversion in the region can be demonstrated in the south-west of the Cheshire Basin, where the Carboniferous succession was deformed and then deeply eroded prior to Permo-Triassic deposition. Similarly on the northern margin of the Needwood Basin, north-west-trending folds occur in Carboniferous strata, and are demonstrably of Variscan age. It is possible, that many Variscan structures were modified to varying degrees by subsequent Alpine orogenic events, and that other structures in Carboniferous strata formed entirely later, during Cainozoic (Alpine) compression. However, it is likely that structures in the Carboniferous strata that show evidence of thrusting, and particularly those that are associated with early Permian breccias, are of Variscan origin. It is also likely that some structures in Lower Palaeozoic rocks were reactivated and altered by the Variscan Orogeny.

The orientation of Variscan inversion structures varies systematically around the region, and is independent of the north-north-west–south-south-east directed compression, but dependent upon the trends of lineaments in the underlying Lower Palaeozoic basement, which in many cases were inherited by Upper Palaeozoic normal faults. For this reason, Variscan structures are described in turn according to the early Carboniferous structural domain in which they occur (Figure 36). A map of the subcrop at the Variscan unconformity surface is presented in Figure 37.

VARISCAN STRUCTURES IN THE IAPETUS DOMAIN

Most of the Carboniferous strata of this domain lie beneath the Permo-Triassic Cheshire Basin. Clear evidence of

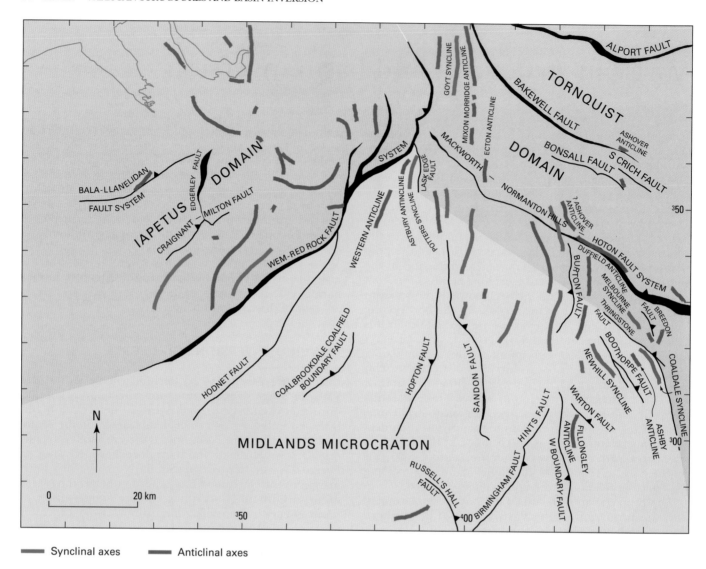

Synclinal axes ▬▬▬ Anticlinal axes

Figure 36 Main Variscan structures of central England and the region.

Variscan reversal of controlling faults can be demonstrated only on four fault complexes, the Wem–Bridgemere–Red Rock Fault System, the Bala–Llanelidan Fault System, the Edgerley Fault and the Craignant–Milton Fault Zone. Other faults may have undergone inversion, but this cannot be proved as the quality of the seismic reflection data is generally poor.

Wem–Bridgemere–Red Rock Fault System

The Wem–Bridgemere–Red Rock Fault System defines the eastern margin of the Iapetus domain and the eastern boundary to the Permo-Triassic Cheshire Basin. In the southern part of the Cheshire Basin, there is considerable evidence that reversal of movement, associated inversion and erosion of strata occurred along the fault system towards the end of Carboniferous times. Seismic reflection data (Figure 38) and evidence from outcrop (Plant et al., 1999) demonstrate the existence of a plunging anticline extending for over 30 km and

trending at a slight angle to the fault; the Carboniferous succession has been truncated beneath the base Permian unconformity, which generally dips to the east. In the hanging-wall block, the entire Carboniferous sequence is absent in places adjacent to the fault system (Mikkelsen and Floodpage, 1997; Chadwick et al., 1999), and Permian rocks rest directly on Silurian strata (Figures 37; 38). In contrast, Westphalian strata occur in the footwall block of the fault (Evans et al., 1993).

To the north-east, a series of ill-defined anticlines trend parallel to the Wem–Bridgemere–Red Rock Fault System (Figures 36; 37), and may be related to inversion on individual faults such as the Alderley and Bridgemere faults (Figure 13). There is also evidence of inversion in the north of the region where much of the Westphalian succession is absent, probably due to erosion, from a southward plunging anticline between the Brook House and Red Rock faults (Figures 38; 39). Inversion appears to have started during Westphalian times, as there is some evidence of erosion beneath the Warwickshire Group, as well as beneath the

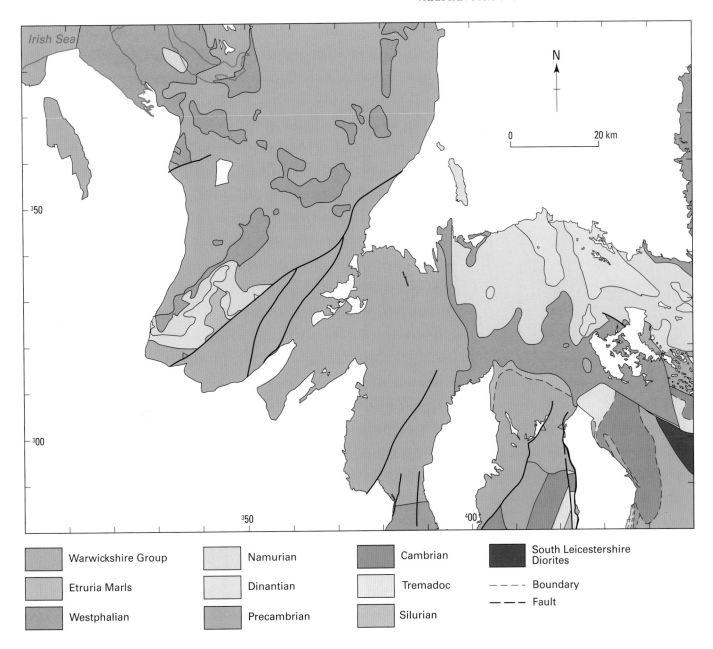

Figure 37   Variscan (base Permo-Traissic) subcrop map.

base of the Permo-Triassic. Correlation of the seismic data with Westphalian outcrops to the east of the fault indicates that erosion has removed strata down to the level of the Arley Mine seam (mid Langsettian) which now lies close to the base Permo-Triassic unconformity. A schematic summary of the movement on the Wem Fault, including later Permo-Triassic reactivation, is presented in Figure 40.

Bala–Llanelidan Fault System

The Bala–Llanelidan Fault System impinges on the western margins of the region (Figures 36; 37). Dominating the structural 'grain' of north Wales, it is an early, long-lived Palaeozoic fault zone in mid-Wales, reactivated as a normal fault in Dinantian times. Within the region,

this fault system is represented by the Bryn Eglwys Fault (Fitches and Campbell, 1987) and the easterly trending Llanelidan Fault, which forms the southern limit of the Vale of Clwyd Basin. The dominant overall sense of downthrow is to the north, typically juxtaposing Lower Palaeozoic rocks against Carboniferous strata (Davies et al., 2004). The Horseshoe Anticline at Hope Hills is a Variscan inversion structure on the Bryn Eglwys Fault. Dinantian strata crop out in the core and are faulted against Coal Measures to the south (Wedd and King, 1924). On the south side of the lineament, the late Duckmantian Coal Measures are considerably thicker than on the north, where the Red Measures facies occur earlier. This may indicate the early effects of Variscan inversion (Davies et al., 2004).

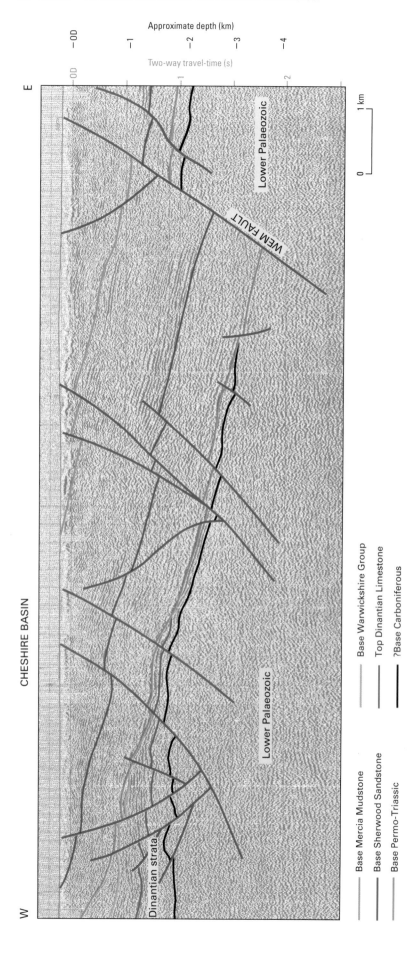

Figure 38 Seismic reflection profile illustrating folded Carboniferous rocks in the hanging-wall block adjacent to the Wem–Bridgemere–Red Rock Fault System. The (south plunging) anticline results from Variscan reversal of movement on the fault, and shows deep erosion with the total removal of Carboniferous rocks revealing Lower Palaeozoic rocks in the core in some areas. Younger, flatter lying post-inversion Permo-Triassic rocks overlie this succession. Location of profile is indicated on Figure 13.

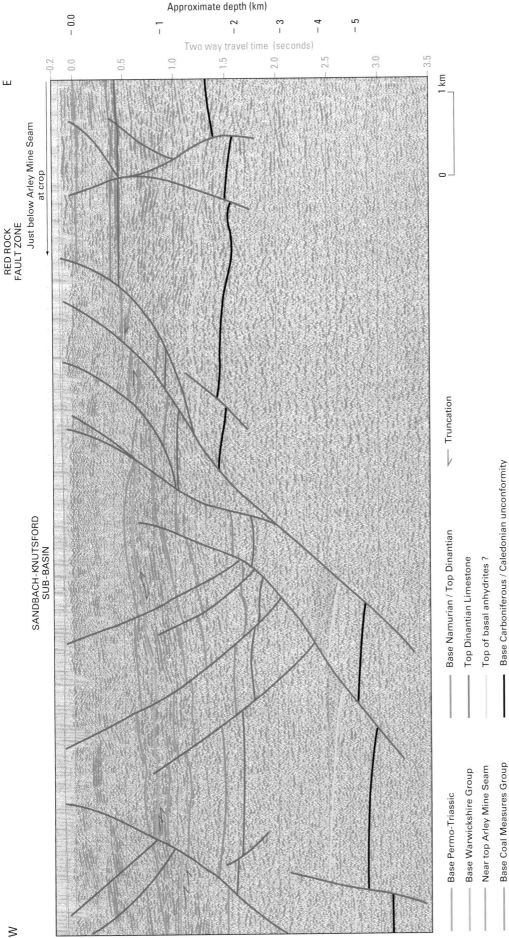

Figure 39 East–west seismic reflection line to illustrate the complex Red Rock Fault Zone, the nature of the Carboniferous basin fill and the 'double unconformity' of the base Warwickshire Group and Base Permo-Triassic in the north of the region. Deep erosion of the Silesian succession is apparent beneath the Base Permian Unconformity, perhaps with the removal of all but the lowest Coal Measures Group in the hanging-wall block adjacent to the fault zone. The development of a wedge-shaped reflection package (yellow) adjacent to the fault zone may also be interpreted as footwall-derived alluvial fan deposits, and evidence for early Carboniferous syndepositional movement on the fault zone. Location of profile is indicated on Figure 13.

Base Permo-Triassic

Base Warwickshire Group

Near top Arley Mine Seam

Base Coal Measures Group

Base Namurian / Top Dinantian

Top Dinantian Limestone

Top of basal anhydrites ?

Base Carboniferous / Caledonian unconformity

Truncation

Figure 40   Cartoon illustrating the structural development of the southern end of the Wem–Bridge-mere–Red Rock Fault System by repeated fault reactivation.

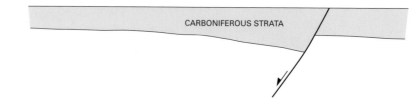

a   Carboniferous syndepositional normal movement

CARBONIFEROUS STRATA

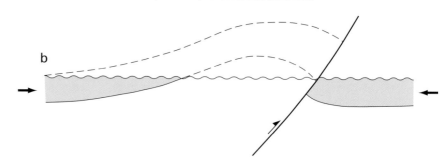

End Carboniferous (Variscan) reversal and inversion

b

c   Permo-Triassic syndepositional normal movement

PERMO-TRIASSIC STRATA

WEM FAULT

Edgerley Fault

In the hanging-wall succession of the Edgerley Fault (Figure 36), evidence of mild Variscan inversion is seen in the development of a local fault-controlled inversion anticline above the base of the Coal Measures. Further substantial normal movement occurred again in Permo-Triassic times, and it is possible that there was some reverse movement, perhaps in Cainozoic times, although this cannot be proved (Figure 22).

Craignant–Milton Fault zone

Seismic data across the Milton Fault provide hints of a complex late Carboniferous history of reactivation and

reversal of movement on the fault (Figure 41) with the development of two angular unconformities: one at the base of the Warwickshire Group (Symon unconformity) and the other at the base of the Permo-Triassic succession. These unconformities demonstrate a similar history to that developed at the base Permo-Triassic during inversion on the Wem Fault to the south, and the Red Rock Fault in the north. The base Warwickshire Group unconformity probably developed at the very onset of the Variscan Orogeny to the south of the area, which culminated in the main Variscan compression. Erosion across the Variscan Foreland in latest Carboniferous and early Permian times resulted in the development of the base Permo-Triassic unconformity (Figure 37). The unconformities developed by uplift, warping and deep erosion of the hanging-wall

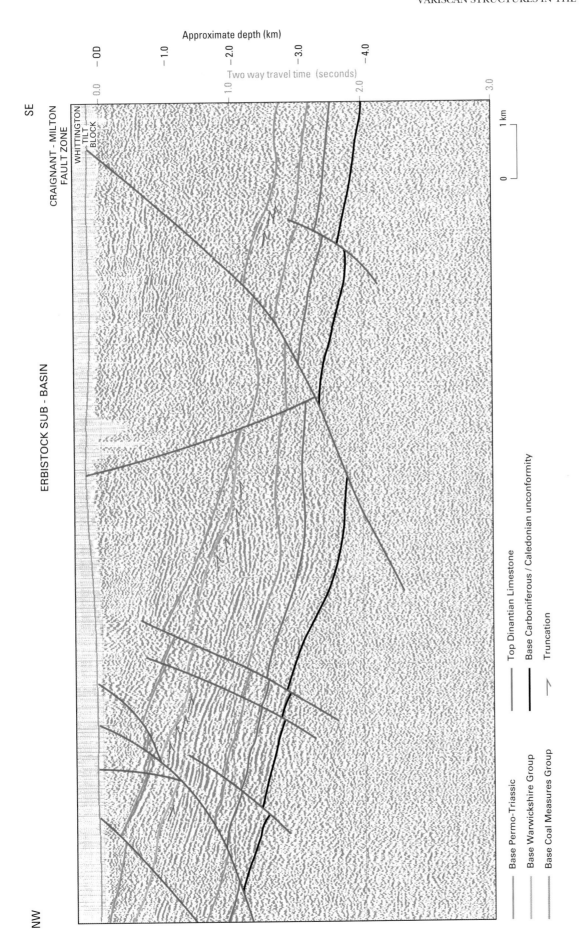

Figure 41   Seismic reflection profile illustrating the Variscan inversion of the Craignant–Milton Fault Zone and the uplift and deep erosion of Carboniferous rocks developed in the hanging-wall of the fault. Two important episodes of inversion may be recognised. A pronounced angular unconformity developed at the base of the Warwickshire Group suggests that a first inversion phase occurred during Bolsovian (Westphalian C) times. A second inversion phase followed in late Carboniferous times and resulted in the renewed reversal of movement on the fault zone uplift with the removal of much of the Warwickshire Group adjacent to the fault zone. Location of profile is indicated on Figure 13.

succession against the fault. Immediately adjacent to the fault, the Warwickshire Group has been removed beneath the base Permian unconformity.

VARISCAN STRUCTURES IN THE MIDLANDS MICROCRATON

Variscan structures show several different trends on the Midlands Microcraton (Figure 36). Structures associated with reversal of the Wem–Bridgemere–Red Rock Fault System trend north-north-east. Eastwards, the structures trend north–south, and in the south and east they trend north-west. This pattern reflects the range in orientation of pre-existing structures. Although some are reactivated Dinantian normal faults, others with fault hades typically as low as 40° are thought more likely to be reactivated thrusts that were initiated during the Acadian (late Caledonian) Orogenic Phase in the early Devonian (Pharaoh et al., 1987a, b).

Faults trending north-west (e.g. Thringstone, Boothorpe, Overseal faults) exhibit a strong Variscan reverse movement, separating domains 5 to 10 km wide, affected by asymmetric folds overturning to the south-west (e.g. Breedon Anticline, Melbourne Syncline, Ashby Anticline). These folds exhibit steep limbs in the footwall blocks of the reverse faults. This pattern of deformation, concentrated in discrete zones, is suggestive of the reactivation of zones of pre-existing anisotropy within the pre-Dinantian basement.

Potteries Syncline, Western and Astbury anticlines

The Western Anticline and its northward continuation the Astbury Anticline lie approximately 6 km east of Stoke-on-Trent, parallel with and in the footwall of the Wem–Bridgemere–Red Rock Fault System (Figure 36). This is an asymmetrical fold with south-easterly vergence towards the Potteries Syncline. It trends north-north-east, extending for over 15 km, and at crop affects mainly Namurian and Westphalian rocks, but with Dinantian rocks in the core of the Astbury Anticline. The structure is periclinal in form, tight in the north becoming more open to the south-west where the western limb dips at 30° to 45° and the eastern limb at 10°. Near Newcastle-under-Lyme the axial zone is flat lying with a sharp transition to the western limb, forming a distinct kink seen in Brown Lees open cast mine (Rees and Wilson, 1998).

The parallelism of these folds with the Red Rock Fault suggests a genetic link (Corfield, 1991; Rees and Wilson, 1998). The south-east vergence of the folds and the Variscan reverse displacement on the Hodnet Fault, which dips north-west and is the south-western continuation of the fault system into the Stoke-on-Trent area (Evans et al., 1993; Rees and Wilson, 1998), suggests that the fault was reactivated during the Variscan Orogeny as a south-east-directed reverse fault, uplifting basement beneath the anticlines.

Russell's Hall Reverse Fault

The north-west-trending Russell's Hall Reverse Fault (Figure 36) almost links the Western and Eastern Boundary faults that delineate the South Staffordshire Coalfield (Waters et al., 1994). It has a net reverse displacement along much of its length. Marked deformation of the footwall sequences is noted along north- or north-north-west-trending sections, whereas north-west-trending sections are single fault planes that show no such deformation of the footwall. This suggests the presence of a lateral ramp (Waters et al., 1994). In its south-eastern reaches, minor anastomosing splays are developed. Further compressional features, located to the north of the fault, are collectively referred to as the Dudley Ridge (Waters et al., 1994). This north-west-trending structure is some 7.5 km long and comprises a series of *en échelon* sigmoidal periclinal folds, in which the axial plane traces range from north-north-west to north-north-east.

On the west of the fault, thick Coal Measures and Etruria Formation are preserved (368 m), and to the east the succession is thinner (67 m), for example in the vicinity of Mucklow Hill. This indicates that the eastern side of the fault was already being uplifted during deposition of the Etruria Formation.

Hopton Fault

Some degree of basin inversion is indicated along the Hopton Fault (Figure 36), where the Warwickshire Group rests with minor angularity below the Permo-Triassic strata in the hanging-wall block.

Birmingham and Western Boundary faults

The Permo-Triassic Knowle Basin is bounded to the west by the Birmingham Fault, and to the east by the Western Boundary Fault that also defines the western margin of the Warwickshire Coalfield (Figures 36; 44). Studies of late Carboniferous and Permian breccias and conglomerates of the Midlands (Wills, 1956) suggest that the basement of the Knowle Basin originally formed part of a horst in late Carboniferous times. Currently, the Western Boundary Fault has a substantial down-to-the-west normal movement, but with subsurface indications of overthrusting towards the east in the Warwickshire Coalfield (Figure 42).

Many seismic profiles reveal a series of minor westerly dipping reverse faults with associated folding of the Coal Measures and basement successions just to east of the Western Boundary fault; these are thought to be part of the overthrust margin. The Western Boundary Fault formed during Permo-Triassic extension as a result of reactivation of an overthrust boundary. This gave rise to a 'short-cut' fault, where the basement occurred near the surface — a common feature in reactivated structures. Cambrian and Tremadoc strata are exposed in the Dosthill inlier in the north-west of the coalfield, and demonstrate this 'short-cut' effect, being bounded to the east by a reverse fault, but in the west by the 'short-cut' normal fault (Figures 42; 43).

Timing of the reverse movement on this Western Boundary Fault is constrained by the isopachs and facies of the Westphalian succession (Map 6). Movement started during deposition of the Etruria Formation, the earliest strata of the Warwickshire Group. The Etruria

Figure 42   Development and structural position of early Permian breccias over the horsts flanking the Knowle Basin. The map shows the location of the breccias. The cross-sections schematically illustrate the inferred end-Carboniferous to early Permian topography, the arrows indicating the direction from which the breccias were sourced.

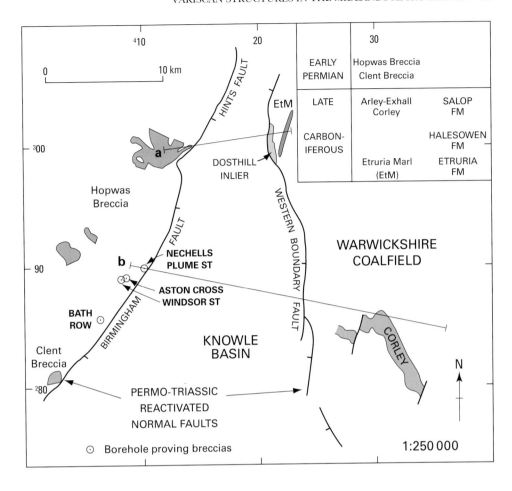

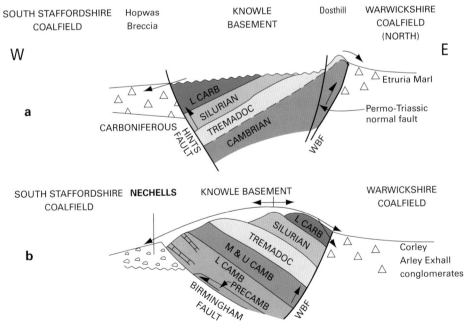

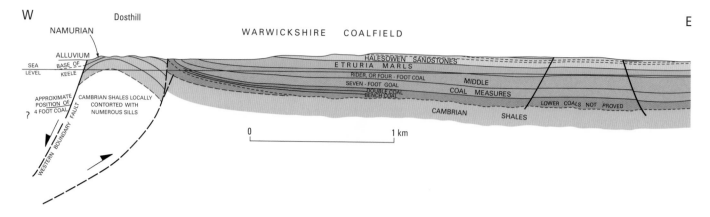

Figure 43   Cross-section illustrating the structure and relationship of the Dosthill inlier to the Western Boundary Fault and the Warwickshire Coalfield.

Formation thickens towards the fault, in contrast to earlier Westphalian formations that thin towards the west (Figure 43). Movement occurred in several phases; the overlying Halesowen Formation is unaffected by the fault, but pebbles of pre-Carboniferous rocks within conglomerates of the Salop Formation suggest a local derivation, probably from the uplifted Knowle basement horst. Characteristic basal Permo-Triassic breccias that occur locally in this area also have been derived from this uplifted basement during the last phase of movement on this fault (Figures 42a, b).

The north-north-east-trending Birmingham Fault is 20 km long and currently downthrows to the east; it passes *en échelon* into the Hints Fault. In the late Carboniferous, the faults acted as reverse faults, uplifting the basement to the Knowle graben to the east, and overthrusting Westphalian strata to the west. A reverse fault is seen on seismic data immediately to the west of the Hints Fault, and is related to this period of thrusting. This is directly analogous and probably related to the overthrust of Westphalian strata on the eastern margin of the Knowle Basin by the Western Boundary Fault.

Fillongley Anticline

The north-east-trending Fillongley Anticline (Figure 36) is thought to be controlled by a westerly dipping reverse fault that splays off the Western Boundary Fault. This fault has also been reversed in post-Carboniferous times, and shows a normal down-to-the-west displacement. Thinning of strata, notably the Etruria Formation, occurs over the anticline but there are no thickness changes in the overlying Halesowen Formation.

Sandon and Burton faults

The Permo-Triassic Needwood Basin is bounded in the west by the Sandon Fault and in the east by the Burton Fault, both trend approximately north–south (Figure 36). The Sandon Fault is 40 km long and currently downthrows to the east; during the Variscan movements, this

was a reverse fault in the northern part with downthrow to the west. The Burton Fault extends about 20 km beyond the postulated boundaries between the Midlands Microcraton and the Tornquist Domain. In the northern part, it formed a reverse fault during the Variscan movements. The Carboniferous succession to the west of the fault was folded into a large north–south-trending southerly plunging anticline, with Dinantian strata in the core, which can be traced northwards to link with the Dinantian outcrops of the Peak District. In the south, the fault bounds a north–south-trending plunging syncline with Coal Measures in the core.

The Carboniferous succession that lies between the Sandon and Burton faults has been subjected to inversion; most of the Westphalian succession was eroded prior to the deposition of the Permo-Triassic strata. This Variscan structural high forms a southward continuation of the ill-defined Pennine inversion that trends approximately north–south (Smith, 1985; Evans et al., 2002).

NW-trending structures in the east

The Boothorpe Fault, the *en échelon* Polesworth Fault and the Warton Fault (Figure 36) are reverse faults that were reactivated as normal faults during Permo-Triassic extension; all trend approximately north-west, dipping to the north-east. The Boothorpe Fault lies subparallel to the Thringstone Fault; the estimated Variscan downthrow to the west was about 320 m, which was followed by Triassic downthrow to the east (Carney et al., 1999). Middle Coal Measures exposed in the South Derbyshire Coalfield are preserved in the associated asymmetric New Hall Syncline, which dips up to 18° in the steep north-east limb adjacent to the Boothorpe Fault.

The Warton Fault thrusts Lower Palaeozoic rocks of the 'Hinckley basement', the concealed northerly extension of the Nuneaton Anticline, over Carboniferous strata to the south-west. Unlike the Knowle horst, the thrust created an asymmetrical uplift, preserving Carboniferous rocks on the eastern side, which, in turn, was overthrust by the Charnian Block along the Thringstone Fault.

The Overseal–Coton Park Fault system forms a kilometre-wide complex, north-west-trending belt of faults and broad periclinal folds (Overseal Anticline, Overseal and Mount Pleasant synclines) within the Middle Coal Measures of the concealed South Derbyshire Coalfield, to the south-east of Burton-on-Trent. The Variscan reverse throw of about 190 m, was reduced in part by post-Triassic normal downthrow to the north-east.

Structures related to the Thringstone Fault

Near Thringstone, Middle Coal Measures (Duckmantian) strata are preserved in the markedly asymmetrical Coalville Syncline that has a steep north-east limb in the footwall (downthrown side) of the Thringstone Fault. Strata are locally vertical in a zone 200 to 300 m wide (Worssam and Old, 1988).

The Ashby Anticline lies to the east and controls the structure of the Leicestershire Coalfield. Lower Coal Measures (Langsettian) in the core show gentle dips; Middle Coal Measures on the north-east limb dip about 5° to the north-east into the Coalville Syncline, marginal to the Thringstone Fault.

VARISCAN STRUCTURES IN THE TORNQUIST DOMAIN

The north-west-trending Dinantian extensional basins that characterise this domain are the Alport and Edale basins and Widmerpool Gulf (Figure 13). They are controlled by faults of similar trend, and all have been mildly inverted. Inversion structures developed along these faults are characterised by broad long-wavelength anticlines (Fraser and Gawthope, 1990; Fraser et al., 1990). Similarly, the faults defining the boundary between the Tornquist Domain and the Midlands Microcraton were reactivated during the Variscan movements, forming north-east-dipping high-angle reverse faults.

In more general terms, Dinantian rocks of the Peak District can be seen to have a broad anticlinal form that is, at least in the south of the Peak District, demonstrably Variscan in origin. This regional inversion feature has an approximately north–south trend that appears to cut across the trend of the Dinantian extensional faults and to be unaffected by them. This 'Pennine Basin Inversion Line' (Smith, 1985) may be related to a deeper and as yet poorly understood structure. It is thought to continue southwards underneath the Permo-Triassic of the Needwood basin, controlled, in part at least, by the approximately north–south-trending Sandon and Burton faults. The inversion line may also be related to the Knowle Basin inversion feature, bounded by the Western Boundary and Birmingham faults (Figure 42).

Breedon Fault and Anticline and Melbourne Syncline

The concealed Breedon Fault (Figure 36) is a north-west-trending, major reverse fault of Variscan age, affecting the relatively thin Dinantian sequence of the

Hathern Shelf. Strata exposed in Breedon and Cloud Hill quarries occupy the steep, western dipping limb of the Breedon Anticline. In Cloud Hill Quarry, the strata are locally vertical or overturned, and the fold is broken by a number of thrust faults generated during flexural-slip (Ambrose and Carney, 1997b). The Breedon Fault is inferred to be a major displacement along the axis of the Breedon Anticline. The broad Melbourne Syncline lies to the west of the fault and is developed mainly in Namurian strata. It is markedly asymmetrical, with steeper dips, up to 65°, on the north-eastern limb adjacent to the Breedon fault, and dips of typically 5° on the south-western limb adjacent to the Thringstone Fault.

Thringstone Fault

The Thringstone Fault lies on the south-west margin of the Charnwood High, locally defining the boundary between the Midlands Microcraton and the Tornquist Domain (Figure 36). It trends north-north-west to north-west, dips at 40° to the north-east and can be traced for about 32 km. Reverse movement of up to 550 m (Worssam and Old, 1988) is estimated during late Carboniferous and early Permian times, emplacing a succession ranging in age from the Precambrian to Namurian over Coal Measures to the south-west (Butterley and Mitchell, 1946).

Lask Edge Fault and Eastern Folds

In the hanging wall of the Lask Edge Fault, the Carboniferous succession is folded into a series of north-trending structures (Figure 36), referred to as the Eastern Folds (Rees and Wilson, 1998). These were formed during the Variscan compression by reactivation of the fault, and include the periclinal Lask Edge, Blackwood, Werrington, Stanley Moor and Overmoor anticlines and the Bagnall and Shaffalong synclines.

Mackworth–Normanton Hills–Hoton Fault system and Duffield Anticline

This major fault system defines the southern margin of the Dinantian Widmerpool half-graben. Reversal during the Variscan compression resulted in the formation of the Duffield Anticline, and strata to the north-west of Derby (Figure 16) were eroded down to the Widmerpool Formation (uppermost Dinantian). Shallow boreholes proved strata of similar facies in the Trent valley, just north of Kings Newton.

Bonsall and South Crich faults

The Bonsall Fault is a reversed fault, subparallel to the Bakewell Fault, which dips at 25 to 40° to the north-east and is 20 km long (Aitkenhead et al., 1985); it is associated with a number of smaller reverse faults to the west. It is not imaged clearly by seismic profiles, but does display a down-to-the-north displacement at basement level in contrast to the down-to-the-south displacement at surface.

The South Crich Fault lies *en échelon* to the Bonsall Fault and forms the south-west boundary to the anticlinal Crich Dinantian inlier. This is also likely to be a reversed fault of Variscan origin, dipping to the north-east and throwing Dinantian against Namurian strata.

Bakewell Fault and Ashover Anticline

This fault, mapped over a distance of 50 km, is largely concealed beneath the late Dinantian shelf sequence; its position corresponds to the Taddington–Bakewell Anticline of Gutteridge (1987). Although this anticline is thought to be the result of anticlinal fold or drape during Holkerian times, the occurrence of the Ashover Anticline along strike suggests there may be a through-going fracture that underwent inversion during the Variscan movements (Smith et al., 1985).

Other folds

The Longstone Edge Anticline is particularly well exposed, with mineralisation along its east-trending axial crest. Other prominent folds include the Calow-Brimington and Ashover anticlines. The synclines, by reason of their axial coalfields (e.g. the Goyt Syncline), are better known than the anticlines (e.g. Mixon-Morridge Anticline, Ecton Anticline). The axial parts of two of these folds, the Ecton Anticline and Dovedale Anticline are spectacularly exposed in the gorges of the Manifold valley and Dovedale.

EIGHT

Post-Variscan structure and stratigraphy

A detailed account of the post-Variscan structure and evolution of the region is beyond the scope of this book; the reader is directed elsewhere for details of this (Evans et al., 1993; Chadwick and Evans, 1995), and for information on the stratigraphy (e.g. Plant et al., 1999; Aitkenhead et al., 2002). A brief summary is given here.

Permian and Triassic rocks form the bulk of the Mesozoic succession at crop in the region; the youngest rocks are the Lias Group of early Jurassic age. All are the remnants of a once more extensive sedimentary cover that was uplifted and eroded in Cainozoic times.

By earliest Permian times, Variscan continental collision had led to final suturing and consolidation of the Pangaean supercontinent. The region lay deep within this continental mass, within a few degrees of the Equator. Variscan basin inversion and regional uplift had resulted in considerable elevation of the land-surface, which underwent progressive peneplanation during Permian times. Contemporaneously, regional sag basins developed in the North Sea region. By late Permian, and particularly, early Triassic times, the north-west European region formed an isthmus between the rapidly developing Arctic–North Atlantic rift system to the north and the Tethys–Central Atlantic–Gulf of Mexico rift-wrench system to the south. Regional crustal extension became established as the dominant tectonic process.

PERMO-TRIASSIC STRUCTURAL EVOLUTION

Reactivation of basement faults (Variscan and older) under an approximately east–west-orientated extensional regime commenced in late Permian times, resulting in the formation of a series of fault-controlled basins in a rift system extending from the English Channel in the south to the East Irish Sea Basin in the north. Those basins lying within the region are, in order of decreasing size, the **Cheshire Basin**, the **Needwood Basin**, the **Stafford Basin**, the **Hinckley Basin,** the **Knowle Basin**, the **Vale of Clwyd Basin** and the **Bratch Graben** (Figure 44). The basins were infilled with Permo-Triassic sediments. There are also Permo-Triassic rocks in the north-east of the region on the western margin of the **East Midlands Shelf**, which was situated on the western margin of the North Sea Basin.

The Cheshire Basin is bounded to the east by the Wem–Bridgemere–Red Rock Fault System. This fault zone, together with the Hodnet and Alderley faults, were controlled by extensional reactivation of an underlying basement thrust and lineament, in the form of an upward-propagating normal fault (Evans et al., 1993; Plant et al., 1999). The throw on the Wem–Bridgemere–Red Rock Fault System gradually diminishes northwards beyond the Bridgemere Fault as the Wem Fault passes into the Red

Rock Fault. Throw on the Red Rock Fault at base Permo-Triassic level decreases from typically 1000 to 2000 m to a few hundred metres or less in the north of the region. Traced southwards, the total throw across the fault zone is in excess of 4000 m at the base of the Permo-Triassic in the south-central section, with throws on the Wem and Bridgemere faults locally in excess of 2500 m (Evans et al., 1993; Chadwick, 1997). Within the Cheshire Basin, two sub-basins, the Wem–Audlem and Sandback–Knutsford sub-basins are bounded by the Edgerley–Waverton and Brook House–King Street fault zones, respectively; both fault zones are reactivated Caledonian structures. The down-to-the-west Hodnet Fault is located in the footwall and splays southwards from the Wem–Bridgemere–Red Rock Fault System. It forms the eastern boundary of the Ternhill Terrace, which separates the Cheshire Basin from the Stafford Basin (Plant et al., 1999).

The Vale of Clwyd Basin is an easterly tilted half-graben, bounded on its eastern side by the north-west-trending Vale of Clwyd Fault System, a series of major, yet relatively poorly understood, subparallel, high-angle down-to-the-west normal faults. It is subdivided into the Rhyll sub-basin in the north and the Ruthin sub-basin in the south, separated by the St Asaph Ridge (Jackson and Mulholland, 1993). It resembles a number of half-grabens developed in the East Irish Sea and surrounding areas of the Cheshire Basin. Due to a lack of seismic reflection data across the Vale, little new detail on the structural history of this area is provided here. Preserved thickness of Permo-Triassic strata is thought to exceed 400 m.

The Stafford Basin is also a half-graben, bounded in the west by the Brewood–Horton faults. Strata thin progressively westward from 600 m near the fault.

The Needwood Basin is faulted on both margins, the Sandon Fault lying on the western margin and the Burton Fault on the east. Preserved thickness of strata ranges up to 600 m.

The Hinckley Basin, which trends north-west, lies in the south-east of the region and is fault-bounded on its western margin. This can be demonstrated in the north along the Warton Fault; elsewhere, however, seismic data are lacking and the relationships at the basin margins remain ambiguous.

The northern part of the Knowle Basin lies within the region, forming a narrow north-south-trending graben. The Birmingham Fault defines the western margin and the Western Boundary Fault (to the Birmingham coalfield) forms the eastern margin. Preserved thickness range to over 1000 m. The Knowle Basin lies above basement rocks that during the Variscan Orogeny formed an uplifted horst, shedding breccias both to the east and west. Movement on the bounding faults, after the Variscan Orogeny reversed, to create the Knowle Basin.

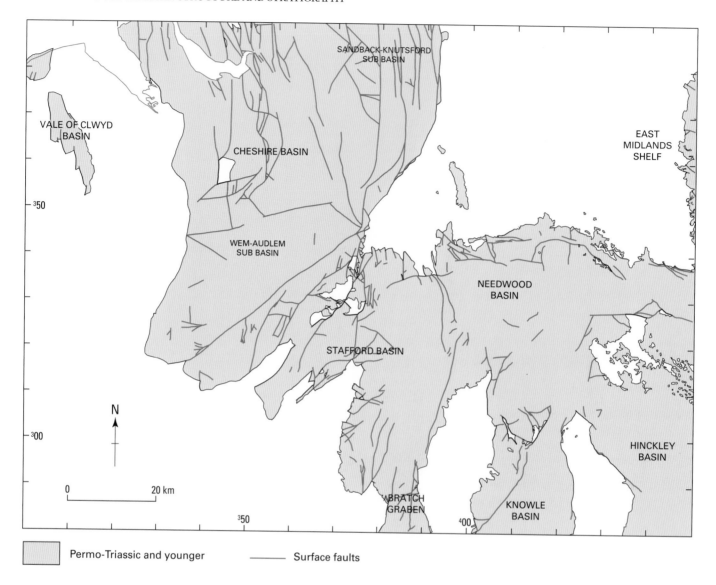

Figure 44   Permo-Triassic basins in the region.

The northern part of the Bratch Graben lies within the region, trending north–south, and bounded on the west by the Enville Fault and on the east by the Western Boundary Fault (to the South Staffordshire Coalfield).

In addition to the major basin-bounding faults, some reactivation of earlier faults occurred. For example, the Clotton Fault, mapped at surface 4 km to the west of the Acton Bridge–Overton–East Delamere Fault Zone, is a down-to-the-east north–south-trending normal fault known to downthrow Permo-Triassic strata by about 300 m (Earp and Taylor, 1986). The Cinderhill Fault, mapped from surface exposure and mine records, forms a hinge zone that was reactivated during Permo-Triassic extension.

Late Permian

East–west-orientated crustal extension causing reactivation of basement faults also produced controlling faults to new sedimentary basins. Intra-basin syndepositional normal faulting produced local depocentres, and stratal thickness exceeds 1800 m in places; the strata are dominantly aeolian sandstones.

Early Triassic

Early Triassic subsidence controlled the deposition of much of the Sherwood Sandstone Group. Strong crustal extension was directed roughly east–west to east-north-east–west-south-west, and produced rapid fault-controlled subsidence. A number of separate, well-defined sub-basin depocentres developed such as the Wem–Audlem and Sandbach–Knutsford sub-basins of Cheshire. The principal phase of normal faulting that controlled basin development probably occurred at this time. More than 3500 m of strata were deposited locally within these basins and sub-basins by the end of the early Triassic.

Table 5 Basin-fill stratigraphy of the Cheshire Basin.

Ma	GROUP	FORMATION	STAGE / AGE	SYSTEM /PERIOD
			TOARCIAN	JURASSIC
190	LIAS	Marlstone Rock	PLIENSBACHIAN	JURASSIC
200	LIAS		SINEMURIAN	JURASSIC
			HETTANGIAN	JURASSIC
210	PENARTH	Lilstock / Westbury	RHAETIAN	TRIASSIC
	MERCIA MUDSTONE	Blue Anchor / Brooks Mill Mudstone	NORIAN	TRIASSIC
220 / 230	MERCIA MUDSTONE	Wilkesley Halite	CARNIAN	TRIASSIC
		Wych Mudstone	LADINIAN	TRIASSIC
240		Byley Mudstone / Northwich Halite / Bollin Mudstone / Tarporley Siltstone / Helsby Sandstone	ANISIAN	TRIASSIC
250	SHERWOOD SANDSTONE	Bulkeley Hill Sandstone / Wilmslow Sandstone / Chester Pebble Beds	OLENEKIAN & INDUAN	TRIASSIC
260	CUMBRIAN COAST	Manchester Marls / Kinnerton Sandstone	TATARIAN & KAZANIAN	PERMIAN
	APPLEBY	Collyhurst Sandstone	KUNGURIAN	PERMIAN
270	APPLEBY		ARTINSKIAN	PERMIAN
280			SAKMARIAN	PERMIAN
290			ASSELIAN	PERMIAN
300			STEPHANIAN	CARBONIFEROUS
			WESTPHALIAN	CARBONIFEROUS

Mid and late Triassic

The uppermost Sherwood Sandstone Group, Mercia Mudstone and Penarth groups were deposited during mid and late Triassic subsidence. Crustal extension and the development of syndepositional normal faulting continued, but were less active than previously. Rates of subsidence decreased gradually with time, and a single depocentre developed in the Cheshire Basin, where it is estimated that sedimentary thickness probably exceeded 5000 m at the end of Triassic times.

PERMO-TRIASSIC STRATIGRAPHY

At the beginning of Permian times, the region lay deep within the Pangaean supercontinent, situated within a few degrees of the Equator. The area was dominated by desert erosion and deposition, and it lay within a zone of easterly winds. A summary of Permo-Triassic lithostratigraphical nomenclature is presented in Table 5.

Initially, Permian deposition was restricted to breccias that accumulated adjacent to faults produced during the Variscan Orogeny. By their nature, these breccias are local and hence have been given a variety of local names. The Alberbury Breccia crops out to the west of Shrewsbury; clasts consist predominantly of Carboniferous Limestone that was sourced to the north of the Wem Fault. The Hopwas Breccia crops out to the north-east of Birmingham, and the Nechells and Quartzite breccias were proved in the Nechells Borehole. The Kenilworth Breccias are known from the southern part of the Warwickshire Coalfield (Mitchell, 1942) and the Clent

Breccia crops out on the south-west margin of the South Staffordshire Coalfield. These are interpreted as breccia fans, and consist of clasts of basement rocks derived from a highland area formed, during the Variscan Orogeny, by uplift of a 'horst' between the Birmingham and Western Boundary Faults, along the site of the present Knowle Basin. The breccias are preserved on the highs (white areas of Figure 44).

As the Permo-Triassic basins started to form, aeolian sands were deposited widely, and preserved as the Collyhurst Sandstone Formation, which is up to 220 m thick. Dolomitic and gypsiferous mudstones of the Manchester Marls Formation mark a disruption of continental deposition in the early part of the Late Permian, when a marine incursion flooded the northern part of the Cheshire Basin. In the south, terrestrial conditions persisted, and the laterally equivalent Bold Formation consists of aeolian sandstones similar to those of the Collyhurst Sandstone. Towards the end of Permian times, the sea retreated and the Kinnerton Sandstone was deposited over most of the region, comprising aeolian sandstones with some interbedded strata of fluvial origin. Continental conditions persisted into Triassic times, and the Kinnerton Sandstone is succeeded by the Chester Pebble Beds Formation. This formation consists of sandstone and conglomerate with pebbles that decrease in abundance northwards. These beds were deposited in a northward flowing river system that entered the Cheshire Basin via the Stafford Basin. The overlying Wilmslow Sandstone Formation contains interbedded siltstone and mudstone; it was deposited within the same river basin, but there is some evidence of aeolian dune sandstone, which was formed by the winds from the east. The succeeding beds of the Bulkeley Hill Sandstone Formation are present only locally. Their deposition was followed by a period of faulting and erosion, marked by the Hardegsen disconformity. The overlying Helsby Sandstone Formation was deposited by rivers flowing from the south-east and under the influence of easterly winds.

The Tarporley Siltstone is the lowest formation of the Mercia Mudstone Group. It was laid down in intertidal and playa environments, and marks a transition to dominantly argillaceous deposition. The succeeding strata are dominated by dolomitic mudstone (Bollin Member, Byley and Wych mudstone formations) or halite (Northwich and Wilkesley halite formations). During this time the basinal areas varied between desert conditions, shallow temporary lakes and marine transgressions or basins of a more lasting nature in which thick halites developed. The detrital sediment was almost entirely fine-grained deposits of aeolian origin or sediment that settled in shallow water. Interbedded sandstone is sparse and probably of fluvial origin. Dolomite and magnesian-bearing clays were deposited from the high concentrations of magnesian minerals in the groundwater at this time. In Carnian times, stable uniform conditions were established over a wide area and the Wilkesley Halite was deposited. The Blue Anchor Formation at the top of the Mercia Mudstone Group marks a change in the pattern of deposition. It is composed of wind-blown detritus, but the dominantly greenish grey colour indicates deposition in reducing conditions, possibly a shallow lake as there is evidence of a freshwater fauna.

The Penarth Group marks a major marine incursion. It consists of mudstone, fine-grained sandstone and limestone with marine fossils.

POST-TRIASSIC STRUCTURAL EVOLUTION

The post-Triassic evolution of the region is poorly constrained owing to the paucity of preserved strata. Regional considerations and depth of burial studies (Chadwick et al., 1995) allow some speculation on the main events

Jurassic

Prior to the onset of North Atlantic sea-floor spreading in mid-Cretaceous times, it is likely that regional crustal extension continued episodically. East–west-directed extension probably continued into early Jurassic times. Continued fault-controlled basin subsidence is indicated by the thick succession of the Lias Group. Extension was probably renewed in late Jurassic times, possibly with a markedly different orientation. The total sedimentary thickness cannot be easily quantified, but may have exceeded 6000 m in places by the end of Jurassic times. The deeper parts of the Permian succession were probably sufficiently deeply buried during this period to have entered the 'oil-window' i.e. suitable hydrocarbon source rocks could have generated oil.

Early Cretaceous

No strata of this age are preserved in the region, and therefore this phase of basin evolution is necessarily speculative. It is likely that crustal extension, associated with sea-floor spreading in the southern part of the North Atlantic between Iberia and America, led to rapid localised basin subsidence. Contemporaneous regional uplift, associated with development of the widespread Late-Cimmerian unconformity (Rawson and Riley, 1982) caused severe erosion of the basin margins, with less severe erosion in the basin depocentres. Thus, at this time any Lower Cretaceous strata that were deposited are likely to have been removed, particularly from the basin edges, together with a substantial thickness of Jurassic and possibly Triassic strata. The deepest parts of the Sherwood Sandstone Group and the Permian succession probably entered the oil-window during this period.

Post-Jurassic movements can be demonstrated on a number of faults, including the Normanton Hills, Sileby and Thringstone faults. These movements are inferred from monoclinal flexuring affecting Triassic strata and the Lias Group around Gotham, with displacements of up to 95 m in the Lias Group along the Normanton Hills Fault (Brandon, 1994; Carney, et al., 2001). Post-Jurassic deformation probably caused the north- to west-north-west-trending faults and gentle synclinal warping of the

Triassic along and to the east of the Thringstone Fault, and further movements of the syn-Triassic fault systems on the north-east margin of the Needwood Basin around Burton upon Trent (Carney et al., 2001).

Late Cretaceous and early Paleocene

The onset of sea-floor spreading between Europe and Canada effectively terminated extension in the region. This phase of basin evolution was probably characterised by regional, post-extensional, shelf subsidence that allowed the deposition of the Chalk. Maximum basin development was probably attained by early Paleocene times, with the accumulation of nearly 6500 m of strata in the basin depocentre.

Alternatively, in the absence of any firm data, it is equally possible that no Chalk was deposited in this region. Offshore, in Cardigan Bay Basin Chalk is absent, although Cainozoic (Tertiary) strata are preserved (Tappin et al., 1994). This suggests that areas between the Celtic Sea and Northern Ireland may have been uplifted early, so that the Chalk was not deposited there. Exotic clasts within the Chalk, Greensand and Carstone of eastern England suggest that some areas to the west may have had only a thin cover of Chalk or none at all.

Renewed subsidence in the Cainozoic is likely as there is evidence of further movement on the faults that controlled the evolution of the Cardigan Bay Basin, and some of these extend through Wales into the Cheshire Basin.

Late Paleocene to present

The dominant structural influences in the Palaeogene and Neogene were the development of the Iceland Plume, associated with the onset of sea-floor spreading between Europe and Greenland, and Alpine continental convergence to the south. Cainozoic uplift probably had two distinct components: a regional uplift, and a superimposed more local uplift of the basin depocentre. The latter was associated with basin inversion and reversal of the major basin-controlling faults. Regional uplift commenced in Paleocene times, with basin inversion perhaps culminating in the Oligocene to Miocene, associated with emplacement of Alpine nappes far to the south. Uplift varied in amount and the regional component is estimated at about 1500 m to well over 2000 m in the basin depocentre, where inversion was most pronounced. Considerable cooling accompanied uplift, with the entire basin-fill probably leaving the oil-window.

NINE

Subsurface economic resources

The region is the cradle of early exploitation of subsurface minerals and energy in the UK. Brine has been extracted from very early times, copper and lead were mined by the Romans, and, in the past, boreholes were drilled to augment the supply of spa waters (Plot, 1686, p.101). Bitumen was heated and marketed as a medicine ('Betton's Oil' patent 1742) and bitumen-rich sandstone was excavated at Row Brook in the 1690s; oil was mined in the vicinity of the Tar Tunnel (Brown and Trinder, 1979) and distilled from coal mine seeps (1847). Ironbridge is known throughout the world as the symbol of the Industrial Revolution. It contains all the elements of progress that contributed to the rapid development of this industrial region in the 18th century, from the mines themselves to the railway lines. Salt mining may have begun in 1670 at Marbury, where an unsuccessful coal borehole led to mining by means of shafts (Sherlock, 1921). It is not known where coal was first mined but there are early references to coal mining in most of the coalfields in the region. James Young of Liverpool, built the first industrial equipment to heat organic shales to produce hydrocarbons. He was advised of the oil seep at Riddings Colliery by Dr Lyon Playfair and sought to replicate the natural transformation of coal to oil. He later obtained fame in Scotland (Redwood, 1922), using richer source rocks. The first countrywide search for oil, during the First World War, drilled nine of its eleven wells in the region and culminated in the discovery of the first English oilfield at Hardstoft (Giffard, 1923).

Coal

Coal Measures are absent from large areas at outcrop and from the pre-Permian subcrop, notably beneath the deepest part of the Needwood and Knowle basins (Figure 38).

There are fifteen separate coalfields within the region (Figure 32). These are clockwise from the north-west: Lancashire, Nottinghamshire–Yorkshire, Leicestershire–South Derbyshire, Warwickshire, South Staffordshire, Wyre Forest, Coalbrookdale, Leebotwood, Shaffalong, Cheadle, Potteries (the last three comprising North Staffordshire), Shrewsbury, Denbighshire and Flintshire. There is however only one pit (Daw Mill Pit) currently active. These coalfields are shown in some detail on the Coal Resources Map of Britain (British Geological Survey, 1999) and more detailed assessments have been made of the coal resources with new technologies in mind (Jones et al., 2004). Eight coalbed methane boreholes have been drilled and more proposed. (Coalmine methane licences have been acquired).

Formerly, the NCB (National Coal Board) sold mine drainage gas to local industry and used some gas at the pitheads at the Point of Ayr, Lancashire and Potteries - collieries (Smith, 1982; Burton, 1984). The Flintshire Coalfield (North Wales) was extensively worked underground and the NCB identified prospects at North and South Dee. The South Lancashire Coalfield is largely worked out, but there are some remaining underground prospects in the south, on the margins of the Cheshire Basin. The potential for underground coal gassification is good in large areas south of the existing workings at Sutton Manor and Parkside.

The Park prospect between the North and South Staffordshire coalfields, and the area around Lichfield are promising for underground mining. There is also good potential for underground coal gassification at Park, along with the southern fringe of the North Staffordshire coalfield and the area just east of the former Lea Hall Colliery.

The Warwickshire Coalfield has underground mining prospects at Hawkhurst Moor, just south of the existing Daw Mill Mine for the Warwickshire Thick Coal. There is some potential for underground mining of coal between the Wyre Forest and the southern edge of the South Staffordshire Coalfield.

The Leicestershire Coalfield is largely worked out, but the South Derbyshire Coalfield has some underground prospects just west of the Netherseal Fault.

Hydrocarbons

Exploration for hydrocarbons in the region has been carried out, in several phases, since the First World War gave impetus to the first systematic search. Long before this time, hydrocarbon seeps in coalmines, houses and at the surface had frightened householders and miners and aroused scientific curiosity (Robinson and Grayson, 1990). One gas seep near Broseley was encouraged as an early tourist attraction (Hopton, 1711) and, when it ceased, exploration was conducted again, eventually proving successful (Mason, 1747). The Coalport Tar Tunnel seep from a sandstone in the Halesowen Formation, which was discovered in 1786, was mined extensively until the 1830s, and is now part of the Ironbridge Gorge tourist site (Brown and Trinder, 1979). Cannel coals and oil shales were exploited during the mid 1800s, representing the earliest phase of hydrocarbon exploration. In the Flint district, a rich oil-bearing shale 10 to 25 cm thick forms the roof to the Cannel Coal and was used for the distillation of paraffin oil at Leeswood Green (Wedd and King, 1924).

Potential source rocks range from early Palaeozoic shales (which underlie parts of the region) to early Namurian shales and Westphalian cannel coals, oil-shales and bituminous coals. Cannel coals and oil-shales are found at several levels in the Flint district (Wedd and King, 1924). They are probably immature, as reasonable amounts of oil were obtained by distillation. Oil-shales were also reported in the Norton and Kidsgrove areas of the Potteries Coalfield by Gibson (1905). Petroleum or saline springs are present in the Astley Deep Pit, east of Standish, and at Rose Bridge and Worthington Hall collieries (Jones et al., 1938; Sherlock, 1921). These localities are, respectively, west, east and north of the Cheshire Basin. It is reasonable to suppose that equivalent rocks lie concealed beneath the Permo-Triassic and Warwickshire Group strata of this basin.

There are several different geographical and geological locations where oil seepage has occurred. The main seeps are from the boundary between the Carboniferous Limestone and the overlying Millstone Grit, bordering the Derbyshire Dome. Inspissated bitumen is found at outcrop (Windy Knoll) and encountered in lead mines and associated drainage channels (soughs). Several coalmines in Lancashire, Flintshire and the Potteries have encountered oil (Strahan, 1920; Kent, 1954). The South Staffordshire Coalfield has notably fewer discoveries. The Warwickshire Coalfield has one large oil discovery but the details could not be confirmed in the BGS archive. In Shropshire, Warwickshire Group sandstones have yielded oil at several localities. The base metal mines of the Shelve and Longmynd have bitumen stains on the ore. A few oil shows are known from Triassic strata, mainly near the Wirral peninsula and at Burton-on-Trent.

Carboniferous rocks in all the coalfields surrounding the Cheshire Basin have fair to good oil shows, comparable to those in the Nottinghamshire–Yorkshire Coalfield (Kent, 1954). Live oil has been encountered in the Coalbrookdale, Lancashire and North Staffordshire coalfields (Strahan, 1920). In some instances this may be interpreted as migrating oil intercepted by mining, although oil-bearing sandstones are also known, for example in the Coalbrookdale area. This oil has a probable local cannel coal source and has migrated to the extremity of the Carboniferous basin (Longmynd–Shelve area).

Lack of hydrocarbon shows in the Cheshire Basin Helsby Sandstone wells has been attributed to an absence of Carboniferous source rocks (Mikkelsen and Floodpage, 1997). However, the present study found that Coal Measures and Warwickshire Group are present in this basin (Figure 37). The quality of seismic reflection data decreases near the Red Rock Fault so the age of strata forming the subcrop hereabouts is unclear. The Halesowen Formation was probably drilled at Knutsford beneath Permian strata and most of the other wells penetrated the Warwickshire Group and Coal Measures strata. Moreover, from wells drilled in the west of the Cheshire Basin and farther east, there is no reason to doubt that Namurian rocks are present beneath most of the basin. A spatially wide correlation of wells suggests that the distinctive Arnsbergian shales can be traced on all sides of the basin.

Potential reservoirs are, in order of increasing age, Helsby Sandstone Formation, Wilmslow Sandstone Formation, Kinnerton Sandstone Formation, Collyhurst Sandstone Formation and Westphalian and Namurian sandstones. These are all proven reservoirs in adjacent basins. Many of the Silesian sandstones in the Milton Green and Blacon East boreholes are thin, but thicker equivalents were found in the Erbistock Borehole. Lower Palaeozoic rocks, notably lower Cambrian and upper Llandovery sandstones are unproven potential reservoirs.

Hardstoft Oilfield was the only commercial oilfield within the region. It was discovered by the first systematic, American-advised search for oil, conducted during and after the First World War on 3rd June 1918 (Strahan, 1920). It produced oil from the top of the Carboniferous Limestone initially at 8 to 10 barrels per day. Production by October 1919 was 849 barrels. This first discovery however proved anomalous, compared with the later discovered and more prolific East Midlands oil province.

There were two gasfields located on surface anticlines in the Coal Measures, on the eastern flank of the Pennines. At Calow Gasfield, the reservoirs are the Westphalian Crawshaw Sandstone and Namurian Chatsworth Grit (Brunstrom, 1966). Adcock (1963) referred only to the wells having been completed as commercial gas wells for the Gas Council. The seal is by shales within the Coal Measures. In the Ironville Gasfield, the reservoir was the Kinderscout Grit (Brunstrom, 1966). Adcock (1963) stated that the Ironville 3 well was completed as a gas producer with a potential of 800 000 cfd.

Coalbed methane

Methane is a by-product of the coalification process, which is the low-grade metamorphism of peat through lignite to coal and anthracite. Some of this methane may migrate from the source rock, but that which remains within the coal is known as coalbed methane. It is either adsorbed onto maceral surfaces or held as free gas within the cleat system of the coal. Coal is known to have a very large internal surface area and consequently can hold large quantities of methane. Coalbed methane is produced from the seam by reducing the pressure that results in desorption of the methane and diffusion through the fracture system to the point of lowest pressure, usually a borehole. Pressure reduction is usually brought about by pumping water from the coals.

Many of the coal seams in the region are gassy, attracting drilling on three UK coalbed methane exploration licenses with more proposed. Table 6 shows the published average methane content of coals in the coalfields of the region. Most coalbed methane produced from the broadly comparable Carboniferous coals in the Warrior Basin of Alabama comes from seams which contain more than 7 m^3/tonne methane. Given that the permeability of the UK Westphalian coals appears to be significantly lower than in the Warrior Basin, 7 m^3/tonne CH4 appears to be a reasonable economic gas content cut-off at present. Thus South Lancashire, North Wales and North Staffordshire coalfields appear to have the best prospects. Coalbed methane exploration

Table 6 Coalfields ranked by methane content.

Coalfield	Mean methane m³/tonne	Mean methane + ethane m³/tonne	Average depth (m)
South Lancashire	8.2	9.48	1080
North Wales	7.1	8.40	1080
North Staffordshire	7.1	7.95	697
South Yorkshire	5.9	7.02	735
Cannock	3.3	3.72	653
Warwickshire	1.7	1.93	766
Leicestershire/ Derbyshire	1.3	1.48	566

Data from Creedy (1991, 1988) and Ayers et al. (1993)
* Part of the Yorkshire/Nottinghamshire Coalfield and its concealed extension

drilling to date bears this out. Wells have been drilled at Yew Tree Farm near Chester, Ince near Ellesmere Port and Rhuddlan in the Clwyd basin. No economic production has been established to date. However, Point of Ayr Colliery, on the north Wales coast, was one of the few places in the UK where significant flows of methane occurred from boreholes drilled in association with coal mining (Creedy, 1999).

Methane/air mixtures may be extracted from abandoned mines, providing they have not been flooded by recovery of mine-water levels since abandonment. An abandoned mine methane extraction plant has been established at Silverdale Colliery, North Staffordshire. The gas is transmitted via the North Staffordshire gas grid to local industry. In the Flintshire Coalfield at Point of Ayr Colliery a methane drainage scheme was required to remove gas from underground workings. Similarly at Parkside Colliery in the Lancashire Coalfield, gas was drained and sold to a Warrington factory. At Wolstanton Colliery in the North Staffordshire Coalfield excess methane was sold to local potteries.

Geothermal energy

In the region, heat flow is around the national average, with no large positive anomalies. The most likely method of heat extraction from the rocks of the region therefore is using the low enthalpy system that attempts to extract hot groundwater directly from deep aquifers. Most Carboniferous and older rocks are likely to have insufficient porosity and permeability at the necessary depths (Gale et al., 1984). However, the presence of warm springs associated with the Carboniferous Limestone in Derbyshire suggests that open fractures at depth locally may enhance the possibilities from rocks of this age. In general however, Permo-Triassic sandstones of the Cheshire Basin are likely to have the most suitable characteristics with, for example, 45 per cent of the Collyhurst Sandstone in the Prees Borehole at depths between 3301 and 3575 m having porosities greater than 20 per cent. It is thought that more generally perhaps 30 and 25 per cent of the Sherwood Sandstone and Permian sandstones, respectively, in the Cheshire Basin will have

suitable characteristics. The total geothermal resource of these two reservoirs in the Cheshire Basin is estimated at 36 and 38 ˘ 10¹⁸ Joules, respectively (Rollin et al., 1995).

Evaporites

Evaporites are widespread in Triassic rocks, most notably in the Cheshire Basin, where the main sources are the Northwich and Wilkesley Halite Formations. Salt has been mined at Meadowbank in two phases (1844 to 1892 and 1928 to present). Total resources in this basin have been estimated at 28 cubic miles (Pugh, 1960). Brine extraction, from the Northwich Halite Formation, is presently by controlled pumping in the Holford and Warmingham brinefields. A total of 5.5 million tons of salt is produced each year from the Cheshire Basin.

In the Stafford and Needwood basins, several natural brine springs led to exploitation in Tudor–Stuart and later times. Boreholes near Stafford indicate that individual halites in these basins may be very thin (0.15 m). The Chartley Borehole in the Needwood Basin found salt at five levels within the Mercia Mudstone Group, near to the Shirleywich and Weston brine springs (Sherlock, 1921).

Gypsum has been mined and quarried from the Mercia Mudstone Group (Tutbury Gypsum) in Staffordshire, Derbyshire and Nottinghamshire since at least mediaeval times (Sherlock and Hollingworth, 1938; Firman, 1989).

Mineral deposits

The history of mining, main mines and subsidiary indications. together with genesis of the mineralisation are covered in detail by Plant et al. (1999). There has been a long history of mining of base metals within the region. The main concentration of lead-zinc deposits are in Dinantian carbonates (Plant and Jones, 1989) on the north-east margin of the Derbyshire Dome and in northeast Wales, where mineralisation is associated with barytes (Smith, 1921) and is generally concentrated on structural highs and anticlines This mineralisation is mostly separate from the copper mineralisation that occurs in Longmyndian, Dinantian and Triassic reservoirs, within and marginal to the Cheshire Basin (Plant et al., 1999) and on the south-west margin of the Derbyshire Dome. Only fluorspar mining continues in the areas formerly worked here.

In the West Shropshire mining region, lead-zinc-barium deposits are found in veins in Ordovician rocks along the Shelve Anticline (Dines, 1958) and copper was mined by the Romans at Llanymynech (Smith, 1921).

There is some evidence for three alignments connecting the known copper mines and shows. Two are in the Cheshire Basin (at the boundary between the Mercia Mudstone and Sherwood Sandstone groups) and the third extends from the Cheshire Basin towards Charnwood. Alderley Edge lies at the apex of two different-trending alignments. In the east, the alignment of mines and veins, from north-west to south-east links Alderley Edge, Mixon, Ecton and Snelston mines with many other smaller sites.

In the western Cheshire Basin, there are two possible alignments of mines from north-east to south-west, linking Gallantry Bank, Eardiston (Triassic reservoirs) and Llanymynech (Dinantian reservoir). In southern Cheshire an alignment of mines includes Hawkstone, Grinshill and small mines with Triassic reservoirs, Westcott and Huglith (both Longmyndian reservoir).

In addition to base metals, fluorspar is mined at two localities (Chance and Eckington), calcite at Arbour Low and limestone at Middleton.

References

Most of the references listed below are held in the Library, British Geological Survey, Keyworth and in Murchison House, Edinburgh. Copies of the references can be purchased subject to current copyright legislation. BGS Library catalogue can be searched online at: http://geolib.bgs.ac.uk

ADAMS, A E, HORBURY, A D, and ABDEL AZIZ, A A. 1990. Controls on Dinantian sedimentation in south Cumbria and surrounding areas of northwest England. *Proceedings of the Geologists' Association*, Vol. 101, 19–30.

ADCOCK, C M. 1963. Natural gas in Britain. *Gas World*, pages 266–268 23 Feb, 291–294 2 Mar, and 321–323, 9 Mar 266–268, 291–294 and 321–323.

AITKENHEAD, N. 1977. Institute of Geological Sciences Borehole at Duffield, Derbyshire. *Bulletin of the Geological Survey of Great Britain*, No. 59, 1–27.

AITKENHEAD, N A, and CHISHOLM, J I. 1982. A standard nomenclature for the Dinantian formations of the Peak District of Derbyshire and Staffordshire. *Institute of Geological Sciences Report*, No. 82/8.

AITKENHEAD, N A, CHISHOLM, J I, and STEVENSON, I P. 1985. Geology of the country around Buxton, Leek and Bakewell. *Memoir of the British Geological Survey*, Sheet 111 (England and Wales).

AITKENHEAD, N, BARCLAY, W J, BRANDON, A, CHADWICK, R A, CHISHOLM, J I, COOPER, A H and JOHNSON, E W. 2002. British regional geology:the Pennines and adjacent areas. Fourth edition. (Keyworth, Nottingham: British Geological Survey.)

ALLEN, J R L. 1960. The Mam Tor Sandstones: a turbidite facies of the Namurian deltas of Derbyshire, England. *Journal of Sedimentary Petrology*, Vol. 30, 193–208.

ALLEN, P M, and JACKSON, A A. 1978. Bryn-teg Borehole, North Wales. *Bulletin of the Geological Survey of Great Britain*, 61.

AMBROSE, K, and CARNEY, J N. 1997. Geology of the Breedon on the Hill area: 1:10 000 Sheet SK42SW. *British Geological Survey Technical Report*, WA/97/42.

ANDERSON, E M. 1951. *The dynamics of faulting*. Second edition. (Edinburgh: Oliver & Boyd Ltd.)

ARNOLD-BEMROSE, H H. 1894a. Geology of the Ashbourne and Buxton branch of the London and North-Western Railway: Ashbourne to Crake Low. *Quarterly Journal of the Geological Society of London*, Vol. 55, 224–238.

ARNOLD-BEMROSE, H H. 1894b. On the microcopical structure of the Carboniferous dolerites and tuffs of Derbyshire. *Quarterly Journal of the Geological Society of London*, Vol. 50, 603–644.

ARNOLD-BEMROSE, H H. 1899. On a sill and faulted inlier in Tideswell Dale (Derbyshire). *Quarterly Journal of the Geological Society of London*, Vol. 55, 239–250.

ARNOLD-BEMROSE, H H. 1907. The toadstones of Derbyshire: their field relations and petrography. *Quarterly Journal of the Geological Society of London*, Vol. 63, 241–281.

ARTHURTON, R S, BURGESS, I C, and HOLLIDAY, D W. 1978. Permian and Triassic. 189–206 in The geology of the Lake District. MOSELEY, F (editor). *Yorkshire Geological Society Occasional Publication*, No. 3.

ARTHURTON, R S, JOHNSON, E W, and MUNDY, D J C. 1988. Geology of the country around Settle. *Memoir of the Geological Survey of Great Britain*, Sheet 60 (England and Wales).

AYERS, W B, TISDALE, R M, LITZINGER, L A, and STEIDL, P F. 1993. Coalbed methane potential of Carboniferous strata in Great Britain. *Proceedings of the 1993 International Coalbed Methane Symposium*, University of Alabama, Tuscaloosa, USA, May 17–21, pp.1–14.

BADHAM, J P N, and HALLS, C. 1975. Microplate tectonics, oblique collisions, and the evolution of the Hercynian orogenic systems. *Geology*, Vol. 3, 373–376.

BAKER, J W. 1971. The Proterozoic history of southern Britain. *Proceedings of the Geologists' Association, London*, Vol. 82, 246–266.

BARBER, A J, and MAX, M D. 1979. A new look at the Mona Complex (Anglesey, North Wales). *Journal of the Geological Society of London*, Vol. 136, 407–432.

BARCLAY, W J, RILEY, N J, and STRONG, G E. 1994. The Dinantian rocks of the Sellafield area, West Cumbria. *Proceedings of the Yorkshire Geological Society*, Vol. 50, 37–49.

BARCLAY, W J, AMBROSE, K, CHADWICK, R A, and PHARAOH, T C. 1997. Geology of the country around Worcester. *Memoir of the British Geological Survey*, Sheet 199 (England and Wales).

BECKINSALE, R D, EVANS, J A, THORPE, R S, GIBBONS, W, and HARMON, R S. 1984. Rb-Sr whole rock ages, $\delta^{18}O$ values and geochemical data for the Sarn Igneous Complex and the Parwyd gneisses of the Mona Complex of Llyn, N Wales. *Journal of the Geological Society of London*, Vol. 141, 701–709.

BEETE-JUKES, J. 1859. The South Staffordshire Coalfield. *Coalfield memoir of the Geological Survey of Great Britain*.

BESLY, B M. 1983. The sedimentology and stratigraphy of red beds in the Westphalian A to C of Central England. Unpublished PhD thesis, University of Keele.

BESLY, B. 1988. Palaeogeographic implications of late Westphalian to early Permian red-beds. 200–221 in *Sedimentation in a synorogenic basin complex: the Upper Carboniferous of northwest Europe*. BESLY, B, and KELLING, G (editors). (Glasgow and London: Blackie.)

BESLY, B, and KELLING, G (editors). 1988. *Sedimentation in a synorogenic basin complex: the Upper Carboniferous of northwest Europe*. (Glasgow and London: Blackie.)

BESLY, B M, BURLEY, S D, and TURNER, P. 1993. The late Carboniferous 'Barren Red Bed' play of the Silver Pit area, southern North Sea. 727-740 in *Petroleum geology of northwest Europe: proceedings from the fourth conference held at the Barbican Centre, London, 29 March–1 April 1992*. PARKER, J R (editor). (London: Geological Society of London.)

BISAT, W S. 1924. Carboniferous goniatites of the north of England and their zones. *Proceedings of the Yorkshire Geological Society*, Vol. 20, 40–124.

BISAT, W S. 1928. Carboniferous goniatite zones of England and their continental equivalents. C I. *Congre. Int. Strat. Géol. Carb. (Heereln)*, 117–133.

BLAKE, J F. 1890. On the Monian and basal Cambrian rocks of Shropshire. *Quarterly Journal of the Geological Society of London*, Vol. 46, 386–420.

BLAND, B H. 1994. Trace fossils in the Swithland Formation. *Transactions of the Leicester Literary and Philosophical Society*, Vol. 8, 27.

BLUCK B J, COPE, J C W, and SCRUTTON, C T. 1992. Devonian. 153 in Atlas of palaeogeography and lithofacies. COPE, J C W, INGHAM, J K, and RAWSON, P F (editors). *Geological Society of London Special Memoir*, No. 13.

BOTT, M H P. 1967. Geophysical investigations of the northern Pennine basement rocks. *Proceedings of the Yorkshire Geological Society*, Vol. 36, 481–495.

BOTT, M H P, and JOHNSON, G A L. 1967. The controlling mechanism of Carboniferous cyclic sedimentation. *Quarterly Journal of the Geological Society, London*, Vol. 122, 421–441.

BOULTON, W S. 1926. Evidence for an easterly extension of the Warwickshire Coalfield. *Transactions of the Institute of Mining Engineers of London*, Vol. 70, 69–78.

BRANDON, A. 1994. Geological notes and local details for 1:10 000 Sheet SK52SW (Normanton on Soar). *British Geological Survey Technical Report*, WA/94/60.

BRANDON, A, AITKENHEAD, N A, CROFTS, R G, ELLISON, R A, EVANS, D J, and RILEY, N J. 1998. Geology of the country around Lancaster. *Memoir of the British Geological Survey*, Sheet 59, (England and Wales).

BRASIER, M D, HEWEITT, R A, and BRASIER, C J. 1978. On the late Precambrian–early Cambrian Hartshill Formation of Warwickshire. *Geological Magazine*, Vol. 115, 21–36.

BRIDGE, D McC. 1991. Sheet SP 38 NE, Bedworth. *British Geological Survey Technical Report Series*, WA/91/58.

BRIDGE, D McC, CARNEY, J N, LAWLEY, R S, and RUSHTON, A W A. 1998. Geology of the country around Coventry and Nuneaton. *Memoir of the British Geological Survey*, Sheet 169 (England and Wales).

BRISTOW, C S. 1988. Controls on the sedimentation of the Rough Rock Group (Namurian) from the Pennine Basin of northern England. 114–131 in *Sedimentation in a synorogenic basin complex: the Upper Carboniferous of northwest Europe*. BESLY, B M, and KELLING, G (editors). (Glasgow and London: Blackie.)

BRISTOW, C S, BROADHURST, F M, and SIMPSON, I M. 1967. Sedimentary infilling of fossils and cavities in limestone at Treak Cliff, Derbyshire. *Geological Magazine*, Vol. 104, 443–448.

BRITISH GEOLOGICAL SURVEY. 1985. Atlas of onshore sedimentary basins in England and Wales: post-Carboniferous tectonics and stratigraphy. WHITTAKER, A (editor). Glasgow: Blackie & Son Ltd.)

BRITISH GEOLOGICAL SURVEY. 1994. East Irish Sea (Special Sheet Edition). 1:250 000 (Edinburgh, Scotland: British Geological Survey.)

BRITISH GEOLOGICAL SURVEY. 1999. Coal Resources Map of Great Britain. (Chapman, G R.)

BROWN, I, and TRINDER, B. 1979. The tar tunnel. (Ironbridge: Ironbridge Gorge Museum Trust.)

BRUNSTROM, R G W. 1966. Indigenous petroleum and natural gas in Britain. *Institute of Petroleum*, Vol. 1 5–27.

BURTON, J B. 1984. Colliery methane utilisation schemes within the western area. *The Mining Engineer*, Sept 1984, 175–180

BURGESS, I C. 1982. Stratigraphical distribution of Westphalian volcanic rocks to the east and south of Nottingham. *Proceedings of the Yorkshire Geological Society*, Vol. 44, 29–45.

BUTCHER, N J D, and FORD, T D. 1973. Carboniferous Limestone of Monsdal Dale, Derbyshire. *Mercian Geologist*, Vol. 4, 179–196.

BUTTERLEY, A D, and MITCHELL, G H. 1946. Driving of two drifts by the Desford Coal Co. Ltd at Merry Lees, Leicestershire. *Transactions of the Institution of Mining Engineers*, Vol. 104, 703–713.

CALVER, M A. 1968. Distribution of Westphalian marine faunas in northern England and adjoining areas. *Proceedings of the Yorkshire Geological Society*, Vol. 37, 1–72.

CALVER, M A, and SMITH, E G. 1974. Westphalian of north Wales. 169–183 in *Upper Palaeozoic and post-Palaeozoic rocks of Wales*. OWEN, T R (editor). (Cardiff: Cardiff University Press.)

CAMPBELL, S D G, and HAINS, B A. 1988. Deeside (North Wales) thematic mapping. *British Geological Survey Technical Report*, WA/88/2.

CARNEY, J, GLOVER, B J, and PHARAOH, T C. 1992. Pre-conference field excursion guide: Midlands. *British Geological Survey Technical Report*, WA/92/72.

CARNEY, J N, AMBROSE, K, and BRANDON, A. 2001. Geology of the country between Loughborough, Burton and Derby. *Sheet Description of the British Geological Survey*, Sheet 141 Loughborough (England and Wales.)

CHADWICK, R A. 1997. Fault analysis of the Cheshire Basin, north-west England. 297–313 in Petroleum geology of the Irish Sea and adjacent areas. MEADOWS, N S, TRUEBLOOD, S P, HARDMAN, M, and COWAN, G (editors). *Geological Society of London Special Publication*, No. 124.

CHADWICK, R A, and EVANS, D J. 1995. The timing and direction of Permo-Triassic rifting in southern Britain. 161–192 in Permo-Triassic Rifting in the UK. BOLDY, S R, and HARDMAN, R F P (editors). *Geological Society of London Special Publication*, No. 91.

CHADWICK, R A, and SMITH, N J P. 1988. Short paper: evidence of negative structural inversion beneath central England from new seismic reflection data. *Journal of the Geological Society of London*, Vol. 145, 519–522.

CHADWICK, R A, HOLLIDAY, D W, HOLLOWAY, S, and HULBERT, A G. 1993. The evolution and hydrocarbon potential of the Northumberland–Solway Basin. 717–726 in *Petroleum geology of northwest Europe: proceedings from the fourth conference held at the Barbican Centre, London, 29 March–1 April 1992*. PARKER, J R (editor). (London: Geological Society of London.)

CHADWICK, R A, KIRBY, G A, and BAILY, H E. 1994. Post-Triassic structural evolution of north-west England and adjacent parts of the East Irish Sea. *Proceedings of the Yorkshire Geological Society*, Vol. 50, 91–102.

CHADWICK, R A, HOLLIDAY, D W, HOLLOWAY, S, and HULBERT, A G. 1995. Structure and evolution of the Northumberland–Solway Basin and adjacent areas. *Subsurface Memoir of the British Geological Survey*.

CHADWICK, R A, EVANS, D J, ROWLEY, W J, SMITH, N J P, WALKER, A S D, BIRCH, B, and BULAT, J. 1999. Chapter 3 Structure and evolution of the basin. 41–89 in The Cheshire Basin. Basin evolution, fluid movement and mineral resources in a Permo-Triassic rift setting. PLANT, J A, JONES, D G, and Haslam, H W (editors). (Keyworth, Nottingham: British Geological Survey.)

CHARSLEY, T J. 1984. Early Carboniferous rocks of the Swinden No.1 Borehole, west of Skipton, Yorkshire. *British Geological Survey Report*, No. 84/1, 5–12.

CHERRY, J L. 1877. Sectional reports. No.1: Geology. *North Staffordshire Naturalists' Field Club*, 23–25.

CHISHOLM, J I. 1977. Growth faulting and sandstone deposition in the Namurian of the Stanton Syncline, Derbyshire. *Proceedings of the Yorkshire Geological Society*, Vol. 41, 305–323.

CHISHOLM, J I. 1981. Growth faulting in the Almscliff Grit (Namurian E1) near Harrogate, Yorkshire. *Transactions of the Leeds Geological Association*, Vol. 9, 61–70.

CHISHOLM, J I. 1990. The Upper Band–Better Bed sequence (Lower Coal Measures, Westphalian A) in the central and south Pennine area of England. *Geological Magazine*, Vol. 127, 55–74.

CHISHOLM, J I., CHARSLEY, T J, and AITKENHEAD, N. 1988. Geology of the country around Ashbourne and Cheadle. *Memoir of the British Geological Survey*, Sheet 124 (England and Wales).

CLARKE, W J. 1901. The unconformity in the Coal Measures of the Shropshire Coalfield. *Quarterly Journal of the Geological Society of London*, Vol. 57, 86–95.

COBBOLD, E S. 1900. Geology of the Church Stretton district. 1–115 in *Church Stretton Vol. 1*. CAMPBELL-HYSLOP C W (editor.) (Shrewsbury: L Wilding.)

COBBOLD, E S. 1925. Unconformities in south Shropshire. *Proceedings of the Geologists' Association*, Vol. 36, 364–367.

COLLAR, F A. 1974. A geophysical interpretation of the structure of the Vale of Clwyd, North Wales. *Geological Journal*, Vol. 9, 65–76.

COLLINSON, J D. 1968. Deltaic sedimentation units in the Upper Carboniferous of northern England. *Sedimentology*, Vol. 10, 233–254.

COLLINSON, J D. 1969. Sedimentology of the Grindslow Shales and the Kinderscout Grit: a deltaic complex in the Namurian of northern England. *Journal of Sedimentary Petrology*, Vol. 39, 194–221.

COLLINSON, J D. 1988. Controls on Namurian sedimentation in the Central Province basins of northern England. 85–100 in Sedimentation in a synorogenic basin complex: the Upper Carboniferous of northwest Europe. BESLY, B, and KELLING, G (editors.) (London and Glasgow: Blackie.)

COLLINSON, J D, and BANKS, N L. 1975. The Haslingden Flags (Namurian G1) of south-east Lancashire: bar finger sands in the Pennine Basin. *Proceedings of the Yorkshire Geological Society*, Vol. 40, 431–458.

COLLINSON, J D, JONES, C M, and WILSON, A A. 1977. The Marsdenian (Namurian R2) succession west of Blackburn: implications for the evolution of Pennine delta systems. *Geological Journal*, Vol. 12, 1, 59–76.

COLLINSON, J D, HOLDSWORTH, B K, JONES, C M, and MARTINSEN, O J. 1992. Discussion of: 'The Millstone Grit (Namurian) of the southern Pennines viewed in the light of eustaically controlled sequence stratigraphy' by W A Read. *Geological Journal*, Vol. 27, 173–180.

COPE, F W. 1936. The Cyrtina septosa Band in the Lower Carboniferous succession of north Derbyshire. *Summary of the Proceedings of the Geological Survey Great Britain*, for 1934, Pt 2, 48–51.

COPE, F W. 1937. Some features of the D$_1$–D$_2$ limestones of the Miller's Dale region, Derbyshire. *Proceedings of the Yorkshire Geological Society*, Vol. 23, 178–195.

COPE, F W. 1939a. Oil occurrences in south-west Lancashire. *Bulletin of the Geological Survey of Great Britain*, No. 2, 18–25.

COPE, F W. 1939b. The mid-Visean (S2-D1) succession in north Derbyshire and north-west England. *Proceedings of the Yorkshire Geological Society*, Vol. 24, 60–66.

COPE, F W. 1946. The correlation of the Coal Measures of the Cheadle Coalfield, North Staffordshire. *Transactions of the Institution of Mining Engineers*, Vol. 105, 75–97.

COPE, F W. 1949. Woo Dale Borehole near Buxton, Derbyshire. *Quarterly Journal of the Geological Society of London*, Vol. 105, iv.

COPE, F W. 1966a. The Butterton Dyke near Keele and Butterton, Staffordshire. *North Staffordshire Journal of Field Studies*, 5, 25–37.

COPE, F W. 1966b. The Lower Carboniferous succession in the Wye valley region of north Derbyshire. *Journal of the Manchester Geological Association*, Vol. 1, 125–145.

COPE, J C W. 1979. The age of the volcanic rocks in the Woo Dale Borehole, Derbyshire. *Geological Magazine*, Vol. 116, 319–320.

COPE, J C W, GUION, P D, SEVASTOPULO, G D, and SWAN, A R H. 1992. Carboniferous. 67–86 in Atlas of palaeogeography and lithofacies. COPE, J C W, INGHAM, J K, and RAWSON, P F (editors). *Geological Society of London Special Memoir*, No. 13.

CORFIELD, S M. 1991. The Upper Palaeozoic to Mesozoic structural evolution of north Staffordshire and adjoining areas. Unpublished PhD thesis, University of Keele.

CORFIELD, S M, GAWTHORPE, R L, GAGE, M, FRASER, A J, and BESLY, B M. 1996. Inversion tectonics of the Variscan foreland of the British Isles. *Journal of the Geological Society of London*, Vol. 153, 17–32.

COWARD, M P. 1990. The Precambrian, Caledonian and Variscan framework to north-west Europe. 1–34 in Tectonic events responsible for Britain's oil and gas reserves. HARDMAN, R F P, and BROOKS, J (editors). *Geological Societ of London Special Publication*, No. 55.

CREEDY, D P. 1988. Geological controls on the formation and distribution of gas in British Coal Measure strata. *International Journal of Coal Geology*, Vol. 10, 1–31.

CREEDY, D P. 1991. An introduction to geological aspects of methane occurrence and control in British deep coal mines. *Quarterly Journal of Engineering Geology*, Vol. 24, 209–220.

CREEDY, D P. 1999. Coalbed methane — the R and D needs of the UK. *DTI Cleaner Coal Technology Programme, Report*, No. R163.

CRITCHLEY, M F. 1984. Variscan tectonics of the Alston Block, northern England. 139–146 in Variscan tectonics of the North Atlantic region. HUTTON, D H W, and SANDERSON, D J. (editors). *Geological Society of London Special Publication*, No. 14.

DALZIEL, I W D. 1997. Neoproterozoic-Palaeozoic geography and tectonics: review, hypothesis, environmental speculation. *Bulletin of the Geological Society of America*, Vol. 109, 16–42.

DAVIES, J R, RILEY, N J, and WILSON, D. 1989. Distribution of Chadian and earliest Arundian strata in north Wales: implications for Dinantian (Carboniferous) lithostratigraphy and palaeogeography. *Geological Journal*, Vol. 24, 31–47.

DAVIES, J R, WILSON, D, and WILLIAMSON, I T. 2004 Geology of the country around Flint. *Memoir of the British Geological Survey*, Sheet 108 (England and Wales).

DEARNLEY, R. 1966. Ignimbrites from the Uriconian and Arvonian. *Bulletin of the Geological Survey of Great Britain* No. 24, 1–6.

DEWEY, J F. 1969. Evolution of the Caledonian–Appalachian Orogen. *Nature*, Vol. 222, 124–129.

DEWEY, J F. 1982. Plate tectonics and the evolution of the British Isles. *Journal of the Geological Society of London*, Vol. 139, 371–412.

DINES, H G. 1958. West Shropshire mining region. *Bulletin of the Geological Survey of Great Britain*, No. 14, 1–43.

DREWERY, S, CLIFF, R A, and LEEDER, M R. 1987. Provenance of Carboniferous sandstones from U-Pb dating of detrital zircons. *Nature (London)*, Vol. 325, 50–53.

DUNHAM, K C. 1973. A recent deep borehole near Eyam, Derbyshire. *Nature, Physical Sciences*, Vol. 241, 84–85.

DUNHAM, K C, and WILSON, A A. 1985. Geology of the Northern Pennine Orefield: Volume 2, Stainmore to Craven. *Economic Memoir of the British Geological Survey.*

EARP, J R, and CALVER, M A. 1961. Exploratory boreholes in the North Staffordshire Coalfield. *Bulletin of the Geological Survey of Great Britain*, No. 17, 153–190.

EARP, J R, and HAINS, B A. 1971. *British regional geology: the Welsh Borderland.* Third edition. (London: HMSO for the Institute of Geological Sciences.)

EARP, J R, and TAYLOR, B J. 1986. Geology of the country around Chester and Winsford. *British Geological Survey Memoir*, Sheet 109 (England and Wales).

EASTWOOD, T. 1935. British regional geology: northern England. First edition. (London: HMSO for the Institute of Geological Sciences.)

EBDON, C C, FRASER, A J, HIGGINS, A C, MITCHENER, B C, and STRANK, A R E. 1990. The Dinantian stratigraphy of the East Midlands: a seismostratigraphic approach. *Journal of the Geological Society of London*, Vol. 147, 519–536.

EDEN, R A, STEVENSON, I P, and EDWARDS, W. 1957. Geology of the country around Sheffield. *Memoir of the Geological Survey of Great Britain*, Sheet 100 (England and Wales).

EDWARDS, W N. 1951 [published 1952]. The concealed coalfield of Yorkshire and Nottinghamshire. Third edition. *Coalfield memoir of the Geological Survey of Great Britain.*

EDWARDS, W N. 1954. British regional geology: Pennines and adjacent areas. Third edition. (London: HMSO.)

EDWARDS, W N. 1967. Geology of the country around Ollerton. *Memoir of the Geological Survey, Great Britain*, Sheet 113 (England and Wales).

ELLIOT, R E. 1968a. Deltaic processes and episodes: the interpretation of productive Coal Measures occurring in the East Midlands. *Mercian Geologist*, Vol. 3, 111–135.

ELLIOT, R E. 1968b. Facies, sedimentation successions and cyclothems in productive Coal Measures in the East Midlands, Great Britain. *Mercian Geologist*, Vol. 2, 351–371.

EVANS, D J, and KIRBY, G A. 1999. The architecture of concealed Dinantian carbonate sequences over the Central Lancashire and Holme highs, northern England. *Proceedings of the Yorkshire Geological Society*, Vol. 52, 297–312.

EVANS, D J, REES, J G, and HOLLOWAY, S. 1993. The Permian to Jurassic stratigraphy and structural evolution of the central Cheshire Basin. *Journal of the Geological Society of London*, Vol. 150, 857–870.

EVANS, D J, WALKER, A S D, and CHADWICK, R A C. 2002. The Pennine Anticline, northern England — a continuing enigma? *Proceedings of the Yorkshire Geological Society*, 54, 17–34.

EVANS, W B, WILSON, A A, TAYLOR, B J, and PRICE, D. 1968. Geology of the country around Macclesfield, Congleton, Crewe and Middlewich. *Memoir of the British Geology Survey*, Sheet 110 (England and Wales).

FALCON, N L, and KENT, P E. 1960. Geological results of petroleum exploration in Britain. *Geological Society of London, Memoir*, No. 2.

FALCON-LANG, H J. 1999a. Early Carboniferous (Asbian–Brigantian) seasonal tropical climate of northern Britain. *Palaios.* Vol. 14, 116–126.

FALCON-LANG, H J. 1999b. Early Carboniferous (Courceyan–Arundian) monsoonal climate of the British Isles: evidence from growth rings in fossil woods. *Geological Magazine*, Vol. 136, 177–187.

FAREY, J. 1811. *General view of the agriculture and minerals of Derbyshire: with observations on the means of their improvement, Board of Agriculture and Internal Improvement.* Vol. 1. (London: B Macmillan.)

FIELDING, C R. 1984a. A coal depositional model for the Durham Coal Measures of north-east England. *Journal of the Geological Society of London*, Vol. 141, 919–931.

FIELDING, C R. 1984b. Upper delta-plain lacustrine and fluviolacustrine facies from the Westphalian of the Durham Coalfield. *Sedimentology*, Vol. 31, 547–567.

FIELDING, C R. 1986. Fluvial channel and overbank deposits from the Westphalian of the Durham Coalfield, north-east England. *Sedimentology*, Vol. 33, 119–140.

FIELDING, C R, and JOHNSON, G A L. 1987. Sedimentary structures associated with extensional fault movement from the Westphalian of NE England. 511–516 in Continental extensional tectonics. COWARD, M P, DEWEY, J F, and HANCOCK, P L (editors). *Geological Society of London Special Publication*, No. 28.

FITCH, F J, MILLER, J A, GRASTY, A L, and MENEISY, M Y. 1969. Isotopic age determinations on rocks from Wales and the Welsh Borders. 23–46 in Pre-Cambrian and Lower Palaeozoic rocks of Wales. WOOD, A (editor). (Cardiff: University of Wales Press.)

FITCHES, W R, and CAMPBELL, S D G. 1987. Tectonic evolution of the Bala Lineament in the Welsh Basin. *Geological Journal*, Vol. 22, 131–153.

FITTON, J G, and HUGHES, D J. 1970. Volcanism and plate tectonics in the British Ordovician. *Earth and Planetary Science Letters*, Vol. 8, 223–228.

FIRMAN, R J. 1989. A tale of two excursions; geological, historical and environmental aspects of gypsum in Derbyshire and Staffordshire. *East Midlands Geological Society*, Nottingham, United Kingdom.

FORD, T D (editor). 1977. *Limestones and caves of the Peak District.* (Northwich: Geo Abstracts.)

FORD, T D. 1999. The growth of geological knowledge in the Peak District. *Mercian Geologist*, Vol. 14, 161–190.

FOSTER, D, HOLLIDAY, D W, JONES, C M, OWENS, B, and WALSH, A. 1989. Concealed Upper Palaeozoic rocks of Berkshire and South Oxfordshire. *Proceedings of the Geologists' Association*, Vol. 100, 395–407.

FOX-STRANGWAYS, C. 1905. Geology of the country between Derby, Burton-on-Trent, Ashby-de-la-Zouch and Loughborough. *Memoir of the British Geological Survey*, Sheet 141 (England and Wales).

FRASER, A J, and GAWTHORPE, R L. 1990. Tectono-stratigraphic development and hydrocarbon habitat of the Carboniferous in northern England. 49–86 in Tectonic events responsible for Britain's oil and gas reserves. HARDMAN, R F P, and BROOKS, J (editors). *Geological Society of London Special Publication*, No. 55.

FRASER, A J, NASH, D F, STEELE, R P, and EBDON, C C. 1990. A regional assessment of the intra-Carboniferous play of northern England. 417–439 in Classic petroleum provinces. BROOKS, J (editor). *Geological Society of London Special Publication*, No. 50.

FROST, D V, and SMART, J O O. 1979. Geology of the country north of Derby. *Memoir of the Geological Survey*, Sheet 125 (England and Wales).

FROST, R T C, FITCH, F J, and MILLER, J A. 1981. Age and nature of the crystalline basement of the North Sea Basin. 43–57 in *Petroleum geology of the continental shelf of north-west Europe: proceedings of the second Conference on Petroleum*

Geology. Organized by the Institute of Petroleum and held in London, 4–6 March 1980. ILLING, L V, and HOBSON, G D (editors). (London: Heyden, on behalf of the Institute of Petroleum.)

FULTON, I M, and WILLIAMS, H. 1988. Palaeogeographical change and controls on Namurian and Westphalian A/B sedimentation at the southern margin of the Pennine Basin, central England. 178–199 in *Sedimentation in a synorogenic basin complex: the Upper Carboniferous of northwest Europe.* BESLY, B M, and KELLING, G (editors). (Glasgow and London: Blackie.)

GALE, I N, EVANS, C J, EVANS, R B, SMITH, I F, HOUGHTON, M T, and BURGESS, W G. 1984. The Permo-Triassic aquifers of the Cheshire and West Lancashire Basins. *Investigation of the Geothermal Potential of the UK.* (Keyworth, Nottingham: British Geological Survey.)

GARNER, R. 1844. *The natural history of the county of Staffordshire.* (London: J Van Voorst.)

GAWTHORPE, R L. 1987. Tectono-sedimentary evolution of the Bowland Basin, northern England, during the Dinantian. *Journal of the Geological Society of London,* Vol. 144, 59–71.

GAWTHORPE, R L, GUTTERIDGE, P, and LEEDER, M R. 1989. Late Devonian and Dinantian basin evolution in northern England and north Wales. 1–23 *in* The role of tectonics in Devonian and Carboniferous sedimentation in the British Isles. ARTHURTON, R S, GUTTERIDGE, P, and NOLAN, S C (editors). *Yorkshire Geological Society, Occasional Publication,* No. 6.

GEIKE, A. 1897. *Ancient volcanoes of Great Britain,* Vol. 2, 8–22. (London: Macmillan.)

GEORGE, T N. 1958. Lower Carboniferous palaeogeography of the British Isles. *Proceedings of the Yorkshire Geological Society,* Vol. 31, 227–318.

GEORGE, T N, JOHNSON, G A L, MITCHELL, M, PRENTICE, J E, RAMSBOTTOM, W H C, SEVASTOPULO, G D, and WILSON, R B A. 1976. A correlation of Dinantian rocks in the British Isles. *Geological Society of London, Special Report,* No. 7.

GIBBONS, W. 1983. The Monian Penmynydd zone of metamorphism in Llyn, North Wales. *Geological Journal,* Vol. 18, 1–21.

GIBBONS, W. 1987. The Menai Strait Fault system: an early Caledonian terrane boundary in north Wales. *Geology,* Vol. 15, 744–747.

GIBBONS, W. 1990. Transcurrent ductile shear zones and the dispersal of the Avalon superterrane. 407–423 *in* The Cadomian Orogeny. D'LEMOS, R S, STRACHAN, R A, and TOPLEY, C G (editors). *Geological Society of London, Special Publication.* No. 51.

GIBBONS, W, and HORAK, J M. 1996. The evolution of the Neoproterozoic Avalonian subduction system: evidence from the British Isles. 269–280 in Avalonian and related peri-Gondwana terranes of the circum-Atlantic. NANCE, R D, and THOMPSON, M D (editors). *Geological Society of America Special Paper,* No. 304.

GIBBONS, W, and MURPHY, J B. 1995. Mylonitic mafic granulite in fault megabreccia at Clarke Head, Nova Scotia: a sample of Avalonian lower crust? *Geological Magazine,* Vol. 132, 81–90.

GIBSON, W. 1899. *Summary of progress of the Geological Survey of Great Britain for 1888,* 122–129.

GIBSON, W. 1905. Geology of the North Staffordshire Coalfields. *Coalfield memoir of the Geological Survey of Great Britain.*

GIBSON, W. 1925. Geology of the country around Stoke on Trent (second edition). *Memoir of the Geological Survey,* Sheet 123 (England and Wales).

GIBSON, W, and HIND, W. 1899. On the agglomerates and tuffs in the Carboniferous Limestone Series of Congleton Edge. *Quarterly Journal of the Geological Society of London,* Vol. 55, 548–559.

GIFFARD, H P W. 1923. The recent search for oil in Great Britain. *Transactions of the Institution of Mechanical Engineers,* Vol. 115, 221–250.

GILLIGAN, A. 1920. Petrography of the Millstone Grit of Yorkshire. *Quarterly Journal of the Geological Society of London,* Vol. 75, 251–294.

GLENNIE, K W. 1986. Chapter Two: Structural framework and the pre-Permian history of the North Sea area. 25–60 in *Introduction to the petroleum geology of the north Sea.* Second edition. GLENNIE, K W (editor). JAPEC (UK), (Oxford: Blackwell Scientific Publications.)

GLOVER, B W. 1990. Geology of the Halesowen District. *British Geological Survey Technical Report Series,* WA/90/74.

GLOVER, B W. 1991. Geology of the Womborne district. *British Geological Survey Technical Report Series,* WA/91/76.

GLOVER, B W, POWELL, J H, and WATERS, C N. 1993. Etruria Formation (Westphalian C) palaeoenvironments and volcanicity on the southern margin of the Pennine Basin, UK. *Journal of the Geological Society of London,* Vol. 150, 737–750.

GLOVER, B W, LENG, M J, and CHISHOLM, J I. 1996. A second major fluvial sourceland for the Silesian Basin of northern England. *Journal of the Geological Society of London,* Vol. 153, 901–906.

GREEN, P F. 1986. On the thermo-tectonic evolution of Northern England: evidence from fission track analysis. *Geological Magazine,* Vol. 123, 493–506.

GREIG, D C, WRIGHT, J E, HAINS, J A, and MITCHELL, G H. 1968 Geology around Church Stretton, Craven Arms, Wenlock Edge and Brown Clee. *Memoir of the Geological Survey of Great Britain,* Sheet 166 (England and Wales).

GSGB. 1857. Old series sheet 72SW. (Solid edition). 1:63 360. Geological Survey of Great Britain (England and Wales).

GSGB. 1972. Oswestry Sheet 137 (Solid edition). Geological Survey of Great Britain (England and Wales).

GSGB. 1978. Shrewsbury Sheet 152 (Solid edition). Geological Survey of Great Britain (England and Wales).

GUION, P D. 1984. Crevasse splay deposits and roof rock quality in the Threequarters Seam (Carboniferous) in the East Midlands Coalfield, UK. 291–308 *in* Sedimentology of coal and coal-bearing strata. RAHMANI, R A, and FLORES, R M (editors). *International Association of Sedimentologists Special Publication,* No. 7.

GUION, P D. 1987. The influence of a palaeochannel on seam thickness in the Coal Measures of Derbyshire, England. *Journal of Coal Geology,* Vol. 7, 269–299.

GUION, P D, and FIELDING, C R. 1988. Westphalian A and B sedimentaion in the Pennine Basin, UK. 153–177 in *Sedimentation in a synorogenic basin complex: the Upper Carboniferous of northwest Europe.* BESLY, B M, and KELLING, G. (editors). (London and Glasgow: Blackie.)

GUTTERIDGE, P. 1987. Dinantian sedimentation and the basement structure of the Derbyshire dome. *Geological Journal,* Vol. 22, 25–41.

GUTTERIDGE, P. 1991. Aspects of Dinantian sedimentation in the Edale Basin, north Derbyshire. *Geological Journal,* Vol. 26, 33–59.

HAINS, B A. 1991. Applied geological mapping in the Wrexham area: geology and land-use planning. *British Geological Survey Technical Report Series,* WA/91/4.

HAINS, B A, and HORTON, A. 1969. *British regional geology: central England.* Third edition. (London: HMSO for the Institute of Geological Sciences.)

HALL, E. 1832. A mineralogical and geological map of the Coalfield of Lancashire, with parts of Yorkshire, Cheshire and Derbyshire. 1:65 000 scale (Manchester)

HAMBLIN, R J O, and COPPACK, B C. 1995. Geology of Telford and the Coalbrookdale Coalfield. *Memoir of the British Geological Survey,* Sheet 152–153 (England and Wales).

HARRIS, A L, and FETTES, D J (editors). 1988. The Caledonian–Appalachian Orogen. *Geological Society of London Special Publication,* No. 38.

HAWKINS, P J. 1978. Relationship between diagenesis, porosity reduction and oil emplacement in late Carboniferous sandstone reservoirs, Bothamsall Oilfield, East Midlands. *Journal of the Geological Society of London,* Vol. 135, 7–24.

HECKEL, P H. 1986. Sea-level curve for Pennsylvanian eustatic marine transgressive depositional cycles along mid-continent outcrop belt, North America. *Geology,* Vol. 14, 330–334.

HIND, W. 1904. Whitsuntide excursion to North Staffordshire. *Proceedings of the Geologists' Association,* Vol. 18, 173–184.

HIND, W, and STOBBS, J T. 1906. The Carboniferous succession below the Coal Measures in North Shropshire, Denbighshire and Flintshire. *Geological Magazine,* Vol. 43, 385–400, 445–459, 496–507.

HOARE, R H. 1959. Red beds in the Coal Measures of the West Midlands. *Transactions of the Institution of Mining Engineers,* Vol. 119, 185–195.

HOLDSWORTH, B K. 1963. Prefulvial, autogeosynclinal sedimentation in the Namurian of the southern Central Province. *Nature* (London), Vol. 199, 133–135.

HOLDSWORTH, B K, and COLLINSON, J D. 1988. Millstone Grit cyclicity revisited. 132–152 in *Sedimentation in a synorogenic basin complex: the Upper Carboniferous of northwest Europe.* BESLY, B M, and KELLING, G (editors). (Glasgow and London: Blackie.)

HOPTON, R. 1711. An account of the eruption of a burning spring at Broseley, Shropshire. *Philisophical Transactions,* Vol. 27–28, 475–476.

HORÁK, J M. 1993. The late Precambrian Coedana and Sarn Complexes, north-west Wales — a geochemical and petrological study. Unpublished PhD Thesis University of Wales.

HORÁK, J M, DOIG, R, EVANS, J A, and GIBBONS, W. 1996. Avalonian magmatism and terrane linkage: new isotopic data from the Precambrian of north Wales. *Journal of the Geological Society of London,* Vol. 153, 91-99.

HOWELL, H H. 1859. Geology of the Warwick Coalfield and the Permian rocks and Trias of the surrounding district. *Coalfield memoir of the Geological Survey of England and Wales.*

HUDSON, R G S, and COTTON, G. 1945. The Lower Carboniferous in a boring at Alport, Derbyshire. *Proceedings of the Yorkshire Geological Society,* Vol. 25, 254–330.

HULL, E. 1860. Geology of the Leicestershire coal-field and the country around Ashby-de-la-Zouch. *Coalfield memoir of the Geological Survey of England and Wales.*

INESON, P R, and WALTERS, S G. 1983. Dinantian extrusive activity in the south Pennines. *Mercian Geologist,* Vol. 10, 88–100.

JACKSON, D I, and MULHOLLAND, P. 1993. Tectonic and stratigraphic aspects of the east Irish Sea Basin and adjacent areas: contrasts in their post-Carboniferous structural styles. 791–808 in *Petroleum geology of northwest Europe: proceedings from the fourth conference held at the Barbican Centre, London, 29 March–1 April 1992.* PARKER, J R (editor). (London: Geological Society of London.)

JACKSON, D I, MULHOLLAND, P, JONES, S M, and WARRINGTON, G. 1987. The geological framework of the East Irish Sea Basin. 191–203 in *Petroleum geology of northwest Europe.* BROOKS, J, and GLENNIE, K (editors). (London: Graham and Trotman.)

JACKSON, J W. 1923. The relation of the Edale Shales to the Carboniferous Limestone in North Derbyshire. *Geological Magazine,* Vol. 62, 267–274.

JAMES, J H. 1956. The structure and stratigraphy of part of the Precambrian outcrop between Church Stretton and linley, Shropshire. *Quarterly journal of the Geological Society,* Vol. 112, 315–337.

JONES, C M. 1980. Deltaic sedimentation in the Roaches Grit and associated sediments (Namurian R2b) in the south-west Pennines. *Proceedings of the Yorkshire Geological Society,* Vol. 43, 39–67.

JONES, D G, and OWEN, T R. 1961. The age and relationships of the Cornbrook Sandstone. *Geological Magazine,* Vol. 98, 285–294.

JONES, N S, HOLLOWAY, S, CREEDY, D P, GARNER, K, SMITH, N J P, BROWNE, M A E, and DURACAN, C. 2004. UK Coal Resource for new exploitation technologes final report. *British Geological Survey Commissioned Report,* CR/04/015N.

JONES, P A. 1981. National Coal Board Exploration in Leicestershire. *Transactions of the Leicester Literary and Philosophical Society,* Vol. 75, 34–40.

JONES, R C B, and LLOYD, W. 1942. The stratigraphy of the Millstone Grit of Flintshire. *Journal of the Manchester Geological Association,* Vol. 1, 247–262.

JONES, R C B, TONKS, L H, and WRIGHT, W B. 1938. Wigan district; explanation of Sheet 84 (England and Wales). *Memoir of the Geological Survey of Great Britain.*

JONES, T A. 1921. A contribution to the microscopic study of the Carboniferous Limestone of north Wales. *Proceedings of the Liverpool Geological Association,* Vol. 13, 78–99.

JUKES, J BEETE. 1859. South Staffordshire coalfield. Second edition. *Coalfield memoir of the Geological Survey of England and Wales.*

KEAREY, P. 1991. A possible basaltic deep source of the south-central England magnetic anomaly. *Journal of the Geological Society of London,* Vol. 148, 775–780.

KENT, P E. 1954. Oil occurrences in coal Measures in England. *Bulletin of the American Association of Petroleum Geologists,* Vol. 38, 8, 1699–1713.

KENT, P E. 1966. Structure of the concealed Carboniferous rocks of north-eastern England. *Proceedings of the Yorkshire Geological Society,* Vol. 35, 3, 323–352.

KENT, P E. 1974. Structural history. 13–28 in The geology and mineral resources of Yorkshire. RAYNER, D H, and HEMINGWAY, J E (editors). *Yorkshire Geological Society, Occasional Publications,* No. 2.

KEPPIE, J D. 1985. The Appalachian collage. 1217–1226 in *The Caledonide orogen: Scandinavia and related areas.* GEE, D G, STURT, B A (editors). (New York: John Wiley and Sons.)

KING, W W. 1921. The plexography of south Staffordshire in Avonian times. *Transactions of the Institution of Mining Engineers,* Vol. 61, 151–168.

KIRBY, G A, AITKENHEAD, N A, BAILY, H E, CHADWICK, R A, EVANS, D J, HOLLIDAY, D W H, HOLLOWAY, S, HULBERT, A G, and SMITH, N J P. 2000. The structure and evolution of the Craven Basin and adjacent areas. *Subsurface Memoir of the British Geological Survey.*

KIRTON, S R. 1984. Carboniferous volcanicity in England with special reference to the Westphalian of the East and West Midlands. *Journal of the Geological Society of London*, Vol. 141, 161–170.

KNOWLES, B. 1964. The radioactive content of the Coal Measures sediments in the Yorkshire–Derbyshire Coalfield. *Proceedings of the Yorkshire Geological Society*, Vol. 34, 413–450.

KOKELAAR, B P, HOWELLS, M F, BEVINS, R E, ROACH, R A, and DUNKLEY, P N. 1984. The Ordovician marginal basin of Wales. 245–270 in Volcanic and associated sedimentary and tectonic processes in modern and ancient marginal basins. KOKELAAR, B P, and HOWELLS, M F (editors). *Geological Society of London, Special Publication*, No. 16.

LACEY, W S. 1952a. Correlation of the Lower Brown Limestone of north Wales with part of the Lower Carboniferous succession in Scotland and northern England. Report of the 18th International Geological Congress Great Britain (1948), 10, 18-25.

LACEY, W S. 1952b. Additions to the Lower Carboniferous flora of north Wales. *C R III Int. Congr. Strat. Carbonif.* (Heerlen 1951), 2, 373–377.

LACEY, W S. 1962. Welsh Lower Carboniferous plants: the flora of the Lower Brown Limestone in the Vale of Clwyd, north Wales. *Palaeontographica*, Bd 111, 126–158.

LAPWORTH, C. 1879. On the tripartite classification of the Lower Palaeozoic rocks. *Geological Magazine*, Vol. 9, 563–569.

LEE, A G. 1988. Carboniferous basin configuration of central and northern England modelled using gravity data. 69–84 in *Sedimentation in a synorogenic basin complex: the Upper Carboniferous of northwest Europe*. BESLY, B M, and KELLING, G (editors). (London and Glasgow: Blackie.)

LEE, M K, PHARAOH, T C, and SOPER, N J. 1990. Structural trends in central Britain from images of gravity and aeromagnetic fields. *Journal of the Geological Society, London*, Vol. 147, 241–258.

LEEDER, M R. 1982. Upper Palaeozoic basins of the British Isles — Caledonide inheritance versus Hercynian plate margin processes. *Journal of the Geological Society of London*, Vol. 139, 479–491.

LEEDER, M R. 1987. Tectonic and palaeogeographic modles for Lower Carboniferous Europe. 1–20 in *European Dinantian environments*. MILLER, J M, ADAMS, A E, and WRIGHT, V P (editors). (Chichester: Wiley.)

LEEDER, M R. 1988. Recent developments in Carboniferous geology: a critical review with implications for the British Isles and NW Europe. *Proceedings Geologists' Association*, Vol. 99, 73–100.

LEEDER, M R, and HARDMAN, M. 1990. Carboniferous geology of the southern North Sea Basin and controls on hydrocarbon prospectivity. 87–105 in Tectonic events responsible for Britain's oil and gas reserves. HARDMAN, R F P, and BROOKS, J (editors). *Geological Society of London, Special Publication*, No. 55.

LEGGETT, J K, MCKERROW, W S, and EALES, M H. 1979. Southern Uplands of Scotland, a lower Palaeozoic accretionary prism. *Journal of the Geological Society of London*, Vol. 136, 755–770.

LEWIS, C L E, GREEN, P F, CARTER, A, and HURFORD, A J. 1992. Elevated K/T palaeotemperatures throughout northwest England: three kilometers of Tertiary erosion? *Earth and Planetary Science Letters*, Vol. 112, 131–145.

LLEWELLYN, P G, and STABBINS, R. 1968. Demonstration: core material from the Anhydrite Series, Carboniferous Limestone, Hathern Borehole, Leicestershire. *Proceedings of the Geological Society of London*, Vol. 1650, 171–186.

LLEWELLYN, P G, and STABBINS, R. 1970. The Anhydrite Series, Lower Carboniferous, Leicestershire, England. *Transactions of the Institute of Mining and Metallurgy*, Vol. 79b, B1–15.

LYNAS, B D T. 1988. Evidence for dextral oblique-slip faulting in the Shelve Ordovician inlier, Welsh Borderland: implications for the south British Caledonides. *Geological Journal*, Vol. 23, 39–57.

MACNIOCAILL, C, VAN DER PLUIJM, B A, and VAN DER VOO, R. 1997. Ordovician palaeogeography and the evolution of the Iapetus Ocean. *Geology*, Vol. 25, 159–162.

MACDONALD, R, GASS, K N, THORPE, R S, and GASS, I G. 1984. Geochemistry and pertogenesis of the Derbyshire Carboniferous basalts. *Journal of the Geological Society of London*, Vol. 141, 147–159.

MAGRAW, D, and RAMSBOTTOM, W H C. 1956. A deep borehole for oil at Croxteth Park, near Liverpool. *Liverpool and Manchester Geological Journal*, Vol. 1, 512–535.

MAGUIRE, P K H. 1987. Charm II: a deep reflection profile within the central England microcraton. *Journal of the Geological Society of London*, Vol. 144, 661–670

MARTINSEN, O J. 1993. Namurian (late Carboniferous) depositional systems of the Craven–Askrigg area, northern England: implications for sequence stratigraphic models. 247–281 in Stratigraphy and facies associations in a sequence stratigraphic framework. POSAMENTIER, H W, SUMMERHAYES, C P, HAQ, B U, and ALLEN, G P (editors). *International Association of Sedimentologists, Special Publication*, No. 18.

MARTINSEN, O J, COLLINSON, J D, and HOLDSWORTH, B K. 1995. Millstone Grit cyclicity revisited, II: sequence stratigraphy and sedimentary responses to changes of relative sea-level. *Special Publications of the International Association of Sedimentologists*, No. 22, 305–327.

MASON, C. 1747. A letter concerning Spelter, melting iron with pit-coal and a burning well at Broseley. *Philisophical Transactions of the Royal Society*, Vol. 44/II, 370–373.

MAYHEW, R W. 1967. The Ashover and Chatsworth Grits in north-east Derbyshire. 94–103 in *Geological excursions in the Sheffield region*. NEVES, R, and DOWNIE, C (editors). (Sheffield: J W Northend.)

MAYNARD, J R. 1992. Sequence stratigraphy of the Upper Yeadonian of northern England. *Marine and Petroleum Geology*, Vol. 9, 197–207.

MAYNARD, J R, and LEEDER, M R. 1992. On the periodicity and magnitude of Late Carboniferous glacio-eustatic sea level changes. *Journal of the Geological Society of London*, Vol. 149, 303–311.

MCCABE, P J. 1977. Deep distributary channels and giant bedforms in the Upper Carboniferous of the Central Pennines, northern England. *Sedimentology*, Vol. 24, 271–290.

MCCABE, P J. 1978. The Kinderscoutian delta (Carboniferous) of northern England: a slope influenced by density currents. 116–126 in *Sedimentation in submarine canyons, fans and trenches*. STANLEY, D J, and KELLING, G (editors). (Stroudsburg: P A Dowden, Hutchinson and Ross.)

MCKERROW, W S. 1988. Wenlock to Givetian deformation in the British Isles and the Canadian Appalachians. 437–448 in The Caledonian–Appalachian orogen. HARRIS, A L, and FETTES, D J (editors). *Geological Society of London, Special Publication*, Vol. 38.

McKerrow, W S, MacNiocaill, C, and Dewey, J F. 2000. The Caledonian orogeny redefined. *Journal of the Geological Society of London*, Vol. 157, 1149–1154.

Merriman, R J, Pharaoh, T C, Woodcock, N H, and Daly, P. 1993. The metamorphic history of the concealed Caledonides of eastern England and their foreland. *Geological Magazine*, Vol. 130, 613–620.

Mikkelsen, P W, and Floodpage, J B. 1997. The hydrocarbon potential of the Cheshire Basin. 161–183 in Petroleum geology of the Irish Sea and adjacent areas. Meadows, N S, Trueblood, S P, Hardman, M, and Cowan, G (editors). *Geological Society of London, Special Publication*, No. 124.

Miller, J, and Grayson, R F. 1982. The regional context of Waulsortian facies in northern England. 17–33 in *Symposium on the palaeoenvironmental setting and distribution of the Waulsortian facies*. Bolton, K, Lane, H R, and Lemone, D U (editors). (El Paso: The El Paso Geological Society and the University of Texas.)

Mitchell, G H. 1942. Geology of the Warwickshire coalfield. *Geological Survey Great Britain, war time pamphlet*, No. 25.

Mitchell, G H, and Stubblefield, C J. 1941. The Carboniferous Limestone of Breedon Cloud, Leicestershire, and the associated inliers. *Geological Magazine*, Vol. 78, 201–219.

Mitchell, G H, and Stubblefield, C J. 1945. The geology of the northern part of the South Staffordshire coalfields (Cannock Chase region). *Geological Survey Great Britain, war time pamphlet*, No. 43, 1–47.

Mitchell, G H, Pocock, R W, and Taylor, J H. 1961. Geology of the country around Droitwich, Abberley and Kidderminster. *Memoir of the Geological Survey of Great Britain*, Sheet 182 (England and Wales).

Molyneux, S G. 1987a. Acritarchs from the Barnt Green Volcanic beds. British Geological Survey, Unpublished *Palaeontological Report*, PD/87/425.

Molyneux, S G. 1987b. Microfossils from the Lickey Quartzites. British Geological Survey, Unpublished. *Palaeontological Report*, PD87/382.

Morris, P G. 1969. Dinantian and Namurian stratigraphy, east and south-east of Leek, North Staffordshire. *Proceedings of the Geologists' Association*, Vol. 80, 145–175.

Morton, G H. 1870. The Mountain Limestone of Flintshire and part of Denbighshire. *Geological Magazine*, Vol. 7, 526–527.

Morton, G H. 1878. The Carboniferous Limestone and Millstone Grit of North Wales. *Proceedings of the Liverpool Geological Society*, Vol. 3, 152–205, 299–325, 371–431.

Morton, G H. 1886. The Carboniferous Limestone and Cefn-y-Fedw Sandstone of Flintshire. *Proceedings of the Liverpool Geological Society*, Vol. 4, 297–320, 381–403.

Morton, G H. 1898. The Carboniferous limestone of the Vale of Clwyd. *Proceedings of the Liverpool Geological Association*, Vol. 8, 181–204.

Moseley, F. 1978. Geology of the English Lake District: an introductory review. 1–16 in Geology of the Lake District. Moseley, F (editor). *Yorkshire Geological Society Occasional Publication*, No. 3.

Moseley, J B, and Ford, T D. 1985. A stratigraphic revision of the Late Precambrian rocks of the Charnwood Forest, Leicestershire. *Mercian Geologist*, Vol. 10, 1–18.

Murchison, R I. 1835. On the Silurian System of Rocks. *London and Edinburgh Philosophical Magazine*, Vol. 7, 46–52.

Murchison, R I. 1839. *Silurian system.* (London: John Murray.)

Murchison, R I. 1854. *Siluria: a history of the oldest known rocks containing organic remains, with a brief sketch of the distribution of gold over the earth.* (London: Murray.)

Musset, A E, Dagley, P, and Skelhorn, R R. 1988. Time and duration of activity in the British Tertiary Igneous Province. 337–348 in Early Tertiary volcanism and the opening of the north-east Atlantic. Morton, A C, and Parson, L M (editors). *Geological Society of London, Special Publication*, No. 39.

Nance, R D, and Murphy, J B. 1996. Basement isotopic signatures and Neoproterozoic palaeogeography of Avalonian Cadomian and related terranes in the circum-North Atlantic. 333–346 in Avalonian and related peri-Gondwanan terranes of the circum-north Atlantic. Nance, R D, and Thompson, M D (editors). *Geological Society of America Special Paper*, No. 304.

Neaverson, E. 1929. Faunal horizons in the Carboniferous Limestone of the Vale of Clwyd. *Proceedings of the Liverpool Geological Society*, Vol. 15, 111–133.

Neaverson, E. 1945. Carboniferous rocks between Abergele and Denbigh. *Proceedings of the Liverpool Geological Society*, Vol. 19, 52–68.

Neaverson, E. 1946. Carboniferous Limestone Series of north Wales: conditions of deposition and interpretation of its history. *Proceedings of the Liverpool Geological Society*, Vol. 19, 113–144.

Noble, S R, Tucker, R D, and Pharaoh, T C. 1993. Lower Palaeozoic and Precambrian igneous rocks from eastern England, and their bearing on late Ordovician closure of the Tornquist Sea: constraints from U-Pb and Nd isotopes. *Geological Magazine*, Vol. 130, 738–747.

Okolo, S A. 1983. Fluvial distributary channels in the Fletcher Bank Grit (Namurian R$_2$b) at Ramsbottom, Lancashire, England. 421–433 in Modern and ancient fluvial systems. Collinson, J D, and Lewin, J (editors). *International Association of Sedimentologists*, Special Publication, No. 6.

Old, R A, Bridge, D C M, and Rees, J G. 1989. Geology of the Coventry area. *British Geological Survey, Onshore Geology Series, Technical Report Series*, WA/89/29.

Old, R A, Hamblin, R J O, Ambrose, K, and Warrington, G. 1991. Geology of the country around Redditch. *Memoir of the Geological Survey*, Sheet 183 (England and Wales).

Parkinson, D. 1950. The stratigraphy of the Dovedale area, Derbyshire and Staffordshire. *Quarterly Journal of the Geological Society of London*, Vol. 105, 265–294.

Parsons, L M. 1922. Dolomitisation in the Carboniferous Limestone of the Midlands. *Geological Magazine*, Vol. 59, 51–63 and 104–117.

Patchett, P J, Gale, N H, Goodwin, R, and Humm, M J. 1980. Rb-Sr whole-rock isochron ages of late Precambrian to Cambrian igneous rocks from southern Britain. *Journal of the Geological Society of London*, Vol. 137, 649–656.

Pauley, J C. 1990a. The Longmyndian Supergroup and related Precambrian sediments of England and Wales. 5–27 in *Avalonian and Cadomian geology of the North Atlantic*. Strachan, R A, and Taylor, G K (editors). (London and Glasgow: Blackie.)

Pauley, J C. 1990b. Sedimentology, structural evolution and tectonic setting of the late Precambrian Longmyndian Supergroup of the Welsh Borderland, UK. *Geological Society of London Special Publication*, No. 51, 341–351.

Pharaoh, T C. 1999. Palaeozoic terranes and their lithosperic boundaries within the Trans-European suture zone (2002): a review *Technophysics*, 314, 17–41.

PHARAOH, T C, and CARNEY, J. 2000. Chapter 1: Introduction to the Precambrian rocks of England and Wales. 1–15 in *Precambrian rocks of England and Wales.* Geological Conservation Review Series, No 20. (Peterborough: Joint Nature Conservation Committee.)

PHARAOH, T C, and GIBBONS, W. 1994. Chapter 10: Precambrian rocks in England and Wales south of the Menai Strait Fault System. 85–97 in *A revised correlation of Precambrian rocks in the British Isles.* GIBBONS, W, HARRIS, A L (editors). (London: Geological Society of London.)

PHARAOH, T C, MERRIMAN, R J, WEBB, P C, and BECKINSALE, R D. 1987a. The concealed Caledonides of eastern England: preliminary results of a multidisciplinary study. *Proceedings of the Yorkshire Geological Society,* Vol. 46, 355–369.

PHARAOH, T C, WEBB, P, THORPE, R S, and BECKINSALE, R D. 1987b. Geochemical evidence for the tectonic setting of late Proterozoic volcanic suites in the central UK. 541–552 in Geochemistry and mineralisation of Proterozoic volcanic suites. PHARAOH, T C, BECKINSALE, R D, RICKARD, D T (editors). *Geological Society of London, Special Publication,* No. 33.

PHARAOH, T C, MERRIMAN, R J, EVANS, J A, BREWER, T S, WEBB, P C, and SMITH, N J P. 1991. Early Palaeozoic arc-related volcanism in the concealed Caledonides of southern Britain. *Annales de la Société Géologique de Belgique,* Vol. 114, 63–91.

PHARAOH, T C, BREWER, T S, and WEBB, P C. 1993. Subduction-related magmatism of late Ordovician age in eastern England. *Geological Magazine,* Vol. 130, 647–656.

PHARAOH, T C, ENGLAND, R, and LEE, M K. 1995. The concealed Caledonide basement of eastern England and the southern North Sea — a review. 330–346 in The Trans-European Suture Zone: EUROPROBE in Liblice 1993. GEE, D G, BECKHOLMEN, M (editors). *Studia Geophysica et Geodaetica,* Vol. 39, 330–346.

PIDGEON, R T, and AFTALION, M. 1978. Cogenetic and inherited zircon U-Pb systems in Palaeozoic granites from Scotland and England. 183–220 in Crustal evolution in northwest Britain and adjacent regions. BOWES, D R, and LEAKE, B E (editors). *Geological Journal Special Issue,* No. 10.

PLANT, J A, and JONES, D G. 1989. *Metallogenic models and exploration criteria for buried carbonate-hosted ore deposits — a multidisciplinary study in eastern England.* (Keyworth, Nottingham: British Geological Survey and the Institution of Mining and Metallurgy.)

PLANT, J A, JONES, D G, and HASLAM, H W (editors). 1999. *The Cheshire Basin. Basin evolution, fluid movement and mineral resources in a Permo-Triassic rift setting.* (Keyworth, Nottingham: British Geological Survey.)

PLOT, R. 1686. The natural history of Staffordshire.

POCOCK, R W, and WHITEHEAD, T H. 1948. *British regional geology: the Welsh Borderland.* Second edition. (London: HMSO.)

POCOCK, R W, WHITEHEAD, T H, WEDD, C B, and ROBERTSON, T. 1938. Shrewsbury district including the Hanwood Coalfield. *Memoir of the Geological Survey of Great Britain,* Sheet 152 (England and Wales).

POOLE, E G, and WHITEMAN, A J. 1966. Geology of the country around Nantwich and Whitchurch. *Memoir of the British Geological Survey,* Sheet 122 (England and Wales).

POWELL, D W. 1956. Gravity and magnetic anomalies in North Wales. *Quarterly Journal of the Geological Society of London,* Vol. 111, 375–397.

POWELL, J H, CHISHOLM, J I, BRIDGE, D C M, GLOVER, B W, and BESLY, B. 2000. Stratigraphical framework for Westphalian to early Permian red-bed successions of the Pennine Basin. *British Geological Survey Research Report,* RR/00/01.

POWELL, J H, GLOVER, B W, and WATERS, C N. 1992. A geological background for planning and development in the 'Black Country'. *British Geological Survey, Onshore Geology Series, Technical Report,* WA/92/33.

POWELL, J H, GLOVER, B W, and WATERS, C N. 2000. Geology of the country around Birmingham. *Memoir of the Geological Survey of Great Britain,* Sheet 168 (England and Wales).

PRENTICE, J E. 1951. Carboniferous Limestone of the Manifold valley region, north Staffordshire. *Quarterly Journal of the Geological Society of London,* Vol. 106, 171–209.

PRENTICE, J E. 1952. Note on previous paper (Prentice, 1951). *Quarterly Journal of the Geological Society of London,* Vol. 107, 335.

PRIGMORE, J K, BUTLER, A J, and WOODCOCK, N H. 1997. Rifting during separation of Eastern Avalonia from Gondwana: evidence from subsidence analysis. *Geology,* Vol. 25, 3, 203–206.

PUGH, W. 1960. Triassic salt: discoveries in the Cheshire-Shropshire Basin. *Nature, London,* Vol. 187, 278–279.

RAMSAY, A C. 1881. Geology of north Wales. Second edition. *Memoir of the Geological Survey of Great Britain,* Vol. 3.

RAMSBOTTOM, W H C. 1969. The Namurian of Britain. *Compte Rendu 6e Congrès International de Stratigraphie et de Géologie du Carbonifère, Sheffield,* 1967, Vol. 1, 219–232.

RAMSBOTTOM, W H C. 1973. Transgressions and regressions in the Dinantian: A new synthesis of British Dinantian stratigraphy. *Proceedings of the Yorkshire Geological Society,* Vol. 39, 567–607.

RAMSBOTTOM, W H C. 1974. The Namurian of north Wales. 161–167 in *The Upper Palaeozoic and post-Palaeozoic rocks of Wales.* OWEN, T R (editor). (Cardiff: University of Wales Press.)

RAMSBOTTOM, W H C. 1977. Major cycles of transgression and regression (mesothems) in the Namurian. *Proceedings of the Yorkshire Geological Society,* Vol. 41, 261–291.

RAMSBOTTOM, W H C, RHYS, G H, and SMITH, E G. 1962. Boreholes in the Carboniferous rocks of the Ashover district, Derbyshire. *Bulletin of the Geological Survey, Great Britain,* Vol. 19, 75–168.

RAMSBOTTOM, W H C, CALVER, M A, EAGAR, R M C, HODSON, F, HOLLIDAY, D W, STUBBLEFIELD, C J, and WILSON, R B. 1978. A correlation of Silesian rocks in the British Isles. *Geological Society of London, Special Report,* No. 10.

RAWSON, P F, and RILEY, L A. 1982. Latest Jurassic–early Cretaceous events and the 'Late-Cimmerian unconformity' in the North Sea area. *Bulletin of the American Association of Petroleum Geologists,* Vol. 66/12, 2628–2648.

READ, W A. 1988. Controls on Silesian sedimentation in the Midland Valley of Scotland. 222–241 in *Sedimentation in a synorogenic basin complex: the Upper Carboniferous of northwest Europe.* BESLY, B M, and KELLING, G (editors). (Glasgow and London: Blackie.)

READ, W A. 1991. The Millstone Grit (Namurian) of the southern Pennines viewed in the light of eustatically controlled sequence stratigraphy. *Geological Journal,* Vol. 27, 173–180.

READING, H G. 1964. A review of the factors affecting the sedimentation of the Millstone Grit (Namurian) in the Central Pennines. 340–346 in Deltaic and shallow marine deposits. VAN STRAATEN, L M J V (editor). *Developments in Sedimentology,* Vol. 1. (Amsterdam and London: Elsevier.)

REDWOOD, B. 1922. Treatise on petroleum. (London: Charles Griffin and Co. Ltd.)

REES, J G, and WILSON, A A. 1998. Geology of the country around Stoke-on-Trent. *British Geological Survey Memoir*, Sheet 123 (England and Wales).

REES, J G, CORNWELL, J D, DABEK, Z K, and MERRIMAN, R J. 1996. The Apedale tuffs, North Staffordshire: probable remnants of a late Asbian/Brigantian (P1a) volcanic centre. 345–357 *in* Recent advances in Lower Carboniferous geology. STROGEN, P, SOMERVILLE, I D, and JONES, G L (editors). *Geological Society of London, Special Publication*, No. 107.

RILEY, N J. 1986. Dinantian calcareous microbiotas from BGS Rotherwood Borehole, SK 34580 15587 (SK31NW/260), 1" 155. *BGS Technical Report Series*, PD 86/184

RILEY, N J. 1988. Ammonoid biostratigraphy of Core 1, Shell, Blacon East 1Bh, SJ 379 668, near Chester, Sheet 109. *British Geological Survey Technical Report*, WH/88/206c.

RILEY, N J. 1990. Stratigraphy of the Worston Shale Group (Dinantian), Craven Basin, north-west England. *Proceedings of the Yorkshire Geological Society*, Vol. 48, 163–187.

RILEY, N J. 1997. Foraminiferal biostratigraphy of the Carboniferous interval in Fina Long Eaton 1 Borehole. *British Geological Survey Technical Report*, WH/97/46C.

RIPPON, J H. 1984. The Clowne Seam Marine Band and overlying sediments in the Westphalian B of north Derbyshire. *Proceedings of the Yorkshire Geological Society*, Vol. 45, 27–43.

RIPPON, J H. 1996. Sand body orientation, palaeoslope analysis and basin-fill implications in the Westphalian A-C of Great Britain. *Journal of the Geological Society of London*, Vol. 153, 881–900.

ROBINSON, N, and GRAYSON, R. 1990. Natural methane see pages in the Lancashire Coalfield. *Land and Minerals Surveying*, Vol. 8, 333–340.

ROLLIN, K E, KIRBY, G A, ROWLEY, W J, and BUCKLEY, D K. 1995. Atlas of geothermal resources in Europe: UK Revision. *British Geological Survey Technical Report*, WK/95/07.

SADLER, H E, and WYATT, R J. 1966. A lower Carboniferous S₂ inlier near Hartington, Derbyshire. *Proceedings of the Geologists' Association*, Vol. 77, 55–64.

SCHOFIELD, K, and ADAMS, A E. 1985. Stratigraphy and depositional environments of the Woo Dale Limestones Formation (Dinantian), Derbyshire. *Proceedings of the Yorkshire Geological Society*, Vol. 45, 225–233.

SCOTESE, C R, and MCKERROW, W S. 1990. Revised world maps and introduction. 1–21 in Palaeozoic palaeogeography and biogeography. MCKERROW, W S, and SCOTESE C R (editors). *Geological Society of London, Memoir*, No. 12.

SCOTESE, C R, BAMBACH, R K, BARTON, C, VAN DER VOO, R, and ZIEGLER, A M. 1979. Palaeozoic basemaps. *Journal of Geology*, Vol. 87, 217–277.

SCOTT, M. 1861. On the 'Symon Fault' in the Coalbrookdale coalfield. *Quarterly Journal of the Geological Society of London*, Vol. 17, 457–467.

SELLWOOD, E B, and THOMAS J M. 1986. Variscan facies and structure in central south-west England. *Journal of the Geological Society of London*, Vol. 143, 99–207.

SHACKLETON, J S. 1962. Cross strata from the Rough Rock (Millstone Grit Series) in the Pennines. *Geological Journal*, Vol. 3, 109–118.

SHERLOCK, R L. 1921. Rock salt and brine. *Memoir of the British Geological Survey Special Reports on the mineral resources of Great Britain*, No. 18.

SHERLOCK, R L, and HOLLINGWORTH, S E. 1938. Volume III: Gypsum and anhydrite and celstine and strontianite. Third edition. *Memoir of the British Geological Survey Special Reports on the mineral resources of Great Britain.*

SHIRLEY, J. 1959. The Carboniferous Limestone of the Moneyash–Wirksworth area, Derbyshire. *Quarterly Journal of the Geological Society of London*, Vol. 114, 411–429.

SHOTTON, F W. 1927. The conglomerates of the Enville Series of the Warwickshire Coalfield. *Quarterly Journal of the Geological Society of London*, Vol. 83, 604–621.

SIBLEY, T F. 1908. The faunal succession in the Carboniferous Limestone (Upper Avonian) of the Midland area (north Derbyshire and north Staffordshire). *Quarterly Journal of the Geological Society of London*, Vol. 64, 34–82.

SMITH, AG, HURLEY, A M, and BRIDEN, J C. 1981. Phanerozoic palaeocontinental world maps. (Cambridge: Cambridge University Press.)

SMITH, B. 1921. Lead and zinc ores in the Carboniferous rocks of north Wales. *Special Reports on the Mineral Resources of Great Britain*, No. 19.

SMITH, B, and GEORGE, T N. 1961. *British regional geology: north Wales.* (London: HMSO.)

SMITH, E G, RHYS, G H, and EDEN, R A. 1967. Geology of the country around Chesterfield, Matlock and Mansfield. *Memoir of the British Geological Survey*, Sheet 112 (England and Wales).

SMITH, K, CRIPPS, A, and EVANS, C J. 1984. *Geothermal potential of Carboniferous rocks in the western Pennines — eastern Cheshire Basin region of north-west England.* Investigation of the geothermal potential of the UK. (Keyworth, Nottingham: British Geological Survey.)

SMITH, K, SMITH, N J P, and HOLLIDAY, D W. 1985. The deep structure of Derbyshire. *Geological Journal*, Vol. 20, 215–225.

SMITH, N J P (compiler). 1985. Map 1: Pre-Permian geology of the United Kingdom (South). 1:100 000: two maps commemorating the 150th anniversary of the British Geological Survey. (Surrey: Cook Hammond and Kell.)

SMITH, N J P. 1987. The deep geology of central England: prospectivity of the Palaeozoic rocks. 217–224 in Petroleum geology of north-west Europe. BROOKS, J, and GLENNIE, K W (editors). (London: Graham and Trotman.)

SMITH, N J P, and RUSHTON, A W A. 1993. Cambrian and Ordovician stratigraphy related to structure and seismic profiles in the western part of the English Midlands. *Geological Magazine*, Vol. 130, 665–671.

SMITH, N T. 1999. Variscan inversion within the Cheshire Basin, England: Carboniferous evolution north of the Variscan Front. *Tectonophysics*, Vol. 309, 211–225.

SMITH, S. F. 1982. The Parkside Colliery Methane Gas Disposal project. *The Mining Engineer*, May 1982, 663–665.

SOMERVILLE, I D, and STRANK, A R E. 1984a. Faunal discoveries from Viséan limestones of North Wales. *Proceedings Geologists' Association*, Vol. 95, 394–395.

SOMERVILLE, I D, and STRANK, A R E. 1984b. Discovery of Arundian and Holkerian faunas from a Dinantian platform succession in north Wales. *Geological Journal*, Vol. 19, 85–104.

SOMERVILLE, I D, MITCHELL, M, and STRANK, A R E. 1986. An Arundian fauna from the Dyserth area, North Wales and its correlation within the British Isles. *Proceedings of the Yorkshire Geological Society*, 46, 57–75.

SOMERVILLE, I D, STRANK, A R E, and WELSH, A. 1989. Chadian faunas and flora from Dyserth: depositional environments and palaeogeographic setting of Viséan strata in north-east Wales. *Geological Journal*, Vol. 24, 49–66.

SOPER, N J, and HUTTON, D W H. 1984. Late Caledonian sinistral displacements in Britain: implications for a three plate collision model. *Tectonics*, Vol. 3, 781–794.

SOPER, N J, WEBB, B C, and WOODCOCK, N J. 1987. Late Caledonian (Acadian) transpression in north-west England: timings, geometry and geotectonic significance. *Proceedings of the Yorkshire Geological Society*, Vol. 46, 175–192.

SORBY, H C. 1859. On the structure and origin of the Millstone Grit in south Yorkshire. *Proceedings of the Yorkshire Geological and Polytechnic Society*, Vol. 3, 669–675.

SOWERBUTTS, W T C. 1987. Magnetic mapping of the Butterton Dyke: an example of detailed geophysical surveying. *Journal of the Geological Society of London*, Vol. 144, 29–33.

SOWERBUTTS, W T C. 1988. Discussion on the magnetic mapping of the Butterton Dyke: an example of detailed geophysical surveying. *Journal of the Geological Society of London*, Vol. 145, 181–184.

SPEARS, D A. 1964. Radioactivity of the Mansfield Marine Band, Yorkshire. *Geochimica Cosmochemica. Acta*, Vol. 28, 673–681.

SPINK, K. 1965. Coalfield geology of Leicestershire and South Derbyshire: the exposed coalfield. *Transactions of the Leicester Literary and Philosophical Society*, Vol. 59, 41–98.

STEVENSON, I P, and GAUNT, G D. 1971. Geology of the country around Chapel en le Frith. *Memoir of the British Geological Survey*, Sheet 99 (England and Wales).

STONEHOUSE, T H. 1951. Recent provings of concealed extensions of the coalfields of Shropshire and south Staffordshire. *Transactions of the Institution of Mining Engineers*, Vol. 110, 289–300.

STRAHAN, A. 1885. Geology of the coasts adjoining Rhyl, Abergele and Colwyn, with notes by R H Tiddeman. *Memoir of the Geological Survey of Great Britain*, Quarter-sheet 79NW (England and Wales).

STRAHAN, A. 1890. The geology of the neighbourhoods of Flint, Mold and Ruthin. *Memoirs of the Geological Survey of Great Britain*.

STRAHAN, A. 1920. Mineral oil, Kimmeridge oil-shale, lignites, jets, cannel coals and natural gas. Second edition. *Memoir of the Geological Survey, Special Report on Mineral Resources of Great Britain*, Vol. 7.

STRAHAN, A, and WALKER, A O. 1879. Occurrence of pebbles with Upper Ludlow fossils in the Lower Carboniferous conglomerates of north Wales. *Quarterly Journal of the Geological Society of London*, Vol. 35, 268–274.

STRANK, A R E. 1985. Dinantian biostratigraphy of a deep borehole near Eyam. *Geological Journal*, Vol. 20, 227–237.

STRANK, A R E. 1986. Foraminiferal biostratigraphy of the Woo Dale Borehole, Derbyshire and the age of the Dinantian-basement unconformity. *Journal of Micropalaeontology*, Vol. 5, 1–4.

STRANK, A R E. 1987. Stratigraphy and structure of Dinantian strata in the East Midlands. 157–175 in *European Dinantian environments*. MILLER, J, ADAMS, A E, and WRIGHT, V P (editors). (London, New York, Chichester: John Wiley and Sons Ltd.)

STUBBLEFIELD, C J, and TROTTER, F M. 1957. Divisions of the Coal Measures on Geological Survey maps in England and Wales. *Bulletin Geological Survey Great Britain*, No.13, 1–5.

SUMBLER, M G. 1985a. Geological notes and local details for 1:10 000 sheets: SP37NE (south-east Coventry). *British Geological Survey, Onshore Geology Series*, WA/DM/84/36.

SUMBLER, M G. 1985b. Geological notes and local details for 1:10 000 sheets: SP37SE (Bubbenhall). *British Geological Survey, Onshore Geology Series*, WA/DM/84/37.

TAPPIN, D R, CHADWICK, R A, JACKSON, A A, WINGFIELD, R T R, and SMITH, N J P. 1994. *The geology of Cardigan Bay and the Bristol Channel. UK Offshore Regional Report*. (London: HMSO for British Geological Survey.)

TAYLOR, B J, BURGESS, I C, LAND, D H, MILLS, D A C, SMITH, D B, and WARREN, P T. 1971. *British regional geology: northern England*. Fourth edition. (London: HMSO.)

TAYLOR, K, and RUSHTON, A W A. 1971. The pre-Westphalian geology of the Warwickshire Coalfield. *Bulletin of the Geological Survey of Great Britain*, No. 35.

THORPE, R S, BECKINSALE, R D, PATCHETT, P J, PIPER, A , DAVIES, G R, and EVANS, J A. 1984. Crustal growth and late Precambrian– early Palaeozoic plate tectonic evolution of England and Wales. *Quarterly Journal of the Geological Society of London*, Vol. 141, 521–536.

THORPE, R S, GASKARTH, J W, and HENNEY, P. 1993. Tectonic setting of Caledonian minor intrusions of the English Midlands. *Geological Magazine*, Vol. 130, 657–663.

TOGHILL, P. 1992. The Shelveian event, a late Ordovician tectonic episode in Southern Britain (Eastern Avalonia). *Proceedings of the Geologists' Association*, Vol. 103, 31–35.

TORSVIK, T H. 1998. Palaeozoic palaeogeography: a north Atlantic viewpoint. *Geologiska Föreningens i Stockholm Förhendlinger*, Vol. 120, 109–118.

TORSVIK, T H, and TRENCH, A. 1991. The Ordovician history of the Iapetus Ocean in Britain: new palaeomagnetic constraints. *Journal of the Geological Society of London*, Vol. 148, 423–425.

TRENCH, A, and TORSVIK, T H. 1992. Palaeomagnetic constraints on the Early-Middle Ordovician palaeogeography of Europe: recent advances. 255–259 in *Global perspectives on Ordovician geology*. 6. (Rotterdam–Brookfield, Netherlands: A A Balkema.)

TRENCH, A, TORSVIK, T H, and McKERROW, W S. 1992. The palaeogeographic evolution of southern Britain during Early Paleozoic times: a reconcilliation of palaeomagnetic and biographic evidence. *Tectonophysics*, Vol. 201, 75–83.

TREWIN, N H. 1968. Potassium bentonites in the Namurian of Staffordshire and Derbyshire. *Proceedings of the Yorkshire Geological Society*, Vol. 37, 73–91.

TREWIN, N H, and HOLDSWORTH, B K. 1972. Further K-bentonites from the Namurian of Staffordshire. *Proceedings of the Yorkshire Geological Society*, Vol. 39, 87–89.

TREWIN, N H, and HOLDSWORTH, B K. 1973. Sedimentation in the Lower Namurian rocks of the North Staffordshire Basin. *Proceedings of the Yorkshire Geological Society*, Vol. 39, 3, 371–408.

TROTTER, F M. 1929. The Tertiary uplift and resultant drainage of the Alston Block and adjacent areas. *Proceedings of the Yorkshire Geological Society*, 21. 161–180

TROTTER, F M. 1953a. Exploratory borings in south-west Lancashire. *Bulletin of the Geological Survey*, No. 5, 61–80

TROTTER, F M. 1953b. Reddened beds of Carboniferous age in north-west England and their origin. *Proceedings of the Yorkshire Geological Society*, Vol. 29, 1–20.

TROTTER, F M. 1954. Reddened beds in the Coal Measures of south Lancashire. Bulletin of the Geological Survey of Great Britain, Vol. 5, 61-80.

TRUEMAN, A E. 1946. Stratigraphical problems in the Coal Measures of Europe and north America. *Quarterly Journal of the Geological Society of London*, Vol. 102, 49–86.

TRUEMAN, A E. 1947. Stratigraphical problems in the Coal Measures of Great Britain. *Quarterly Journal of the Geological Society*, Vol. 103, 65–104.

TRUEMAN, A E. 1954. *Coalfields of Great Britain*. (London: Arnold.)

TUCKER, R D, and PHARAOH, T C. 1991. U-Pb zircon ages for Late Precambrian igneous rocks in southern Britain. *Journal of the Geological Society of London*, Vol. 148, 435–443.

TURNER, J S. 1949. The deeper structure of central and northern England. *Proceedings of the Yorkshire Geological Society*, Vol. 27, 280–297.

VAN GROOTEL, G, VERNIERS, J, GEERKENS, B, LADURON, D, VERHAEREN, M, HERTOGEN, J, and DE VOS, W. 1997. Timing of magmatism, foreland basin development, metamorphism and inversion in the Anglo-Brabant fold belt. *Geological Magazine*, Vol. 134, 607–616.

VAN STAAL, C R, DEWEY, J F, MacNIOCAILL, C, and McKERROW, W S. 1998. The Cambrian-Silurian tectonic evolution of the northern Appalachians and British Caledonides: history of a complex, west and south-west Pacific-type segment of Iapetus. 199–242 in: Lyell: the Past is the key to the present. BLUNDELL, D J, and SCOTT, A C (editors). *Geological Society of London Special Publications*, 143, 199–242.

VAUGHAN, A. 1905. The palaeontological sequence in the Carboniferous Limestone of the Bristol area. *Quarterly Journal of the Geological Society of London*, Vol. 61, 181–307.

VEEVERS, J J, and POWELL, C McA. 1987. Late Palaeozoic glaciations in Gondwanaland reflected in transgressive-regressive depositional sequences in Euramerica. *Bulletin of American Geological Society*, Vol. 98, 474–487.

VERMA, Y K. 1981. Studies in virgin strata temperatures with special reference to the NCB's Western Area mines. *The Mining Engineer*, Vol. 141, 655–663.

WALKDEN, G M. 1977. Volcanic and erosive events on an upper Visean carbonate platform, north Derbyshire. *Proceedings of the Yorkshire Geological Society*, Vol. 41, 347–366.

WALKER, R G. 1966. Shale Grit and Grindslow Shales: transition from turbiditic to shallow water sediments in the Upper Carboniferous of northern England. *Journal of Sedimentary Petrology*, Vol. 36, 90–114.

WALKER, W T. 1914. Some observations on the Liassic outcrop near Whitchurch (Shropshire). *Proceedings of the Liverpool Geological Society*, Blundell, D J, and Scott, A C (editors), Vol. 12, 72–87.

WALTERS, S G, and INESON, P R. 1981. A review of the distribution and correlation of igneous rocks in Derbyshire, England. *Mercian Geologist*, Vol. 8, 81–132.

WANLESS, H R, and SHEPARD, F P. 1936. Sea level and climate changes related to Late Palaeozoic cycles. *Bulletin of American Geological Society*, Vol. 47, 1177–1206.

WARREN, P T, PRICE, D, NUTT, M J C, and SMITH, E G. 1984. Geology of the country around Rhyl and Denbigh. *Memoir of the British Geological Survey*, Sheets 95 and 107 and parts of sheets 94 and 106 (England and Wales).

WARRINGTON, G, AUDLEY-CHARLES, M G, ELLIOT, R E, EVANS, W B, IVIMEY-COOK, H C, KENT, P E, ROBINSON, P L, SHOTTON, F W, and TAYLOR, F M. 1980. A correlation of Triassic rocks in the British Isles. *Geological Society of London Special Report*, No. 13.

WATERS, C N, GLOVER, B W, and POWELL, J H. 1994. Structural synthesis of south Staffordshire, UK: implications for the Variscan evolution of the Pennine Basin. *Journal of the Geological Society of London*, Vol. 151, 697–713.

WATSON, W. 1811. A delineation of the strata of Derbyshire: forming the surface from Bolsover in the east to Buxton in the west. (Sheffield: W Todd.)

WEDD, C B, and KING, W B R. 1924. Geology of the country around Flint, Hawarden and Caergwrle. *Memoir of the Geological Survey of Great Britain*, Sheet 108 (England and Wales).

WEDD, C B, SMITH, B, and WILLS, L J. 1928. Geology of the country around Wrexham: Part I. Lower Palaeozoic and Lower Carboniferous Rocks. British Geological Survey Memoir, England and Wales, Sheet 121 (England and Wales).

Wedd, C B, Smith, B, and Wills, L J. 1928. The geology of the country around Wrexham: Part II. Coal Measures and Newer Formations. *Memoir of the Geological Survey of Great Britain*, Sheet 121 (England and Wales).

WEDD, C B, SMITH, B, KING, W B R, and WRAY, D A. 1929. The country around Oswestry. *Memoir of the Geological Survey of Great Britain*, Sheet 137 (England and Wales).

WELSH, A, and OWENS, B. 1983. Early Dinantian miospore assemblages from the Caldon Low borehole, Staffordshire, England. *Pollen Spores*, Vol. 25, 253–264.

WHITEHEAD, T H, and EASTWOOD, T. 1927. Geology of the southern part of the South Staffordshire Coalfield. *Coalfield memoir of the Geological Survey of Great Britain*.

WHITEHEAD, T H, ROBERTSON, T, POCOCK, R W, and DIXON, E E L. 1928. The geology of the country between Wolverhampton and Oakengates. *Memoir of the Geological Survey of Great Britain*, Sheet 153 (England and Wales).

WHITEHURST, J. 1778. *An inquiry into the original state and formation of the Earth*. (Second edition 1786). (London: W Bent.)

WHITTAKER, A, HOLLIDAY, D W, and PENN, I E. 1985. Geophysical logs in British stratigraphy. *Geological Society of London Special Report*, No. 15.

WHITTARD, W F. 1952. A Geology of South Shropshire. *Proceedings of the Geologists' Association*, Vol. 63, 143–197.

WILLIAMS, A, STRACHAN, I, BASSETT, D A, DEAN, W T, INGHAM, J K, WRIGHT, A D, and WHITTINGTON, H B. 1976. A correlation of Ordovician rocks in the British Isles. *Geological Society of London Special Report*, No. 3.

WILLIAMS, G D, and CHAPMAN, T J. 1986. The Bristol–Mendip foreland thrust belt. *Journal of the Geological Society of London*, Vol. 143, 63–73.

WILLS, L J. 1948. *Palaeogeography of the Midlands*. (Liverpool: Liverpool University Press.)

WILLS, L J. 1951. *Palaeogeographical atlas of the British Isles and adjacent parts of Europe*. (Glasgow and London: Blackie and Son Ltd.)

WILLS, L J. 1956. *Concealed coalfields*. (Glasgow and London: Blackie and Son Ltd.)

WILLS, L J. 1973. Palaeogeological map of the Palaeozoic floor below Permian and Mesozoic formations in England and Wales. *Geological Society of London, Memoir*, No. 7.

WILLS, L J. 1978. A palaeogeographic map of the Lower Palaeozoic floor below the cover of Upper Devonian, Carboniferous and later formations. *Geological Society of London, Memoir*, No. 8.

WILSON, C D V. 1959. Geophysical investigations in the Vale of Clwyd. *Liverpool and Manchester Geological Journal*, Vol. 2, 253–270.

WILSON, D, DAVIES, J R, WATERS, R A, and ZALASIEWICZ, J A. 1992. A fault-controlled depositional model for the Aberystwyth Grits turbidite system. *Geological Magazine*, Vol. 129, 595–607.

WOLFENDEN, E B. 1958.   Palaeoecology of the Carboniferous reef complex and shelf limestones in north-west Derbyshire. *Bulletin of American Geological Society*, Vol. 69, 871–898.

WOOD, D S. 1974.   The base and correlation of the Cambrian rocks of north Wales.   47–66 in *The Precambrian and Lower Palaeozoic rocks of Wales*. WOOD, A (editor).   (Cardiff: University of Wales Press.)

WOODCOCK, N H. 1984a.   Early Palaeozoic sedimentation and tectonics in Wales.   *Proceedings of the Geologists' Association of London*, Vol. 95, 323–335.

WOODCOCK, N H. 1984b.   The Pontesford Lineament, Welsh Borderland.   *Journal of the Geological Society of London*, Vol. 141, 1001–1014.

WOODCOCK, N H. 1991.   The Welsh, Anglian and Belgian Caledonides compared.   5–18 in *Proceedings of the International Meeting on the Caledonides of the Midlands and the Brabant Massif*. ANDRE, L, HERBOSCH, A, VANGUESTAINE, M, and VERNIERS, J (editors).   *Annales Soc. Géol. Belg.*, Vol. 114.

WOODCOCK, N H, and GIBBONS, W. 1988.   Is the Welsh Borderland Fault System a terrane boundary?   *Journal of the Geological Society of London*, Vol. 145, 915–933.

WOODCOCK, N H, PHARAOH, T C. 1993.   Silurian facies beneath East Anglia.   *Geological Magazine*, Vol. 130, 681–690.

WOODLAND, A W, and EVANS, W B. 1964.   The geology of the South Wales Coalfield, Part IV, the country around Pontypridd and Maesteg.   *Memoir of the Geological Survey of Great Britain*, Sheet 248 (England and Wales).

WORSSAM, B C, and OLD, R A. 1988.   Geology of the country around Coalville.   *Memoir of the British Geological Survey*, Sheet 155 (England and Wales).

WRIGHT, W B, SHERLOCK, R L, WRAY, D A, LLOYD, W, and TONKS, L H. 1927.   Geology of the Rossendale anticline.   *Memoir of the Geological Survey of Great Britain*, Sheet 76 (England and Wales.)

ZIEGLER, P A. 1982.   *Geological atlas of western and central Europe*. (The Hague: Shell International Petroleum Maatschappji BV.)

ZIEGLER, P A. 1990.   *Geological atlas of western and central Europe*. Second edition.   Shell Internationale Petroleum Maatschappij B.V.-Geol. Soc. London. (Amsterdam: Elsevier.)

Appendix 1   Map showing the boundaries of the 1:50 000 geological sheets of the region.

APPENDIX 1

BGS memoirs and other publications of the region

This appendix contains a list of the British Geological Survey 1:50 000 sheet memoirs (Sheet Descriptions and Sheet Explanations) for the region, which have been used as reference sources throughout this book. BGS maps and other publications are available from the Sales Desk, British Geological Survey, Keyworth NG12 5GG (Telephone 0115 936 3241; facsimile 0115 936 3488; e-mail *sales@bgs.ac.uk*; Internet address *http://www.nkw.ac.uk/bgs/home.html*), and at the BGS Edinburgh office (Telephone 0131 667 1000), or through the BGS London Information Office, Natural History Museum (Earth Galleries), South Kensington, London SW7 2DE (Telephone 0171 589 4090), or through Stationery Office stockists and all good booksellers. A catalogue of maps and literature is available on request and can be found on the BGS web site.

BGS memoirs, descriptions and explanations

BGS memoirs, descriptions and explanations are listed by sheet number, and the latest edition of the 1: 50 000 map is shown in italics (see figure, page 106).

† out of print. These may be purchased from BGS libraries as black and white photocopies

Sheet No	Date	Title and author
95/107	1984 *1970/1985*	Rhyl and Denbigh. WARREN, P T
†96	1923 *1975*	Liverpool with Wirral and part of the Flintshire Coalfield. WEDD, C B, SMITH, B, SIMMONS, W C, and WRAY, D A.
98	1963† *1977*	Stockport and Knutsford. TAYLOR, B J, PRICE, R H, and TROTTER, F M.
99	1971 *1977*	Chapel en le Frith. STEVENSON, I P, and GAUNT, G D.
107 see 95		
108	2004 *1999*	Flint. DAVIES, J R, WILSON, D, and WILLIAMSON, I T
109	1986 *1986*	Chester. EARP, J R, and TAYLOR, B J.
110	1968 *1968*	Macclesfield, Congleton, Crewe and Middlewich. EVANS, W B, WILSON, A A, TAYLOR, B J, and PRICE, D.
†110	1906	The geology of the country around Macclesfield, Congleton, Crewe and Middlewich. POCOCK, T I.
111	1985 *1978*	Buxton, Leek and Bakewell. AITKENHEAD, N, CHISHOLM, J I, and STEVENSON, I P.
112	1967 *1963*	Chesterfield, Matlock and Mansfield. SMITH, E G, RHYS, G H, and EDEN, R A.
120	1993	Corwen no memoir
121	1927† *1993*	Wrexham. WEDD CB, SMITH, B, and WILLS, L J.
122	1966† *1967*	Nantwich and Whitchurch. POOLE, E G, and WHITEMAN, A J.
123	1998 *1994*	Stoke on Trent. REES, J G A.
124	1988 *1983*	Ashbourne and Cheadle. CHISHOLM, J I, CHARSLEY, T J, and AITKENHEAD, N.
125	1979 *1972*	Derby. FROST, D V, and SMART, J G O.
†125	1908	Derbyshire and Nottinghamshire Coalfield. GIBSON, W, POCOCK, T I, WEDD, C B, and SHERLOCK, R L.

136	1986	Bala no memoir
137	1929[†] 1999	Oswestry. WEDD, C B, SMITH, B, KING, W B R, and WRAY, D A.
138	1925[†] 1967	Wem. POCOCK, R W, and WRAY, D A
139	1927[†] 1974	Stafford and Market Drayton. WHITEHEAD, T H, DIXON, E E L, POCOCK, R W, ROBERTSON, T, and CANTRILL, T C
140	1955[†] 1982	Burton upon Trent, Rugeley and Uttoxeter. STEVENSON, I P, and MITCHELL, G H
141	2002 2001	Loughborough Sheet Description and Sheet Explanation. CARNEY, J.
150 see 165		
151		
152	1938[†] 1978	Shrewsbury. POCOCK, R W, WHITEHEAD, T H, WEDD, C B, and ROBERTSON, T
153	2002 2001	Telford and Wolverhampton Sheet Description and Sheet Explanation. Bridge, D McC, and Hough, E
154	1919[†] 1926	Lichfield. BARROW, G, GIBSON, W, CANTRILL, T C, DIXON, E E L, and CUNNINGTON, C H
155	1988 1982	Coalville. WORSSAM, B C
165/150	2001 1994	Montgomery and Ordovician rocks around Shelve. CAVE R.

166	1968 1974	Church Stretton, Craven Arms, Wenlock Edge and Brown Clee. GREIG, D C.
167	1947 1975	Dudley and Bridgenorth. WHITEHEAD, T H.
168	2000 1996	Birmingham. POWELL, J H.
169	1998 1994	Coventry and Nuneaton. BRIDGE, D McC.

Other BGS publications relevant to the region

Classical areas of British Geology: Geology of the Church Stretton area. WRIGHT, J E. 1968

Geology of the Craven Arms area. HAINS B A. 1969

Geology of the Wenlock Edge area. HAINS B A. 1970

JACKSON, D I, JACKSON, A A, EVANS, D, WINGFIELD, R T R, BARNES, R P, and ARTHUR, M J. 1996. United Kingdom offshore regional report: the geology of the Irish Sea. (London, HMSO.)

BRITISH GEOLOGICAL SURVEY. 1997. Regional geochemistry of parts of north-west England and north Wales. (Keyworth, Nottingham: British Geological Survey)

Recommended small-scale maps include:

1:1 500 000
Tectonic map of Britain, Ireland and adjacent areas. 1996
Coal Resources map of Britain. 1999
Metallogenic map of Britain and Ireland. 1996

1:1 000 000
Pre-Permian geology of the United Kingdom (South). Map and overlay. 1985
Industrial mineral resources map of Britain. 1996
Building Stone Resources of the United Kingdom.

1:625 000 (about 10 miles to one inch)
Solid geology mapUK, South Sheet. 2001
Quaternary map of the United Kingdom, South, 1977

1:250 000 (about 4 miles to one inch)
52 04W Mid-Wales and Marches, 1990
52 02W East Midlands 1983
53 04W Liverpool Bay 1978
53 02W Humber-Trent 1983

APPENDIX 2

Summary of principal boreholes in the region

Outline records for the boreholes judged to be of particular significance in the elucidation of the subsurface geology of the region are given below. The list is selective and does not include all of the deeper boreholes. The full records are held in the National Geological Records Centre, British Geological Survey, Keyworth, Nottingham NG12 5GG, Tel. 0115 936 3109, Fax 0115 936 3276.

All **depths** are given in metres below Kelly Bushing or other reference level. The depths to the main stratigraphical boundaries is the interpretation of the authors of this book, and may differ in some instances from previously published accounts or from the interpretation on composite logs supplied to the British Geological Survey. Except for those indicated as currently held 'commercial-in-confidence', more details of these boreholes can be found in British Geological Survey records and in the publications cited.

The BGS reference number is a unique number assigned to each borehole. The first two letters of this reference refer to the 100 km grid square, the boundaries of which are indicated in Figure 53. The next two numbers define the 10 km grid square within this area (easting, northing). The following two letters define within which quarter the borehole lies (e.g. NW, SE etc) and the final figure is the number of that borehole within that quarter assigned on a time sequential basis.

Alrewas

BGS record number	SK11SE7
National Grid reference	[4]18636 [3]14067
Surface or reference level (m)	56.69
Drilled by	Shell
Date	1981
Base Permo-Triassic	305
Base Lower Coal Measures	540
Base Millstone Grit	778.46
Base Carboniferous Limestone	996.09
Terminal depth in Old Red Sandstone	1168.3

Bitterns Wood

BGS record number	SJ74SE92
National Grid reference	[3]76625 [3]42868
Surface or reference level (m)	123.33
Drilled by	Hamilton
Date	1989
Base Keele Formation	149.35
Base Halesowen Formation	286.51
Base Etruria Formation	481
Base Lower Coal Measures	1527
Base Millstone Grit	1633
Terminal depth in Carboniferous Limestone	1635.25

Blacon East

BGS record number	SJ36NE23
National Grid reference	[3]37890 [3]66860
Surface or reference level (m)	14.33
Drilled by	Shell
Date	1981
Base Permo-Triassic	416
Base Upper Coal Measures	446
Base Coal Measures	739
Base Millstone Grit	1804
Terminal depth in Carboniferous Limestone	2265.88

Blacon West

BGS record number	SJ36NE24
National Grid reference	[3]36617 [3]66341
Surface or reference level (m)	11.42
Drilled by	Shell
Date	1985
Base Permo-Triassic	57
Base Halesowen Formation	310
Base Lower Coal Measures	763
Terminal depth in Millstone Grit	1339.29

Bosley

BGS record number	SJ96NW13
National Grid reference	[3]93439 [3]67823
Surface or reference level (m)	406.11
Drilled by	BP
Date	1986
Base Millstone Grit	470
Base Carboniferous Limestone	1196
Base Volcanic rocks	1268
Base Carboniferous Limestone	1588
Base Intrusion	1691
Terminal depth in Carboniferous Limestone	2006.5

Calow 1

BGS record number	SK47SW43
National Grid reference	[4]40850 [3]70400
Surface or reference level (m)	128
Drilled by	BP
Date	1957
Base Lower Coal Measures	251.5
Base Millstone Grit	811.68
Terminal depth in Carboniferous Limestone	1132.9

Codsall

BGS record number	SJ80NW69
National Grid reference	[3]83331 [3]05375
Surface or reference level (m)	94.18
Drilled by	Shell
Date	1984
Base Permo-Triassic	640.99
Base Keele Formation	830
Base Halesowen Formation	933
Base Elton Formation	968
Base Much Wenlock Formation	1032
Terminal depth in Coalbrookdale Formation	1188.7

Edgmond

BGS record number	SJ72SW1
National Grid reference	[3]70160 [3]22150
Surface or reference level (m)	86.9
Drilled by	BP
Date	1947
Base Permo-Triassic	152.4
Base Upper Coal Measures	260.6
Terminal depth in Precambrian	270.36

Erbistock

BGS record number	SJ34SW35
National Grid reference	[3]34767 [3]43213
Surface or reference level (m)	63.39
Drilled by	BP
Date	1986
Base Salop Formation	280
Base Halesowen Formation	568
Base Etruria Formation	702.5
Base Lower Coal Measures	1170
Base Millstone Grit	1318.3
Terminal depth in Carboniferous Limestone	1888.4

Gun Hill

BGS record number	SJ96SE18
National Grid reference	[3]97230 [3]61820
Surface or reference level (m)	350.5
Drilled by	BP
Date	1938
Base Millstone Grit	258.2
Base Carboniferous Limestone	420.62
Base Volcanic rocks	432.82
Base Carboniferous Limestone	708.96
Base Volcanic rocks	770.53
Terminal depth in Carboniferous Limestone	1410.92

Hardstoft 3

BGS record number	SK46SW14
National Grid reference	[4]44500 [3]62450
Surface or reference level (m)	190.2
Drilled by	Devonshire
Date	1925
Base Coal Measures	457
Base Millstone Grit	951
Terminal depth in Carboniferous Limestone	1165.86

Heath Farm

BGS record number	SJ90NW49
National Grid reference	[3]93300 [3]09400
Surface or reference level (m)	94.2
Drilled by	Shell
Date	1984
Base Permo-Triassic	160
Base Salop Formation	411
Base Halesowen Formation	465
Base Coal Measures	723
Base Elton Formation	839
Base Much Wenlock Formation	894
Base Coalbrookdale Formation	1153
Base Barr Limestone Formation	1165
Base Upper Llandovery Sandstone	1419
Base Lower Cambrian	1661
Terminal depth in Precambrian	1838.55

Heswall

BGS record number	SJ28SE1
National Grid reference	[3]25260 [3]81610
Surface or reference level (m)	6.1
Drilled by	Belgian Coal Co.
Date	1908
Base Permo-Triassic	717.49
Base Lower Coal Measures	872.64
Terminal depth in Millstone Grit	018.6

Ilkeston

BGS record number	SK44NE47
National Grid reference	[4]47537 [3]45172
Surface or reference level (m)	67.78
Drilled by	BP
Date	1985
Base Lower Coal Measures	433.7
Terminal depth in Millstone Grit	1103.5

Ironville 5

BGS record number	SK45SW67
National Grid reference	[4]42990 [3]51412
Surface or reference level (m)	92.5
Drilled by	BP
Date	1984
Base Lower Coal Measures	279.5
Base Millstone Grit	591.5
Base Carboniferous Limestone	1213
Terminal depth in Tremadoc	1308

Keele

BGS record number	SJ84SW2
National Grid reference	[3]82930 [3]43990
Surface or reference level (m)	154.23
Drilled by	HMG
Date	1943
Base Etruria Formation	274.93
Terminal depth in Lower Coal Measures	1287.48

Knutsford

BGS record number	SJ77NW4
National Grid reference	[3]70270 [3]77860
Surface or reference level (m)	45.7
Drilled by	BGC
Date	1973
Base Permo-Triassic	2821.5
Terminal depth in Halesowen Formation	3045.7

Lees Wood

BGS record number	SJ26SE16
National Grid reference	[3]26360 [3]61800
Surface or reference level (m)	99.97
Drilled by	BP
Date	1955
Base Millstone Grit	278.59
Terminal depth in Carboniferous Limestone	333.76

Maer (Sidway Mill)

BGS record number	SJ73NE3
National Grid reference	[3]76030 [3]39340
Surface or reference level (m)	122
Drilled by	BGS
Date	1962
Base Permo-Triassic	18.36
Base Warwickshire Group	524
Base Halesowen Formation	779.07
Base Etruria Formation	1210.84
Terminal depth in Westphalian C	1269.54

Milton Green

BGS record number	SJ45NW9
National Grid reference	[3]43744 [3]56925
Surface or reference level (m)	19.2
Drilled by	ESSO
Date	1965
Base Quaternary	28.96
Base Erbistock Formation	177
Base Halesowen Formation	457
Base Etruria Formation	527
Base Westphalian C	688
Base Lower Coal Measures	929
Base Millstone Grit	1178
Base Carboniferous Limestone	1499.62
Terminal depth in Arenig	1588.01

Nooks Farm 1A

BGS record number	SJ95NW12
National Grid reference	^{3}91747 ^{3}58032
Surface or reference level (m)	304.19
Drilled by	SHELL
Date	1983

Base Millstone Grit	422
Base Carboniferous Limestone	539
Base Volcanic stones	561
Base Carboniferous Limestone	578
Base Volcanic stones	586
Terminal depth in Carboniferous Limestone	1120

North Stafford

BGS record number	SJ92NW34
National Grid reference	^{3}92740 ^{3}29100
Surface or reference level (m)	94.18
Drilled by	SHELL
Date	1984

Base Permo-Triassic	410
Base Halesowen Formation	545
Base Etruria Formation	631
Base Westphalian C	817
Base Westphalian B	1004
Base Lower Coal Measures	1190
Base Millstone Grit	1814
Terminal depth in Carboniferous Limestone	2403.35

Northwood

BGS record number	SJ84SW145
National Grid reference	^{3}84303 ^{3}41919
Surface or reference level (m)	152.4
Drilled by	FINA
Date	1989

Base Etruria Formation	197.82
Base Westphalian C	585.83
Base Westphalian B	990.6
Base Lower Coal Measures	1420.4
Terminal depth in Millstone Grit	1519.73

Prees

BGS record number	SJ53SE3
National Grid reference	^{3}55720 ^{3}34470
Surface or reference level (m)	96.01
Drilled by	Trend
Date	1973

Base Permo-Triassic	3575
Base Westphalian	3600
Base Ordovician	3800
Terminal depth in Tremadoc	3827.98

Ranton

BGS record number	SJ82SW12
National Grid reference	^{3}84410 ^{3}23620
Surface or reference level (m)	124.18
Drilled by	Shell
Date	1980

Base Permo-Triassic	707
Base Salop Formation	821
Base Halesowen Formation	880
Base Coal Measures	1143
Base Millstone Grit	1407
Base Carboniferous Limestone	1779
Terminal depth in Old Red Sandstone	1859.28

Renishaw

BGS record number	SK47NW6
National Grid reference	^{4}42700 ^{3}77800
Surface or reference level (m)	90.5
Drilled by	HMG
Date	1919

Base Coal Measures	524.26
Base Millstone Grit	1249.68
Terminal depth Carboniferous Limestone	1290.8

Ridgeway

BGS record number	SK48SW14
National Grid reference	^{4}40210 ^{3}80890
Surface or reference level (m)	155.22
Drilled by	HMG
Date	1919

Base Lower Coal Measures	365.76
Terminal depth in Millstone Grit	856.49

Rotherwood

BGS record number	SK31NW260
National Grid reference	^{4}34580 ^{3}15590
Surface or reference level (m)	109.5
Drilled by	BGS
Date	1977

Base Millstone Grit	61.49
Terminal depth in Carboniferous Limestone	173.9

Shuttington Fields

BGS record number	SK20NE2
National Grid reference	^{4}26420 ^{3}06100
Surface or reference level (m)	71.57
Drilled by	NCB
Date	1951

Base Permo-Triassic	269.7
Terminal depth in Tremadoc	297.5

Stoke on Tern 1

BGS record number	SJ62NE1
National Grid reference	^{3}65130 ^{3}26270
Surface or reference level (m)	69.8
Drilled by	BP
Date	1948

Base Keele Formation	193.55
Base Halesowen Formation	341.38
Base Etruria Formation	347.78
Terminal depth in Carboniferous Limestone	558.39

Ternhill

BGS record number	SJ63SW26
National Grid reference	^{3}63150 ^{3}31320
Surface or reference level (m)	69.19
Drilled by	BP
Date	1948

Base Permo-Triassic	434.04
Base Warwickshire Group	613.56
Terminal depth in Carboniferous Limestone	713.23

Ticknall

BGS record number	SK32SE103
National Grid reference	^{4}35910 ^{3}23630
Surface or reference level (m)	100
Drilled by	BGS
Date	1995

Base Carboniferous Limestone	171.19
Terminal depth in Cambrian	209.04

Trickley Lodge

BGS record number	SP19NE22
National Grid reference	[4]16035 [2]98840
Surface or reference level (m)	115.82
Drilled by	NCB
Date	1974
Base Permo-Triassic	593
Base Salop Formation	755
Base Halesowen Formation	832
Terminal depth in Cambrian	880.87

Trusley

BGS record number	SK23NE2
National Grid reference	[4]25480 [3]35880
Surface or reference level (m)	79.25
Drilled by	BGS
Date	1969
Base Permo-Triassic	100.79
Terminal depth in Widmerpool Formation	880.87

Twycross

BGS record number	SK30NW13
National Grid reference	[4]33870 [3]05640
Surface or reference level (m)	122
Drilled by	BGS
Date	1978
Base Permo-Triassic	503.9
Base Intrusion	507
Terminal depth in Cambrian	509

Walsall

BGS record number	SP09NW33
National Grid reference	[4]00930 [2]98050
Surface or reference level (m)	118.3
Drilled by	Co-op
Date	1935
Base Quaternary	12.8
Base Lower Wenlock Limestone	26.8
Base Wenlock Shales	295.66
Base Upper Llandovery Sandstone	381.9
Terminal depth in Lower Cambrian	391.7

Whittington Heath

BGS record number	SK10NW3
National Grid reference	[4]14780 [3]08000
Surface or reference level (m)	76.2
Drilled by	BGS
Date	1948
Base Permo-Triassic	77.09
Base Enville Beds	257.91
Base Keele Formation	452.86
Base Halesowen Formation	534.57
Base Etruria Formation	639.47
Base Westphalian C	772.13
Base Westphalian B	929.54
Base Lower Coal Measures	1134.44
Base Millstone Grit	1194.05
Base Carboniferous Limestone	1194.82
Terminal depth in Old Red Sandstone	1249.22

Woo Dale

BGS record number	SK07SE24
National Grid reference	[4]09850 [3]72840
Surface or reference level (m)	228
Drilled by	ICI
Date	1947
Base Quaternary	3.34
Base Carboniferous Limestone	273.6
Terminal depth in Ordovician	312

Yarnfield

BGS record number	SJ83SE124
National Grid reference	[3]86530 [3]32015
Surface or reference level (m)	97.54
Drilled by	Edinburgh Oil & Gas
Date	1991
Base Permo-Triassic	422.76
Base Salop Formation	493
Base Halesowen Formation	620
Base Etruria Formation	765.66
Base Westphalian C	900
Base Westphalian B	1094.84
Base Lower Coal Measures	1339
Terminal depth in Millstone Grit	1431.34

INDEX

Figures and tables are shown in **bold**

MAPS

Map 1   Depth to Caledonian unconformity.

Map 2   Dinantian isopachs.

Map 3   Depth to top Dinantian/Base Silesian.

Map 4   Namurian isopachs.

Map 5   Depth to top Namurian/Base Pennine Coal Measures.

Map 6   Pennine Coal Measures Group isopachs.

Map 7   Depth to top Pennine Coal Measures Group/Base Warwickshire Group.

Map 8   Warwickshire Group isopachs.

Map 9   Depth to Variscan unconformity.

Map 10   Permian to 'recent' isopachs.

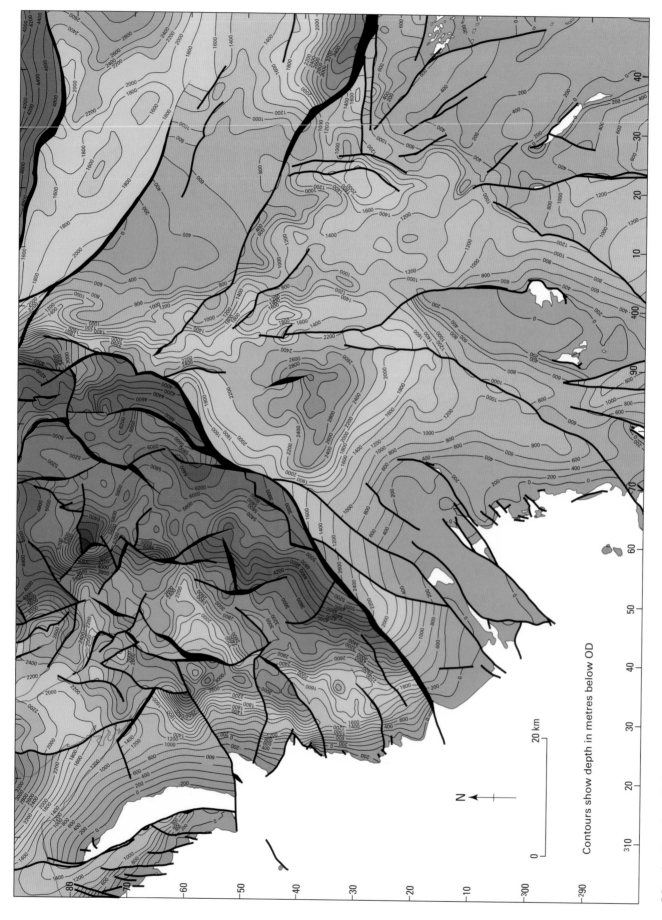

Map 1   Depth to Caledonian unconformity.

Contours show depth in metres below OD

20 km

N

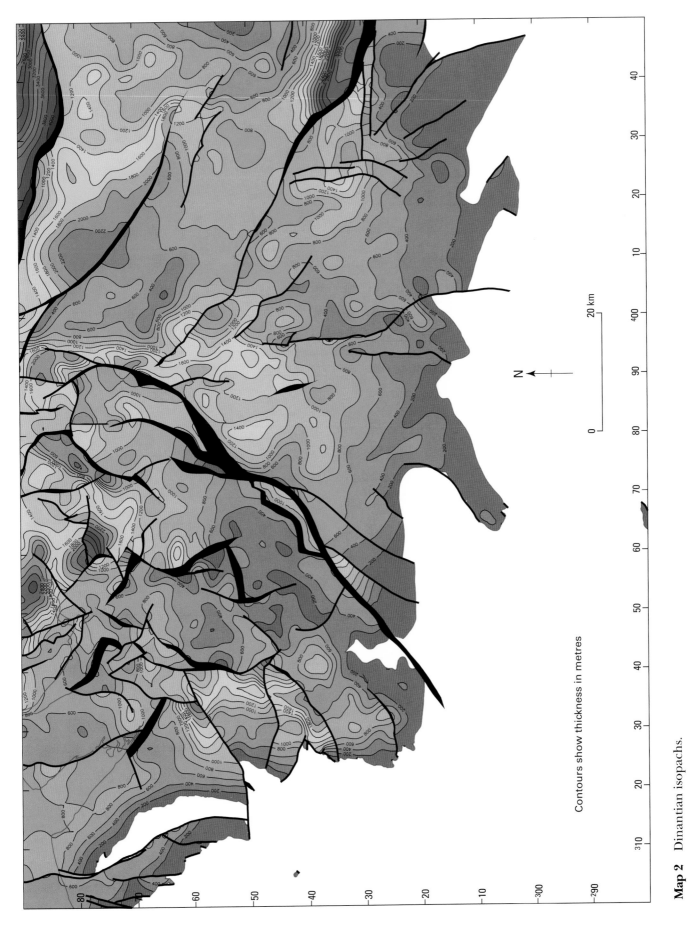

Contours show thickness in metres

20 km

N

0

Map 2 Dinantian isopachs.

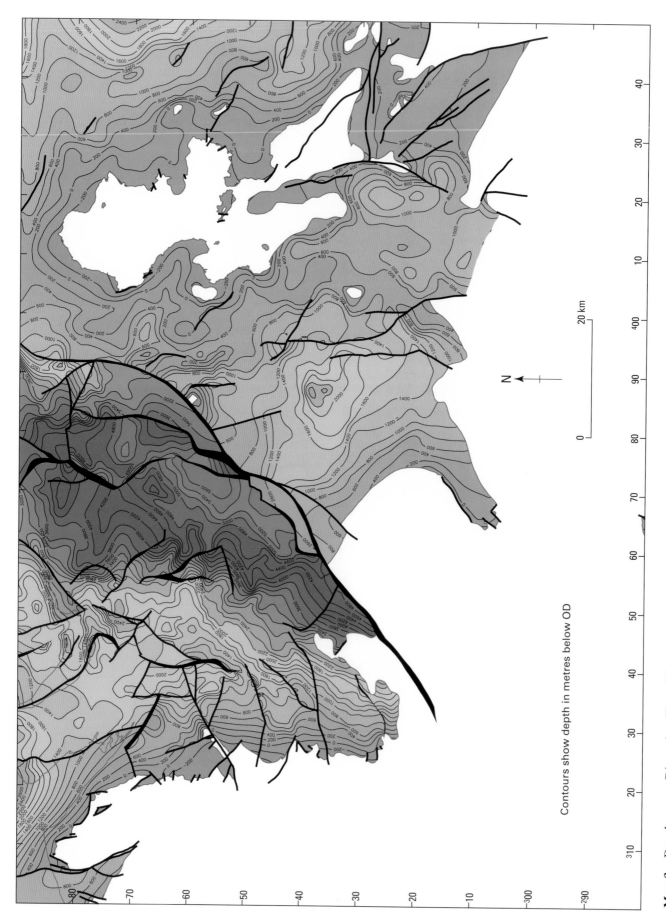

Contours show depth in metres below OD

20 km

N

0

Map 3 Depth to top Dinantian/Base Silesian.

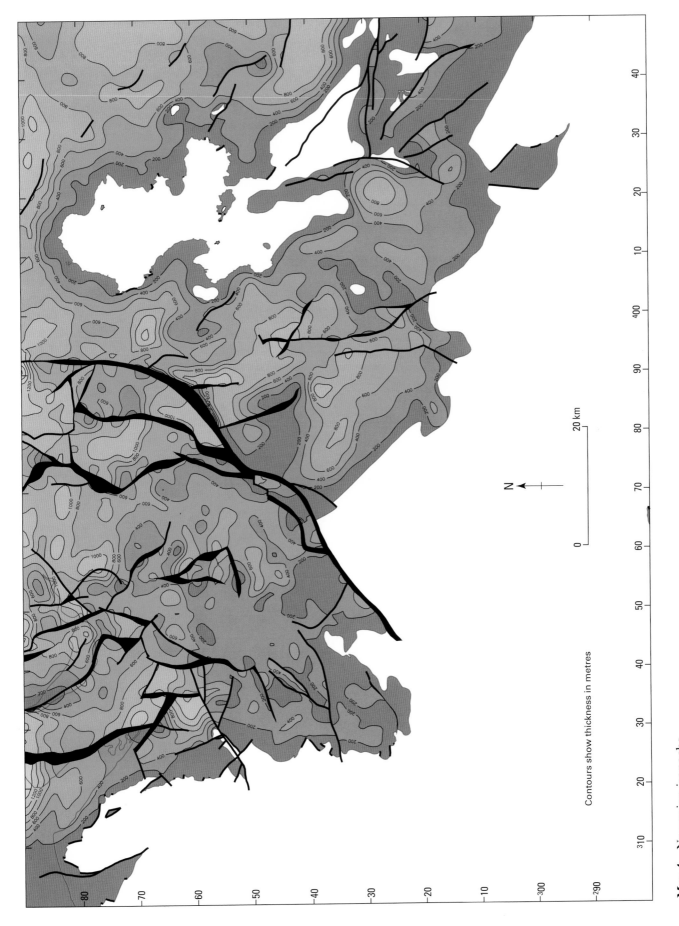

Contours show thickness in metres

20 km

N

0

Map 4 Namurian isopachs.

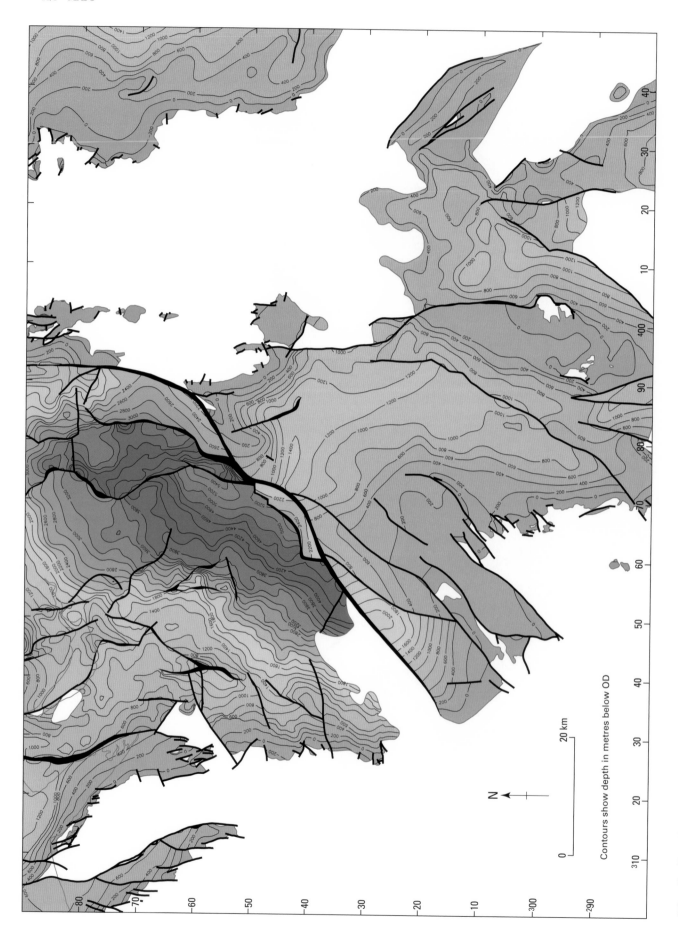

Map 5   Depth to top Namurian/Base Pennine Coal Measures.

Contours show depth in metres below OD

20 km

N

0

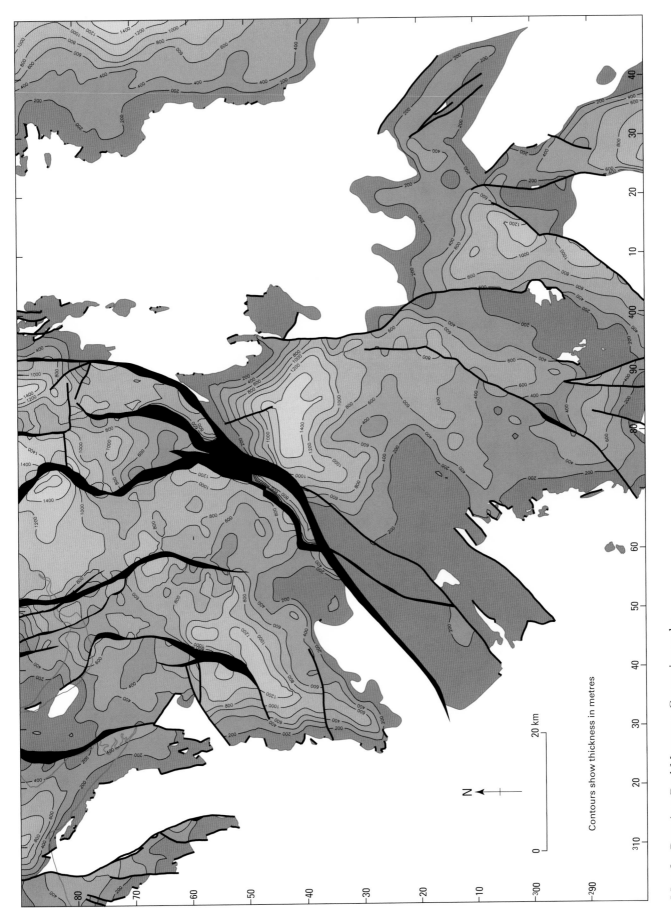

Map 6 Pennine Coal Measures Group isopachs.

Contours show thickness in metres

20 km

N

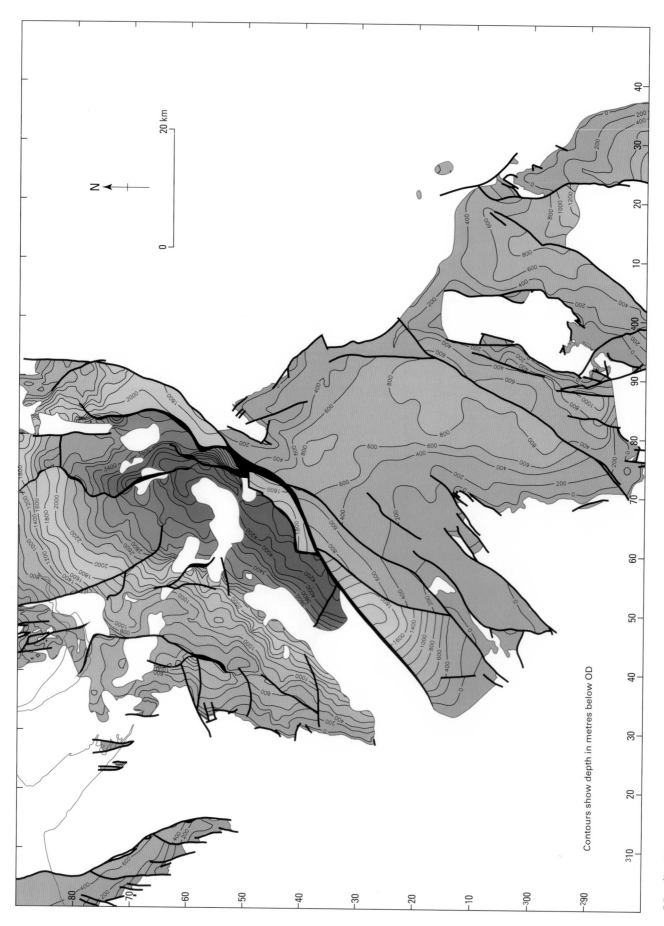

Contours show depth in metres below OD

Map 7   Depth to top Pennine Coal Measures Group/Base Warwickshire Group.

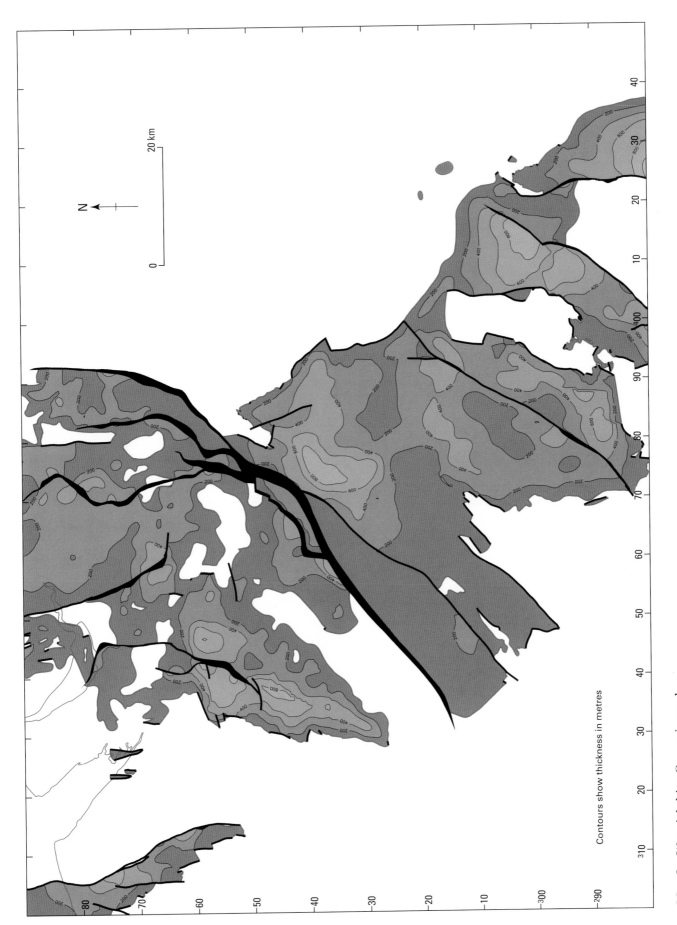

Contours show thickness in metres

20 km

N

Map 8 Warwickshire Group isopachs.

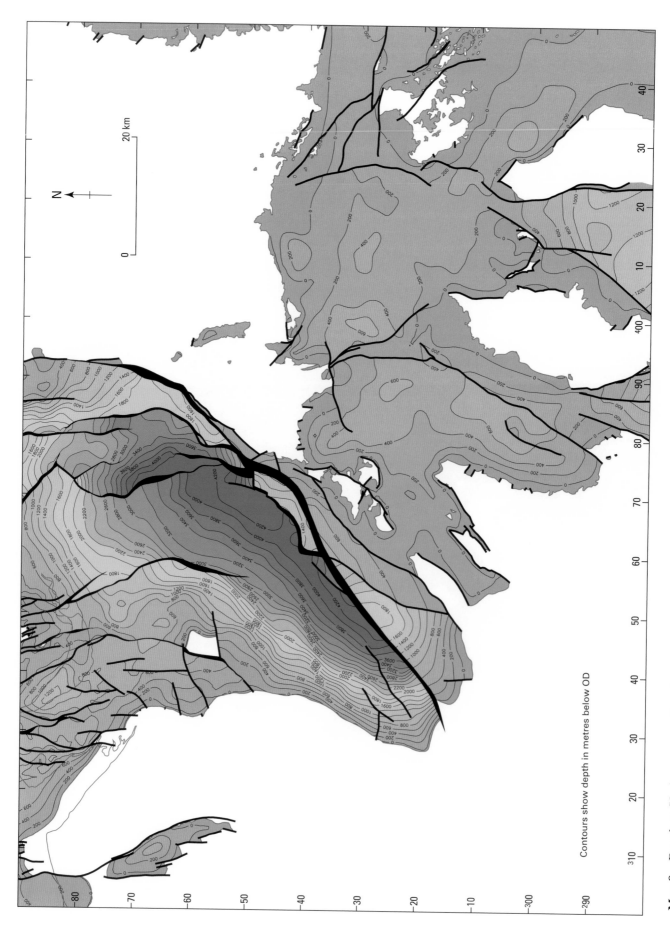

Map 9 Depth to Variscan unconformity.

Contours show depth in metres below OD

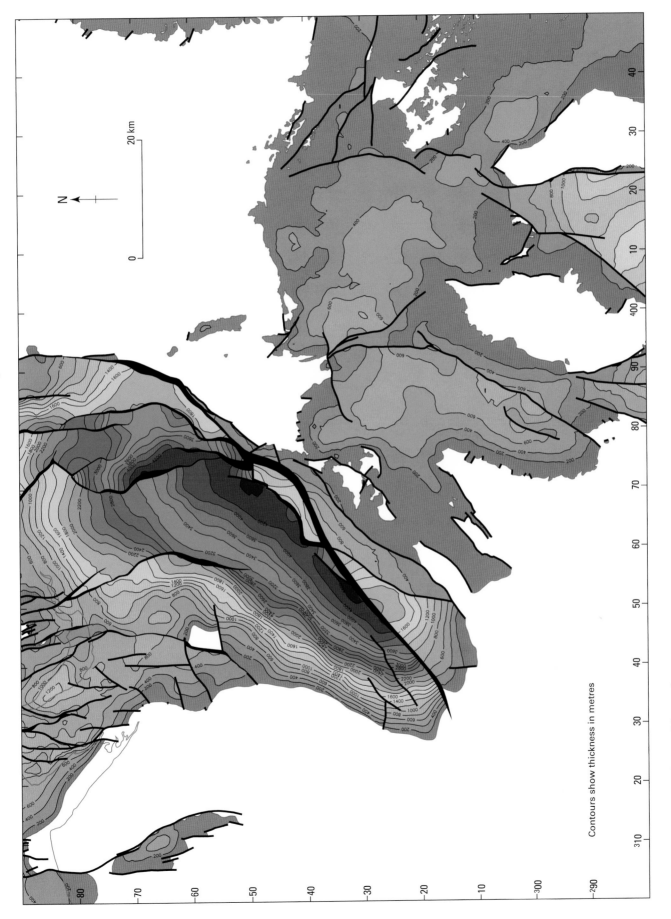

Contours show thickness in metres

Map 10 Permian to 'recent' isopachs.

British Regional Geology

A series of guides to the geology of the United Kingdom.

Each book contains explanatory text, sketch maps, sections and photographs. The areas covered are shown on the index map, and the titles are listed below.

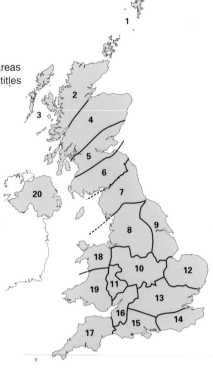

Scotland

England

Wales

Northern Ireland

Ten-mile maps

The Geological Survey publishes two maps of Great Britain at 1:625 000 (about 10 miles to 1 inch). One shows the geology of solid rocks, the other Quaternary geology. Each map comprises two sheets and is available flat, or folded and cased, with overprinted sheet boundaries of the 1:50 000 maps.

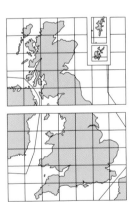

1:250 000 maps

A series of maps showing solid geology, including that of the continental shelf, is available.
Each sheet covers an area of about 1° of latitude by 2° of longitude; coverage is shown by a light tone.

Other series at 1:250 000 cover sea-bed sediments, Quaternary geology, Bouguer gravity anomalies and aeromagnetic anomalies. There is also a map showing the geology of the land area of Northern Ireland.

Structure and evolution of the south-west Pennine Basin and adjacent area

During the exploration of northern and central England for oil and gas in the 1970s and 1980s, numerous seismic reflection surveys were carried out. These provide the principal means of investigating the geological structure and to some extent the stratigraphy of Carboniferous and older rocks below the levels that can be reliably predicted from outcrops, mine workings and most boreholes. In this book, such data have been integrated with as much of the available geological information as possible to produce an account that details the geological evolution of the region from pre-Cambrian to recent times, with particular emphasis on the Carboniferous. It contains a series of structure-contour and preserved-thickness maps at a scale of 1:625 000, which illustrate present-day structure and distribution of rock units.

Carboniferous basin development in the region can be divided broadly into two main phases. In early Carboniferous times, rapidly subsiding, fault controlled, extensional basins developed between structurally elevated emergent blocks. Later, a more regional subsidence followed; this was characterised by a general lack of major fault-control, and resulted in submergence and depositional onlap of the earlier structural highs. Platform carbonates developed across the highs whilst argillaceous sedimentation dominated in basinal areas. In Namurian times, a delta system prograded across the region, mainly from the north and east, and supplied enormous quantities of feldspathic clastic material. These delta deposits infilled the remaining topographic depressions and show much variation in facies and thickness. Small deltas also built out into this region from rivers flowing off the London–Brabant Massif to the south, supplying protoquartzitic clastic material. During Westphalian times, thickness variations were less marked with a more uniform distribution of facies. However, rivers were now supplying increasing quantities of clastic material from an emergent source to the west. There is growing evidence that during Bolsovian (Westphalian C) times, the first effects of the Variscan Orogeny were being felt across the Variscan Foreland. This affected the deposition and distribution of Bolsovian and Westphalian D sequences, culminating, at the end of the Carboniferous, with strong folding in places and partial reversal of some of the earlier basin-controlling normal faults. Deposition ceased with regional uplift and widespread erosion ensued.

A period dominated by extensional faulting occurred from Permian to early Cretaceous times and was followed by further regional subsidence until early Palaeocene times. Regional uplift with superimposed basin inversion then commenced, and triggered a period of erosion that has probably continued until the present day.

British Geological Survey

Kingsley Dunham Centre
Keyworth
Nottingham NG12 5GG
Telephone 0115 936 3100
Fax 0115 936 3200

Murchison House
West Mains Road
Edinburgh EH9 3LA
Telephone 0131 667 1000
Fax 0131 668 2683

Maclean Building
Crowmarsh Gifford
Wallingford
Oxfordshire OX10 8BB
Telephone 01491 838800
Fax 01491 692345

Columbus House
Greenmeadow Springs
Tongwynlais
Cardiff CF15 7NE
Telephone 029 2052 1962
Fax: 029 2052 1963

Forde House
Park Five Business Centre
Harrier Way, Sowton
Exeter EX2 7HU
Telephone 01392 445271
Fax 01392 445371

Geological Survey of Northern Ireland
Colby House
Stranmillis Court
Belfast BT9 5BF
Telephone 028 9038 8462
Fax 028 9038 8461

Natural History Museum Earth
Galleries
Exhibition Road
London SW7 2DE
Telephone 020 7589 4090
Fax 020 7589 8270

Web site: http://www.bgs.ac.uk

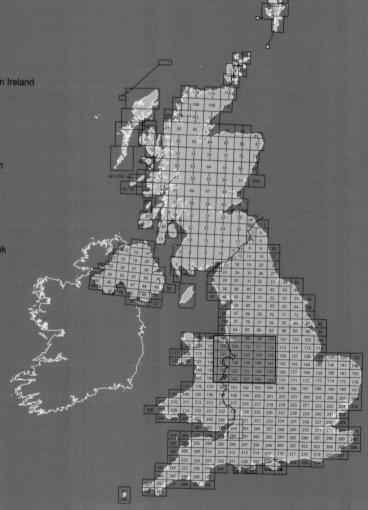

ISBN 0852725183

9 780852 725184

Price code GX